PHYSICO-CHEMICAL CONSTANTS

OF PURE ORGANIC COMPOUNDS

VOL. 2

Volume I published 1950

PHYSICO-CHEMICAL CONSTANTS
OF
PURE ORGANIC COMPOUNDS
VOLUME 2

by

J. TIMMERMANS

HONORARY PROFESSOR OF PHYSICAL CHEMISTRY

FREE UNIVERSITY, BRUSSELS

DIRECTOR, BUREAU OF PHYSICO-CHEMICAL STANDARDS

ELSEVIER PUBLISHING COMPANY

AMSTERDAM - LONDON - NEW YORK

1965

ELSEVIER PUBLISHING COMPANY
335 JAN VAN GALENSTRAAT, P.O. BOX 211, AMSTERDAM

AMERICAN ELSEVIER PUBLISHING COMPANY, INC.
52 VANDERBILT AVENUE, NEW YORK, N.Y. 10017

ELSEVIER PUBLISHING COMPANY LIMITED
RIPPLESIDE COMMERCIAL ESTATE
BARKING, ESSEX

LIBRARY OF CONGRESS CATALOG CARD NUMBER 50-9668

PRINTED IN THE NETHERLANDS

PREFACE

This is the first supplement to my book "Physico-Chemical Constants of Pure Organic Compounds", published in 1950 by Elsevier; and includes new data until the end of 1964, with some Addenda and Corrigenda to the former volume. In collecting these data I was once more struck by the fact that this branch of science still largely fails to attract the attention of French, German and Russian chemists, although it is extensively studied in the United States of America and in the British Commonwealth. This is particularly true for the measurement of calorimetric constants which are so useful in thermodynamic work.

In this work, the methods and conventions used are the same as in the former volume (see pages 3 and 16 of that work) with only two exceptions:

(a) The viscosity (η) is given in centipoise units multiplied by different factors which are specified in each case.

(b) With only a very few exceptions, the calorific values are always given in calories and not in joules.

Corrigenda to the former volume are clearly indicated by "N.B." accompanied by the number of the corresponding page in that volume.

Where an English translation of a Russian periodical is available, the page number of the edition in English is given first, followed by the page number (in brackets) of the Russian original.

I would like to take this opportunity of heartily thanking my collaborators and all colleagues who were so kind as to point out errors, gaps or misprints in the original tables, and I hope that they will continue to send me their criticisms in the future.

I also wish to thank the editorial staff of Elsevier very heartily for the exceptional care with which they corrected the proofs to the best of their ability in order to enhance the usefulness of this book.

Brussels, January 1965   JEAN TIMMERMANS

CONTENTS

1. HYDROCARBONS

A. PARAFFINS

METHANE CH$_4$

(See also Addenda, p. 433)

Saturated vapour pressure

t°	P atm	t°	P atm	
— 163.78	0.8470	— 112.11	16.369	HESTERMANS and WHITE (1961)
158.82	1.2574	105.65	20.995	,,
155.90	1.5596	101.77	25.043	,,
153.18	1.8941	96.72	28.801	,,
146.66	2.9217	93.14	32.461	,,
138.69	4.9851	89.40	36.642	,,
131.23	6.9641	85.92	40.922	,,
126.62	8.7147	— 83.64	43.953	,,
121.55	11.006			,,
— 118.04	12.823			,,
— 141.38	3.969	— 117.33	13.552	EUCKEN and BERGER (1934)
137.01	4.840	115.88	14.520	,,
133.29	5.808	113.11	16.359	,,
132.48	6.776	111.54	18.492	,,
127.74	7.744	107.31	20.425	,,
126.66	9.809	104.14	23.006	,,
124.75	10.675	99.77	26.812	,,
123.15	11.713	96.93	29.427	,,
121.80	11.713	94.05	32.528	,,
— 119.08	12.681	93.15	33.493	,,
		— 92.12	34.558	,,

Boiling point: — 161.74° HESTERMANS and WHITE (1961)

Triple point: — 182.50°; p mm: 87.60 ARMSTRONG, BRICKWEDDE and SCOTT (1953)

Transition point: — 252.76° MILLER and SMYTH (1957)

Transition under high pressure: STEVENSON (1957)

N.B. (p. 20): KEYES, TAYLOR and SMITH (1922) give the vapour pressure, the density and the specific heat on a less pure sample.

Viscosity (Vapour): RONDENKO (1944)

t°	η	t°	η
— 172.0	0.00098	— 118.6	0.00067
— 147.3	0.00090	— 106.1	0.000635
— 139.0	0.00082	— 104.8	0.000625

DEUTEROMETHANES

Triple point

	$t°$	p mm	
CH_3D	— 182.754	84.52	ARMSTRONG, BRICKWEDDE and SCOTT (1953)
CH_2D_2	— 183.009	81.80	,,
CHD_3	— 183.211	80.12	,,

TETRADEUTEROMETHANE CD_4

Triple point: — 183.364°; p mm: 79.13 ARMSTRONG, BRICKWEDDE and SCOTT (1953)

Transition point: — 251.46 MILLER and SMYTH (1957)

Specific heat: BARTHOLOME, DRIKOS and EUCKEN (1938)

$t°$	ε_p	$t°$	ε_p	$t°$	ε_p
— 253.03	5.07	— 250.70	6.86	— 246.88	22.2
252.21	5.68	250.00	6.75	246.72	28.9
252.19	6.17	249.76	6.92	246.61	43.1
251.55	14.35	248.97	7.98	246.47	36.3
251.46	14.55	248.87	8.17	246.42	47.4
251.45	59.1	248.54	8.78	246.33	63.1
251.33	84.5	248.07	9.82	246.19	22.6
251.21	85.78	247.37	12.12	246.15	13.60
251.14	47.2	247.43	13.13	245.78	7.97
251.04	17.31	247.28	12.88	245.24	7.71
— 250.84	10.18	— 247.18	13.91	244.74	7.72
				— 243.66	7.64

ETHANE C_2H_6

Critical constants: WHITEWAY and MASON (1953)

cr. $t° = 32.17°$ cr. d $= 0.215$

Vapour pressure: CLARK and DIN (1950)

$t°$	p mm	
— 88.46	760	
— 85.26	900	

PV values: MICHELS, VAN STRAATEN and DAWSON (1954)

d/t	0°	25°	50°	75°	100°	125°	150°
18.9467	0.82686	0.93648	1.04366	1.14933	1.25361	1.35707	1.46010
23.6822	0.78355	0.89762	1.00853	1.11735	1.22459	1.33075	1.43640
28.4297	0.74112	0.85984	0.97432	1.08637	1.19642	1.30523	1.41334
32.9968	0.70111	0.82441	0.94239	1.05744	1.17023	1.28156	1.39208
36.2913	—	0.79944	0.92000	1.03724	1.15195	1.26510	1.37733
37.7952	—	0.78832	0.90992	1.02808	1.14367	1.25759	1.37065
42.5282	—	0.75381	0.87890	1.00003	1.11835	1.23489	1.35042
43.8355	—	0.74438	0.87051	0.99251	1.11171	1.22885	1.34496
47.0833	—	0.72166	0.85011	0.97407	1.09498	1.21393	1.33183
51.7918	—	0.68948	0.82132	0.94816	1.07169	1.19315	1.31334
53.4437	—	0.67836	0.81139	0.93924	1.06374	1.18600	1.30700
65.2258	—	0.60373	0.74487	0.87949	1.01026	1.13864	1.26554
79.4868	—	—	0.67301	0.81508	0.95318	1.08872	1.22276
98.2775	—	—	0.59223	0.74313	0.89030	1.03534	1.17898
120.7238	—	—	0.51499	0.67523	0.83330	0.98998	1.14588
148.2741	—	—	0.44537	0.61762	0.79054	0.96331	1.13625
182.0166	—	—	0.39465	0.58747	0.78407	0.98198	1.18018

Specific heat: MICHELS, VAN STRAATEN and DAWSON (1954)

c_v (cal/mol)	0°	25°	50°	75°	100°	125°	150°
0	9.56	10.26	11.01	11.79	12.59	13.40	14.20
1	9.58	10.28	11.03	11.81	12.60	13.40	14.20
2	9.58	10.30	11.05	11.83	12.62	13.41	14.20
3	9.58	10.32	11.08	11.85	12.63	13.42	14.20
5	9.63	10.37	11.12	11.90	12.66	13.43	14.21
10	9.72	10.49	11.25	12.00	12.74	13.47	14.22
15	9.87	10.63	11.37	12.11	12.81	13.51	14.23
20	10.1	10.75	11.48	12.22	12.88	13.54	14.25
40	—	11.42	12.00	12.62	13.17	13.70	14.33
60	—	12.33	12.53	13.01	13.44	13.84	14.42
80	—	—	12.86	13.31	13.61	14.00	14.5
100	—	—	13.22	13.61	13.82	14.09	14.5
120	—	—	13.45	13.78	13.94	14.15	14.7
140	—	—	13.60	13.80	14.00	14.20	14.6
160	—	—	13.50	13.80	14.00	14.20	14.6
180	—	—	13.40	13.70	13.90	14.10	14.7

PROPANE C₃H₈

Critical constants

cr. t° = 97.30°   cr. p = 42.93 atm. KREGLEWSKI (1953)

Isotherms in the critical region (see author)

Saturated vapour pressure: DANA, JENKINS *et al.* (1926)

t°	p mm	t°	p mm
−43.7	731.1	−62.82	276.3
45.39	658.9	56.74	380.2
48.21	578.5	56.68	381.2
51.03	506.3	51.51	493.8
54.48	427.4	45.90	643.2
51.53	498.3	42.07	763.6
48.47	570.5	38.11	903.8
45.34	658.6	38.06	906.2
42.73	739.9	30.42	1239.1
42.21	759.7	24.08	1578.2
42.21	757.0	16.86	2043.0
36.39	969.9	5.87	2948.0
31.62	1176.8	−1.03	3443.0
26.39	1441.5	+2.48	3790.0
15.97	2115.0	10.15	4774.0
8.70	2699.0	9.52	4691.0
4.55	3098.0	17.93	5896.0
4.54	2945.0	24.93	7077.0
2.67	3269.0	33.94	8734.0
−2.67	3284.0	42.06	10675.0
+0.54	3620.0	50.34	12768.0
—	—	50.34	12800.0

Refractive index: $n_D^{-60°} = 1.3477$ BENOLIEL (1941)

Solid:

Density under high pressure at −196° till 20.000 kg/cm² STEWART and LA ROCK (1958)

Specific heat: SAGE and LACEY (1935)

t° (Vap.)	c_p (cal/g)	t° (Vap.)	c_p (cal/g)	t° (Liq.)	c_p (cal/g)
15.6	0.379	60.0	0.413	23.9	0.601
26.5	0.388	71.1	0.420	37.9	0.640
37.9	0.396	82.7	0.428	54.3	0.695
48.9	0.404	93.3	0.437	65.6	0.770
—	—	104.4	0.444	72.8	0.825

n-BUTANE $\qquad$ C$_4$H$_{10}$

Saturated vapour pressure

t°	p mm	t°	p mm	
56.95	4483	+57.48	4536	Dana, Jenkins et al. (1926)
56.95	4431	57.48	4501	,,
48.93	3648	49.00	3670	,,
48.93	3611	41.27	2877	,,
37.13	2641	31.71	2274	,,
25.54	1875	17.43	1450	,,
18.76	1464	−1.80	731.6	,,
10.27	1128	−18.12	372.2	,,
−0.19	767.3	—	—	,,
−0.19	763.0	—	—	,,
−12.66	466.8			
−13.20	459	−34.72	168	Simons and Mausteller (1952)
−19.53	348	−39.92	127	,,
−26.80	249	—	—	,,

Vapour pressure: CONNOLLY (1962)

t°	P atm	t°	P atm	
71.11	8.20	133.72	27.67	
87.78	11.79	137.78	29.62	
104.44	16.42	151.97	37.35	
121.11	22.28			

Boiling point: −0.55° SIMONS and MAUSTELLER (1952) and BENOLIEL (1941)

Freezing point: −138.3° SIMONS and MAUSTELLER (1952)

Density: $d^{20} = 0.5787$ BENOLIEL (1941)

Refractive index: $n_D^{25} = 1.3600$ dn/dt $= 556 \cdot 10^6$ BENOLIEL (1941)

Specific heat: SAGE and LACEY (1935)

t° (Vap.)	c_p (cal/g)	t° (Vap.)	c_p (cal/g)	t° (Liq.)	c_p (cal/g)
15.6	0.374	60.0	0.408	23.9	0.565
26.5	0.381	71.1	0.414	37.9	0.599
37.9	0.391	82.7	0.424	61.5	0.625
48.9	0.399	93.3	0.433	65.6	0.655
—	—	104.4	0.441	79.4	0.688
—	—	—	—	92.3	0.712

Heat of vaporization: 5685 cal/mol BENOLIEL (1941)

Heat of combustion at 25°: 687.42 kcal/mol PROSEN, MARON and ROSSINI (1951)

Iso-BUTANE $\quad\quad$ C$_4$H$_{10}$

Saturated vapour pressure

t°	p mm	
71.92	8524	Benoliel (1941)

t°	P atm	
71.11	11.00	Connolly (1962)
87.78	15.52	,,
104.44	21.29	,,
121.11	28.56	,,
133.72	35.32	,,
134.62	35.85	,,

b.t. $= -11.82$ d$^{20} = 0.5572$ dd/dt $= 0.00110$ n$_D^{-25°} = 1.3503$ dn/dt $= 570.10^6$
Benoliel (1941)

n-PENTANE $\quad\quad$ C$_5$H$_{12}$

Polyphasic equilibria

Critical constants

cr. t°	cr. p mm	cr. d	
196.62	25316	0.244	Beattie, Levine and Douslin (1951)
196.34	—	—	Ambrose, Cox and Townsend (1960)

Saturated vapour pressure: Beattie, Levine and Douslin (1951)

t°	p mm
100	4441
125	7526
150	11955
175	18114

Freezing point: – 129.75 Doolittle and Peterson (1951)

Boiling point: —11.82 Benoliel (1941)

Density: d$^{20} = 0.5572$ dd/dt $= 0.001110$ Benoliel (1941)

Refractive index: n$_D^{-25} = 1.3503$ dn/dt $= 570 \cdot 10^6$ Benoliel (1941)

Gaseous state

Compressibility: BEATTIE, LEVINE and DOUSLIN (1952)

t°	1.0	1.5	2.0	2.5	3.0	3.5
200	25.70	31.13	33.66	34.63	34.97	35.20
225	28.74	36.27	41.13	44.47	47.16	50.03
250	31.67	41.22	48.32	54.06	59.40	65.38
275	34.55	46.04	55.32	63.53	71.66	80.98
300	37.37	50.76	62.25	72.93	83.96	96.72

	4.0	4.5	5.0	6.0	7.0	d (mol/liter)
200	35.76	37.77	43.95	92.24	262.04	P (atm.)
225	54.08	61.01	74.06	143.55	347.34	,,
250	73.32	85.55	105.27	195.42	—	,,
275	93.09	110.47	137.31	247.45	—	,,
300	113.05	135.93	169.46	298.81	—	,,

Liquid state

Density: DOOLITTLE and PETERSON (1951)

t°	d
−10	0.6548
+20	0.6263

N.B. (p. 33), correct 20° instead of 30° in WIBAUT, HOOG *et al.* (1939)

Viscosity: DOOLITTLE and PETERSON (1951)

t°	$\eta \cdot 10^5$
−10.10	311.7
+20	240.4

Surface tension: JASPER and KRING (1955) (corrects JASPER, KERR and GREGORICH, 1953)

0°: 18.25   10°: 17.15   20°: 16.05   30°: 14.94

Refractive index: DOOLITTLE and PETERSON (1951)

t°	n_D
20°	1.3572

n_D at −60° = 1.3990; at −25° = 1.3816; at +20° = 1.3577 BENOLIEL (1941)

Iso-PENTANE C_5H_{12}

Polyphasic equilibria

Critical temperature: 187.24 AMBROSE, COX and TOWNSEND (1960)

Vapour: *Isotherms, Saturated vapour pressure and d (liq.):* see ISAAC, KUN-LI and CANJAR (1954)

Liquid: n_D at $-60° = 1.3962$; at $-25° = 1.3787$; at $+20° = 1.3540$ BENOLIEL (1941)

Dielectric constant: PHILIPPE and PIETTE (1955)

t°	ε
20.0	2.845
0.0	2.871
−33.5	1.914
−34.0	1.920
−61.0	1.954
−95.5	2.003
−130.5	2.049

Specific heat (Vapour phase): SCOTT, McCULLOUGH *et al.* (1951)

t°	c_p
44.04	29.95
84.99	33.25
129.14	36.72
176.04	40.24
213.89	42.93

Heat of vaporization: SCOTT, McCULLOUGH *et al.* (1951)

at	6.32°	C = 6181	(C = cal/mol)
	25.00°	5937	
	27.85°	5901	

NEOPENTANE C_5H_{12}

Constants

Critical constants: BEATTIE, DOUSLIN and LEVINE (1952)

t° cr.	cr. p mm	cr. d	
160.60	23993	0.2213	

Boiling point +9.41   *Freezing point* −16.8 BENOLIEL (1941)

Gaseous state

Saturated vapour pressure: BEATTIE, DOUSLIN and LEVINE (1951)

t°	P	t°	P	t°	P
50	3.509	100	11.033	158	30.294
57	4.214	125	17.565	160.60	31.572
75	6.494	150	26.673		

$$\log_{10} P \text{ (atm)} = 3.901633 - (1136.462/T) + 4.99118 \cdot 10^{-4}T \; (T = t\,°C + 273.16)$$

Compressibility: BEATTIE, DOUSLIN and LEVINE (1952)

t°	1.0	1.5	2.0	2.5	3.0	3.5	4.0	4.5	5.0	6.0	7.0 d (mol/liter)
160	23.73	28.73	30.84	31.48	31.56	31.58	31.73	33.12	38.56	85.36	258.30 P (atm.)
175	25.46	31.62	35.13	37.12	38.46	39.70	41.77	46.03	55.45	114.62	297.92 ,,
200	28.35	36.51	42.25	46.59	50.43	54.63	60.38	69.68	85.78	165.35	—
225	31.21	41.29	49.18	55.92	62.44	69.85	79.60	94.10	117.24	217.08	—
250	33.96	45.90	55.95	65.11	74.43	85.15	99.10	118.84	149.00	268.83	—
275	36.71	50.49	62.65	74.25	86.41	100.58	118.85	144.02	181.08	320.93	—

Viscosity: McCOUBREY and SINGH (1957)

t°	$\eta \cdot 10^7$	t°	$\eta \cdot 10^7$	t°	$\eta \cdot 10^7$
+32.04	740	77.94	836	158.54	990
51.54	780	124.00	929	+184.54	1053

Refractive index: ASHTON and HALBERSTADT (1958)

t°	$10^6 \, (n-1)$
27.20	1618.06
49.54	1493.26
69.14	1400.89

Liquid state

$d^{20} = 0.5904 \; dd/dt = 0.00108 \; n_D = 1.3503 \; dn/dt = -615.10^6$ BENOLIEL (1941)

Viscosity: PHIBBS (1951)

t°	$\eta \cdot 10^5$	t°	$\eta \cdot 10^5$
−15	431	+10	281
−10	393	15	264
−5	356	20	247
0	328	25	231
+5	303	30	216

Dielectric constant: PHILIPPE and PIETTE (1955)

Crystals

t°	ε	
−35.0	1.710	
63.5	1.678	
98.0	1.651	
124.5	1.637	
146.0	1.600	
−164.0	1.598	
−143.0	1.623	
137.0	1.631	
134.0	1.633	
126.5	1.637	
−100.0	1.654	

Heat of vaporization: 5820 cal/mol BENOLIEL (1941)

n-HEXANE C_6H_{14}

Polyphasic equilibria

Critical temperature: 234.15° AMBROSE, COX and TOWNSEND (1960)

Saturated vapour pressure: AMBROSE, COX and TOWNSEND (1960)

t°	p mm	t°	p mm	t°	p mm	t°	p mm
36.44	243.09	50.60	414.71	60.21	577.82	65.76	692.93
41.05	291.20	53.04	451.99	60.58	585.04	67.55	733.75
44.45	331.27	55.53	493.24	62.33	619.81	67.67	736.17
47.32	368.46	55.69	495.74	64.24	659.78	68.70	761.15
48.98	391.25	57.79	532.74	65.44	685.70	—	—

N.B (p. 43): *Freezing point:* −95.3254 and *suppress triple point* DOUSLIN and HUFFMAN (1946)

Boiling point: 68.67 BROWN (1952)

Constants of state

Density at 25°: 0.65480 Brown (1952)

Surface tension: Jasper and Kring (1955)

t°	γ	t°	γ
0	20.44	40	16.36
10	19.42	50	15.34
20	18.40	60	14.32
30	17.38	—	—

Refractive index n_D

−60°: 1.4135 −25°: 1.3970 +20°: 1.3750 Benoliel (1941)
+25°: 1.3722 Brown (1952)

Specific magnetic susceptibility at 20°: $-0.856 \cdot 10^{-6}$ von Rautenfeld and Steurer (1942)

2-METHYLPENTANE C_6H_{14}

N.B. (p. 47): *Suppress* Kay (1946)

Critical temperature: 224.30° Ambrose, Cox and Townsend (1960)

Boiling point: 60.271 *dt/dp (10 mm):* 0.4141 Forziati, Glasgow Jr. *et al.* (1946)

N.B. (p. 48): *Freezing point:* −153.6135 (and *suppress triple point*) Douslin and Huffman (1946)

Density at 20°: 0.65315 Forziati, Glasgow Jr *et al.* (1946)

N.B. (p. 48): *Suppress* Van Risseghem (1938) and Chavanne and Van Risseghem (1922) and (p. 49): Tongberg and Fenske (1936)

Refractive index n_D

20°: 1.37145   25°: 1.36873 Forziati, Glasgow Jr. *et al.* (1946)

−25°: 1.3945 +20°: 1.3714 Benoliel (1941)

Specific heat (vapour): WADDINGTON, SMITH *et al.* (1949)

p mm	51.95°	89.00°	129.10°	163.05°	198.00°
760.5	—	41.02	44.48	47.34	50.35 cal/mol
455.4	37.45	40.72	—	—	— „
211.9	37.10	40.51	44.21	47.24	50.23 „

Heat of vaporization: WADDINGTON, SMITH *et al.* (1949)

t°	cal/mol
25.0	7144
45.0	6865
60.3	6642

2,3-DIMETHYLBUTANE C_6H_{14}

Critical temperature: 226.78° AMBROSE, COX and TOWNSEND (1960)

Freezing point: −128.010 DOUSLIN and HUFFMAN (1946)

Specific heat (vapour): WADDINGTON, SMITH *et al.* (1949)

t°	cal/mol
68.44	37.78
98.04	40.69
129.14	43.63
162.84	46.73
197.99	49.77

p mm	68.45°	98.05°	129.15°	162.85°	198.00°
760.0	38.62	41.19	43.98	46.94	49.90
284.4	38.10	40.88	43.77	46.81	49.82

Heat of vaporization

t°	cal/mol
22.80	6988
29.87	6900
39.97	6769
57.99	6519

2,2-DIMETHYLBUTANE C_6H_{14}

Critical temperature: 215.58° AMBROSE, COX and TOWNSEND (1960)

Saturated vapour pressure: NICOLINI (1951)

t°	p mm	t°	p mm	t°	p mm
0	110.3	18	242.9	32	414.1
2	121.3	20	263.2	35	461.2
5	138.7	22	284.9	38	512.8
8	159.0	25	319.3	40	550.3
10	173.6	28	357.0	42	589.5
12	189.6	30	384.5	45	650.1
15	213.9	—	—	—	—

Boiling point: 49.9 NICOLINI (1951)

Freezing point: —98.954 DOUSLIN and HUFFMAN (1946)

N.B. (p. 56): In GLASGOW Jr. *et al.*, replace —99.73° by —99.97°

Refractive index n_D at —25°: 1.3929; +20°: 1.3690 BENOLIEL (1941)

n-HEPTANE C_7H_{16}

Polyphasic equilibria

Critical temperature: 267.13° AMBROSE, COX and TOWNSEND (1960)

Saturated vapour pressure: BROWN (1952)

t°	p mm	t°	p mm
40.00	92.51	80.00	428.20
50.00	141.64	90.00	590.14
60.00	210.32	91.00	608.55
70.00	303.79	98.40	760.00

t°	p mm	
50	141	NEFF and HICKMAN (1955)
55	173	,,
60	210	,,

t°	p mm	t°	p mm	t°	p mm	
26.039	48.19	51.373	149.76	92.078	628.32	FORZIATI, NORRIS and ROSSINI
29.813	57.88	55.442	176.26	97.180	732.53	,, (1949)
33.108	67.60	60.902	217.54	97.728	744.49	,,
36.105	77.65	65.916	262.13	98.237	755.75	,,
38.901	88.06	71.966	325.42	98.813	768.63	,,
42.680	104.00	78.202	402.93	99.322	780.20	,,
46.987	124.95	84.856	501.15	—	—	,,
51.9	150.9	—	—	—	—	ROCK and SIEG (1955)

Boiling point: 98.4°   KYLE and REED (1958) and BROWN (1952)

               98.40°   BROWN and EWALD (1951)

               98.422° dt/dp *(10 mm)* = 0.448 POMERANTZ (1952)

               98.427° dt/dp *(10 mm)* = 0.4481 FORZIATI and ROSSINI (1949)

               98.5°   HAMMOND and STOKES (1955)

Freezing point: —90.5983° DOUGLAS, FURUKAWA *et al.* (1954)

                —90.60°   HUFFMAN, GROSS, SCOTT and McCULLOUGH (1961)

                —90.604° POMERANTZ (1952)

                —90.66°   DOOLITTLE and PETERSON (1951)

Constants of state

Density:

t°	d	t°	d	t°	d	
—10	0.7087	+20	0.6839			DOOLITTLE and PETERSON (1951)
+50	0.6582	100	0.6119			,,
20	0.68376	25	0.67951	30	0.67526	FORZIATI and ROSSINI (1949)
19.7	0.6837					ROCK and SIEG (1955)
20	0.68366	25	0.67937			POMERANTZ (1952)
		25	0.6798			BROWN and EWALD (1951)
						KYLE and REED (1958)
		25	0.67958			HAMMOND and STOKES (1955)

Viscosity

t°	$\eta \cdot 10^5$	
—10.10	601.6	DOOLITTLE and PETERSON (1951)
20.00	418.0	,,
50.00	310.0	,,
25.00	388.0	HAMMOND and STOKES (1955)

Surface tension

t°	γ	
0	22.10	JASPER and KRING (1955)
10	21.12	,,
20	20.14	,,
30	19.17	,,
40	18.18	,,
50	17.20	,,
60	16.22	,,
70	15.24	,,
80	14.26	,,
90	13.28	,,
20	20.32	KOEFOED and VILLADSEN (1958)
30	19.30	,,

Refractive index

t°	n_D	t°	n_D	t°	n_D	
−60.0	1.4241	−25.0	1.4093	+20.0	1.3877	BENOLIEL (1941)
+20.0	1.3877	—	—	—	—	HARRISON and MOELWYN-HUGHES (1957)
20.0	1.3876	—	—	—	—	DOOLITTLE and PETERSON (1951)
20.0	1.3877	—	—	—	—	ROCK and SIEG (1955)
20.0	1.38756	25.0	1.38519	—	—	POMERANTZ (1952)
22.6	1.3861	—	—	—	—	HAMMOND and STOKES (1955)
25.0	1.3851	—	—	—	—	BROWN and EWALD (1951)
25.0	1.3852	—	—	—	—	KYLE and REED (1958)
20.0	1.38764	25.0	1.38511	30.0	1.38258	FORZIATI and ROSSINI (1949)

t°	He_r	H_C	Na_D	Hg_{gr}	He_{blue}	H_F	Hg_v	
20	1.38545	1.38572	1.38764	1.38930	1.39149	1.39241	1.39617	FORZIATI (1950)
25	1.38293	1.38320	1.38511	1.38675	1.38893	1.38984	1.39357	,,
30	1.38041	1.38068	1.38258	1.38420	1.38637	1.38727	1.39097	,,

Heat constants

Specific heat: DOUGLAS, FURUKAWA *et al.* (1954)

Crystals

t°	cal/mol	t°	cal/mol	t°	cal/mol	t°	cal/mol
—	—	−223.16	11.91	−173.16	22.17	−123.16	29.320
−268.16	0.0530	218.16	13.21	168.16	22.93	118.16	30.051
263.16	0.4229	213.16	14.45	163.16	23.68	113.16	30.828
258.16	1.360	208.16	15.61	158.16	24.415	108.16	31.648
253.16	2.819	203.16	16.68	153.16	25.135	103.16	32.500
248.16	4.372	198.16	17.70	148.16	25.844	98.16	33.406
243.16	5.992	193.16	18.70	143.16	26.783	93.16	34.675
238.16	7.602	188.16	19.64	138.16	27.234	− 90.598	35.498
233.16	9.120	183.16	20.56	133.16	27.913	—	—
−228.16	10.55	−178.16	21.37	−128.16	28.605	—	—

Liquid

t°	cal/mol	t°	cal/mol	t°	cal/mol	t°	cal/mol	t°	cal/mol
−88.16	48.400	−43.16	48.826	+6.84	52.139	76.84	58.795	176.84	71.187
83.16	48.228	38.16	49.067	11.84	52.555	86.84	59.880	186.84	72.665
78.16	48.130	33.16	49.330	16.84	52.981	96.84	60.996	196.84	74.225
73.16	48.096	28.16	49.609	21.84	53.415	106.84	62.143	206.84	75.912
68.16	48.116	23.16	49.918	25.00	53.695	116.84	63.323	216.84	77.825
63.16	48.186	18.16	50.245	26.84	53.861	126.84	64.539	226.84	80.194
58.16	48.292	13.16	50.586	36.84	54.776	136.84	65.789	236.84	83.680
53.16	48.439	8.16	50.945	46.84	55.728	146.84	67.077	246.84	90.636
−48.16	48.595	−3.16	51.321	56.84	56.714	156.84	68.402		
		+1.84	51.968	66.84	57.719	166.84	69.768		

Heat of melting: HUFFMAN, GROSS, SCOTT and McCULLOUGH (1961)
3355 cal/mol at −90.60°

2-METHYLHEXANE C_7H_{16}

Saturated vapour pressure: FORZIATI, NORRIS and ROSSINI (1949)

t°	p mm	t°	p mm	t°	p mm
18.528	48.08	43.549	149.67	83.769	628.24
22.260	57.77	47.579	176.15	88.814	732.46
25.518	67.51	52.960	217.44	89.357	744.40
28.469	77.55	57.913	262.04	89.860	755.62
31.235	87.97	63.889	325.31	90.430	768.58
34.956	103.90	70.051	402.84	90.936	780.13
39.219	124.84	76.628	501.07	—	—

t°	p mm	t°	p mm	
0.00	17.56	30.00	83.15	HUFFMAN, GROSS, SCOTT and McCULLOUGH (1961)
15.00	40.09	35.00	104.05	,,
20.00	51.63	40.00	129.07	,,
25.00	65.83	45.00	158.79	,,

Boiling point: 90.052° *dt/dp (10 mm):* 0.4431 FORZIATI and ROSSINI (1949)

90.1° BUCK, ELSNER *et al.* (1949)

Density: FORZIATI and ROSSINI (1949)

t°	d	
20	0.67859	
25	0.67439	
30	0.67001	

Refractive index: $n_D^{20°} = 1.3851$ BUCK, ELSNER *et al.* (1949)

t°	He$_{red}$	H$_C$	Na$_D$	Hg$_{gr}$	He$_{blue}$	H$_F$	Hg$_v$	
20	1.38266	1.38293	1.38485	1.38650	1.38869	1.38961	1.39338	FORZIATI (1950)
25	1.38009	1.38036	1.38227	1.38391	1.38609	1.38700	1.39075	,,
30	1.37752	1.37779	1.37969	1.38132	1.38349	1.38439	1.38812	,,

Specific heat: HUFFMAN, GROSS, SCOTT and McCULLOUGH (1961)

Crystals

t°	cal/mol	t°	cal/mol	t°	cal/mol
—260.54	1.385	—240.93	7.722	—200.30	18.720
259.03	1.792	236.36	9.121	196.76	18.150
256.80	2.438	231.32	10.602	189.86	19.366
254.04	3.349	226.51	11.856	187.59	19.748
253.53	3.518	221.89	13.064	181.37	20.842
250.84	4.437	216.64	14.387	173.03	22.162
249.49	4.887	210.83	15.830	163.44	23.713
247.25	5.636	206.88	16.858	153.18	25.385
245.16	6.345	204.27	17.736	143.56	27.007
—243.51	6.891	—202.25	23.577	—135.55	28.439

Liquid

t°	cal/mol	t°	cal/mol	t°	cal/mol
—112.74	43.134	—35.56	47.816	+5.66	51.356
103.86	43.543	24.35	48.678	10.47	51.781
91.45	44.176	12.92	49.665	13.51	52.122
78.46	44.879	3.82	50.467	21.20	52.880
68.69	45.474	—1.31	50.693	22.03	52.913
57.75	46.183	+4.55	51.258	+28.02	53.564
—46.57	46.954				

Heat of fusion at triple point temp. —118.25°: 2195 cal/mol HUFFMAN *et al.* (1961)

3-METHYLHEXANE　　　　　C_7H_{16}

Saturated vapour pressure: FORZIATI, NORRIS and ROSSINI (1949)

t°	p mm	t°	p mm	t°	p mm
19.915	48.08	45.068	149.66	85.529	628.24
23.662	57.77	49.119	176.15	90.602	732.46
26.932	67.50	54.535	217.43	91.148	744.40
29.911	77.55	59.509	262.04	91.655	755.61
32.684	87.97	65.533	325.41	92.229	768.58
36.428	103.89	71.732	402.84	92.737	780.13
40.713	124.84	78.347	501.07	—	—

Boiling point: 91.850° *dt/dp (10 mm):* 0.4459 FORZIATI and ROSSINI (1949)
　　　　　　　91.6°BUCK, ELSNER *et al.* (1949)

Density:

t°	d	
20	0.68713	FORZIATI and ROSSINI (1949)
25	0.68295	
30	0.67852	

Refractive index: $n_D^{20°} = 1.3887°$ BUCK, ELSNER *et al.* (1949)

t°	He$_{red}$	H$_C$	Na$_D$	Hg$_{gr}$	He$_{blue}$	H$_F$	Hg$_v$	
20	1.38643	1.38671	1.38864	1.39029	1.39249	1.39342	1.39719	FORZIATI (1950)
25	1.38390	1.38417	1.38609	1.38773	1.38991	1.39083	1.39457	
30	1.38137	1.38163	1.38354	1.38517	1.38733	1.38824	1.39195	

3-ETHYLPENTANE C_7H_{16}

Saturated vapour pressure: FORZIATI, NORRIS and ROSSINI (1949)

t°	p mm	t°	p mm	t°	p mm
21.126	48.07	42.045	124.84	87.119	628.23
24.900	57.76	46.423	149.66	92.238	732.46
28.182	67.50	50.511	176.15	92.771	744.39
31.179	77.55	55.954	217.43	93.277	755.61
33.971	87.97	60.962	262.03	93.856	768.58
37.734	103.89	73.242	402.84	94.367	780.12

Boiling point: 93.475° *dt/dp (10 mm):* 0.4482 FORZIATI and ROSSINI (1949)
        93.3   BUCK, ELSNER *et al.* (1949)

Triple point: — 118.57 HUFFMAN, GROSS *et al.* (1961)

Density: FORZIATI and ROSSINI (1949)

t°	d	
20	0.69816	
25	0.69395	
30	0.68948	

Refractive index

t°	He$_{red}$	H$_C$	Na$_D$	Hg$_{gr}$	He$_{blue}$	H$_F$	Hg$_v$	
20	1.39120	1.39147	1.39339	1.39504	1.39723	1.39814	1.40189	FORZIATI (1950)
25	1.38866	1.38893	1.39084	1.39248	1.39465	1.39556	1.39929	
30	1.38612	1.38639	1.38829	1.38992	1.39207	1.39298	1.39669	

$n_D^{20°} = 1.3934$ BUCK, ELSNER *et al.* (1949)

Specific heat: HUFFMAN, GROSS, SCOTT and MCCULLOUGH (1961)

t°	cal/mol	t°	cal/mol	t°	cal/mol	t°	cal/mol
	Crystals				Liquid		
−260.64	0.866	−217.62	13.280	−127.96	40.792	−24.97	47.832
258.76	1.301	215.99	13.651	119.90	41.228	24.79	47.837
258.10	1.477	211.45	14.657	111.95	41.670	18.52	48.385
256.74	1.862	209.97	14.985	109.23	41.806	16.08	48.644
255.56	2.227	204.92	15.992	107.23	41.912	13.47	48.851
255.29	2.306	203.57	16.275	103.15	42.195	13.22	48.872
254.42	2.581	198.52	17.262	98.63	42.449	8.08	49.349
252.64	3.185	196.84	17.577	96.73	42.547	4.85	49.648
252.45	3.243	192.22	18.480	93.04	42.828	1.98	49.894
251.83	3.444	189.96	18.906	86.80	43.230	1.46	49.926
249.67	4.180	185.59	19.706	82.16	43.548	−0.92	49.978
249.21	4.334	182.81	20.183	74.28	44.053	+2.59	50.312
248.74	4.493	178.66	20.868	71.02	44.294	6.15	50.670
245.74	5.491	175.58	21.382	61.56	44.951	10.10	51.017
245.27	5.655	171.28	22.081	60.28	45.075	10.49	51.051
245.09	5.719	168.30	22.550	49.33	45.880	11.94	51.181
241.61	6.847	163.34	23.349	49.10	45.901	13.06	51.308
241.00	7.040	160.49	23.804	39.10	46.674	16.18	51.628
240.12	7.321	154.97	24.684	38.33	46.759	22.33	52.205
237.74	8.051	152.64	25.062	36.90	46.847	22.99	52.269
235.32	8.756	146.61	25.999	35.88	46.902	22.99	52.287
233.42	9.290	145.15	26.227	28.72	47.519	24.51	52.417
230.99	9.952	138.64	27.249	−27.10	47.657	+25.64	52.568
228.54	10.598	137.98	27.355	—	—	—	—
225.98	11.255	131.44	28.369	—	—	—	—
223.82	11.806	131.00	28.417	—	—	—	—
219.99	12.730	−126.35	29.206	—	—	—	—
−219.23	12.915	—	—	—	—	—	—

Heat of fusion at triple point temp. —118.57°: 2282 cal/mol HUFFMAN *et al.* (1961)

2,2-DIMETHYLPENTANE   C₇H₁₆

Saturated vapour pressure: FORZIATI, NORRIS and ROSSINI (1949)

t°	p mm	t°	p mm	t°	p mm
12.188	57.76	37.162	176.14	72.968	628.23
15.395	67.50	42.477	217.43	77.970	732.46
18.312	77.54	47.378	262.03	78.508	744.39
21.032	87.97	53.287	325.30	79.005	755.61
24.708	103.89	59.384	402.84	79.573	768.58
28.915	124.83	65.895	501.07	80.074	780.13
33.186	149.66	—	—	—	—

Triple point: — 123.72 HUFFMAN, GROSS *et al.* (1961)

Boiling point: 79.197° *dt/dp (10 mm):* 0.4394 FORZIATI and ROSSINI (1949)

Density

t°	d	
20	0.67385	FORZIATI and ROSSINI (1949)
25	0.66953	
30	0.66508	

Refractive index

t°	He_red	H_C	Na_D	Hg_gr	He_blue	H_F	Hg_v	
20	1.37995	1.38023	1.38215	1.38380	1.38601	1.38699	1.39071	FORZIATI (1950)
25	1.37737	1.37764	1.37955	1.38119	1.38338	1.38435	1.38805	
30	1.37479	1.37505	1.37695	1.37858	1.38075	1.38171	1.38539	

Specific heat: HUFFMAN, GROSS, SCOTT and McCULLOUGH (1961)

t°	cal/mol	t°	cal/mol	t°	cal/mol
Crystals				Liquid	
−258.85	1.893	−199.51	18.464	−118.47	39.554
258.25	2.086	196.78	19.466	113.87	39.872
257.26	2.414	194.54	20.583	113.34	39.916
256.35	2.742	192.54	22.123	106.63	40.413
254.90	3.247	190.67	24.327	104.26	40.572
253.58	3.733	190.61	24.467	98.13	41.056
251.77	4.409	189.50	24.492	94.38	41.325
250.16	4.988	188.74	22.625	88.40	41.805
248.23	5.638	188.34	21.802	78.41	42.626
246.29	6.292	186.57	20.371	68.17	43.488
244.53	6.854	184.33	20.042	57.70	44.405
242.15	7.607	181.87	20.209	47.44	45.341
240.71	8.045	179.25	20.550	37.37	46.304
237.98	8.792	170.70	21.848	30.77	46.941
233.75	9.904	170.70	21.895	21.00	47.932
228.85	11.109	164.63	22.985	11.42	48.917
223.27	12.441	162.69	23.383	−2.02	49.911
218.22	13.596	157.38	24.387	+7.22	50.880
217.62	13.731	150.12	25.886	+16.29	51.902
213.45	14.714	143.24	27.399	+25.21	52.876
208.07	16.062	140.35	28.058	—	—
207.40	16.207	136.36	29.065	—	—
203.20	17.332	134.09	29.765	—	—
−201.97	17.714	−129.58	32.192	—	—

Heat of fusion at triple point temp. −123.72: 1392.2 cal/mol HUFFMAN *et al.* (1961)

2,3-DIMETHYLPENTANE　　　　　C_7H_{16}

Saturated vapour pressure: FORZIATI, NORRIS and ROSSINI (1949)

t°	p mm	t°	p mm	t°	p mm
17.523	48.07	42.786	149.65	83.429	628.23
21.293	57.76	46.849	176.14	88.531	732.46
24.575	67.49	52.290	217.42	89.080	744.39
27.563	77.54	57.295	262.03	89.588	755.60
30.342	87.96	63.333	325.30	90.167	768.58
34.106	103.88	69.562	402.83	90.678	780.12
38.407	124.83	76.209	501.07	—	—

Boiling point: 89.784° *dt/dp (10 mm):* 0.4482 FORZIATI and ROSSINI (1949)
　　　　　　　89.6°　　BUCK, ELSNER *et al.* (1949)

Density: FORZIATI and ROSSINI (1949)

t°	d	
20	0.69508	
25	0.69091	
30	0.68650	

Refractive index

t°	He_red	H_C	Na_D	Hg_gr	He_blue	H_F	Hg_v	
20	1.38977	1.39005	1.39196	1.39362	1.39582	1.39674	1.40054	FORZIATI
25	1.38728	1.38755	1.38945	1.39110	1.39328	1.39419	1.39796	and ROSSINI (1949)
30	1.38479	1.38505	1.38694	1.38858	1.39074	1.39164	1.39538	and FORZIATI (1950)

$n_D^{20°} = 1.3920$ BUCK, ELSNER *et al.* (1949)

2,4-DIMETHYLPENTANE　　　　　C_7H_{16}

Saturated vapour pressure: FORZIATI, NORRIS and ROSSINI (1949)

t°	p mm	t°	p mm	t°	p mm
13.714	57.76	38.623	176.14	74.297	628.23
16.911	67.49	43.919	217.42	79.277	732.46
19.823	77.54	48.801	262.03	79.813	744.39
22.540	87.96	54.688	325.30	80.308	755.60
26.213	103.88	60.764	402.83	80.874	768.58
30.399	124.83	67.251	501.07	81.374	780.12
34.661	149.65	—	—	—	—

Boiling point: 80.500° *dt/dp (10 mm):* 0.4376 FORZIATI and ROSSINI (1949)

Triple point: — 119.18 HUFFMAN, GROSS *et al.* (1961)

Density

t°	d	
20	0.67270	FORZIATI and ROSSINI (1949)
25	0.66832	
30	0.66383	

Refractive index

t°	He_{red}	Hc	Na_D	Hg_{gr}	He_{blue}	H$_F$	Hg_v	
20	1.37927	1.37954	1.38145	1.38308	1.38527	1.38618	1.38993	FORZIATI (1950)
25	1.37666	1.37692	1.37882	1.38044	1.38261	1.38351	1.38723	
30	1.37405	1.37430	1.37619	1.37780	1.37995	1.38084	1.38453	

Specific heat: HUFFMAN, GROSS, SCOTT and McCULLOUGH (1961)

t°	cal/mol	t°	cal/mol	t°	cal/mol	t°	cal/mol
	Crystals				Liquid		
−260.33	1.769	−188.62	18.603	−112.34	40.556	−12.90	49.477
259.12	2.182	182.72	19.662	110.44	40.695	11.01	49.638
257.24	2.807	182.31	19.730	105.17	41.086	2.67	50.574
256.69	2.971	176.44	20.730	101.82	41.356	−0.58	50.779
254.78	3.632	175.68	20.861	96.22	41.774	+1.48	50.987
253.19	4.164	170.25	21.811	86.97	42.511	2.74	51.140
251.78	4.653	168.61	22.090	77.69	43.268	4.80	51.388
248.87	5.592	163.92	22.944	77.44	43.289	7.33	51.672
247.82	5.895	160.61	23.561	67.83	44.111	8.59	51.792
244.10	7.034	157.03	24.258	67.63	44.136	12.65	52.245
243.28	7.263	153.26	24.888	58.02	44.988	13.29	52.314
239.09	8.402	152.23	25.137	57.26	45.048	13.69	52.327
233.65	9.756	149.69	25.639	48.16	45.922	17.19	52.761
228.05	10.993	146.87	26.221	46.15	46.104	17.59	52.772
222.34	12.216	143.60	26.964	42.73	46.427	20.38	53.078
217.05	13.289	141.96	27.343	38.06	46.872	23.62	53.450
216.54	13.379	139.25	27.982	34.44	47.248	26.44	53.758
212.14	14.231	134.74	29.009	32.73	47.415	26.85	53.824
206.54	15.296	132.04	29.776	22.99	48.384	28.00	53.925
200.54	16.383	−126.50	31.993	−22.92	48.444	+33.94	54.596
−194.56	17.478	—	—	—	—	—	—

Heat of fusion at triple point temp. —119.18: 1636 cal/mol HUFFMAN *et al.* (1961)

3,3-DIMETHYLPENTANE C_7H_{16}

Saturated vapour pressure: FORZIATI, NORRIS and ROSSINI (1949)

t°	p mm	t°	p mm	t°	p mm
13.484	48.06	42.904	176.14	79.672	628.23
17.252	57.75	48.365	217.42	84.803	732.45
20.547	67.49	53.396	262.02	85.355	744.38
23.545	77.54	59.466	325.30	85.866	755.60
30.109	103.88	65.727	402.83	86.447	768.57
34.432	124.83	72.411	501.06	86.962	780.12
38.824	149.65	—	—	—	—

Boiling point: 86.064° *dt/dp (10 mm):* 0.4509 FORZIATI and ROSSINI (1949)

Density

t°	d	
20	0.69327	FORZIATI and ROSSINI (1949)
25	0.68908	
30	0.68481	

N.B. (p. 79): Suppress the data of WIBAUT, HOOG, etc. (1939) and SMYTH and STOOPS (1929)

Refractive index

t°	He$_{red}$	H$_C$	Na$_D$	Hg$_{gr}$	He$_{blue}$	H$_F$	Hg$_v$	
20	1.38869	1.38897	1.39092	1.39259	1.39480	1.39572	1.39948	FORZIATI (1950)
25	1.38621	1.38649	1.38842	1.39008	1.39227	1.39318	1.39691	
30	1.38373	1.38401	1.38592	1.38757	1.38974	1.39064	1.39434	

2,2,3-TRIMETHYLBUTANE C_7H_{16}

Saturated vapour pressure: FORZIATI, NORRIS and ROSSINI (1949)

t°	p mm	t°	p mm	t°	p mm
12.555	57.68	38.012	176.06	74.523	628.17
15.833	67.43	43.424	217.34	79.627	732.41
18.804	77.47	48.422	261.95	80.174	744.32
21.571	87.90	54.445	325.22	80.682	755.50
25.313	103.81	60.668	402.77	81.262	768.54
29.599	124.75	67.308	501.01	81.772	780.07
33.960	149.58	—	—	—	—

Triple point: — 24.58 HUFFMAN, GROSS *et al.* (1961)

Transition points: — 187.35 and — 165.15 *ibid.*

Boiling point: 80.882 *dt/dp (10 mm):* 0.4484 FORZIATI and ROSSINI (1949)

Freezing point: −24.930° STREIFF, ZIMMERMAN *et al.* (1948)

Density

t°	d	
20	0.69011	FORZIATI and ROSSINI (1949)
25	0.68588	
30	0.68154	

Refractive index

t°	He$_{red}$	H$_C$	Na$_D$	Hg$_{gr}$	He$_{blue}$	H$_F$	Hg$_v$	
20	1.38719	1.38746	1.38944	1.39112	1.39335	1.39428	1.39807	FORZIATI
25	1.38469	1.38496	1.38692	1.38858	1.39079	1.39171	1.39546	and ROSSINI (1949)
30	1.38219	1.38246	1.38440	1.38604	1.38823	1.38914	1.39285	and FORZIATI (1950)

Specific heat: HUFFMAN, GROSS, SCOTT and McCULLOUGH (1961)

t°	cal/mol	t°	cal/mol	t°	cal/mol	t°	cal/mol
Crystals I		**Crystals II**				**Liquid**	
−143.86	32.673	−260.07	1.731	−192.18	18.040	−20.12	46.319
135.49	33.522	258.81	2.225	189.58	19.181	18.06	46.557
126.00	34.422	256.83	2.930	187.36	27.854	14.16	46.916
116.35	35.403	256.26	3.136	185.72	41.373	11.43	47.273
106.55	36.388	254.40	3.847	184.90	27.490	−2.61	48.187
96.60	37.418	253.16	4.314	183.87	20.900	+6.62	49.077
86.91	38.434	250.99	5.110	181.57	21.509	15.70	50.088
77.46	39.446	249.16	5.740	181.29	21.579	25.02	51.015
70.05	40.211	247.22	6.389	179.11	22.285	33.80	51.913
68.24	40.457	243.93	7.479	176.52	23.223	+40.11	52.610
61.20	41.244	243.33	7.665	176.33	23.320	—	—
58.86	41.519	238.25	9.044	174.03	24.296	—	—
54.66	41.995	232.03	10.185	171.64	25.713	—	—
51.60	42.385	225.90	11.337	170.91	26.278	—	—
45.20	43.161	220.53	12.305	169.38	27.498	—	—
43.15	43.439	219.52	12.500	167.28	31.240	—	—
37.32	44.139	218.60	12.643	165.54	44.805	—	—
36.70	44.175	214.77	13.327	163.78	29.966	—	—
31.41	44.924	213.55	13.546	161.74	29.658	—	—
31.26	44.967	208.92	14.403	159.79	29.677	—	—
−30.22	45.088	208.23	14.544	159.52	29.766	—	—
—	—	203.28	15.444	158.25	29.836	—	—
—	—	202.28	15.644	158.14	30.291	—	—
—	—	198.98	16.317	157.88	29.609	—	—
—	—	−195.21	17.177	−157.03	30.066	—	—

Heat of transition: 39.00 cal/mol at − 186.35

and 50.13 cal/mol at − 165.15 HUFFMAN *et al.* (1961)

Heat of fusion at triple point temp. −24.58: 540.4 cal/mol *ibid.*

n-OCTANE $\qquad$ C_8H_{18}

Critical temperature: 295.41 AMBROSE, COX and TOWNSEND (1960)
$\qquad$ 295.40 KREGLEWSKI (1955)

Boiling point: 124.8 $\quad$ KREGLEWSKI (1955)
$\qquad$ 125.5 $\quad$ KAZANSKI, ROZENGART et al. (1953)
$\qquad$ 125.668 POMERANTZ, FOOKSON et al. (1954)

Freezing point: −56.89 $\quad$ DOOLITTLE and PETERSON (1951)
$\qquad$ −56.864 $\quad$ POMERANTZ, FOOKSON et al. (1954)
$\qquad$ −56.7985 FINKE, GROSS, WADDINGTON and HUFFMAN (1954)

Density

$t°$	d	
−10	0.7265	DOOLITTLE and PETERSON (1951)
20	0.7026	
50	0.6782	
100	0.6350	
20	0.70264	POMERANTZ, FOOKSON et al. (1954)
20	0.7027	KAZANSKI, ROZENGART et al. (1953)

Viscosity

$t°$	$\eta \cdot 10^6$	
−10	8314	DOOLITTLE and PETERSON (1951)
20	5479	
50	3928	

Surface tension: JASPER and KRING (1955)

$t°$	γ	$t°$	γ
0	23.52	60	17.81
10	22.57	70	16.86
20	21.62	80	15.91
30	20.67	90	14.96
40	19.71	100	14.01
50	18.77	—	—

Refractive index

t°	Hα	nD	
20	1.40238	1.39762	DOOLITTLE and PETERSON (1951)
−60		1.4322	BENOLIEL (1941)
−25		1.4170	,,
+20		1.3977	,,
+20		1.3977	POMERANTZ, FOOKSON et al. (1954)

Specific heat:

Vapour: BARROW (1951)

t°	at 760 mm	cal/mol	t°	at 361 mm	cal/mol
132.54		59.02	134.94		58.86
189.34		65.25	188.14		64.86
249.54		70.68	248.14		70.61

Liquid: FINKE, GROSS et al. (1954)

t°	cal/mol	t°	cal/mol	t°	cal/mol	t°	cal/mol
−50.55	55.590	−34.03	56.161	−10.97	57.650	13.11	59.917
46.42	55.696	30.35	56.338	−3.48	58.195	17.33	60.047
42.95	55.790	23.99	56.689	1.28	58.378	24.42	60.680
41.21	55.837	20.40	56.907	+6.19	59.012	—	—
−38.26	55.967	−12.66	57.420	+8.27	59.189	—	—

Crystals: FINKE, GROSS et al. (1954)

t°	cal/mol	t°	cal/mol	t°	cal/mol	t°	cal/mol
−260.56	0.885	−237.25	8.410	−186.99	21.628	−155.43	26.937
258.59	1.335	232.38	10.014	182.95	22.403	148.12	28.090
256.66	1.839	227.44	11.564	179.91	22.952	147.45	28.151
256.42	1.915	222.27	13.121	176.66	23.473	139.53	29.295
254.35	2.543	216.66	14.748	176.48	23.476	139.49	29.307
252.89	2.998	210.51	16.369	172.38	24.240	130.98	30.495
251.51	3.464	205.86	17.472	170.86	24.508	121.77	31.786
249.56	4.118	204.47	17.805	170.11	24.593	112.41	33.036
248.53	4.469	200.24	18.748	165.21	25.413	102.91	34.380
245.90	5.394	198.52	19.149	164.33	25.548	93.73	35.754
245.12	5.666	193.77	20.192	160.10	25.743	84.44	37.254
−241.79	6.839	−188.94	21.236	−156.24	26.837	75.28	38.920
—	—	—	—	—	—	−66.21	41.237

Heat of melting: 4957 cal/mol FINKE, GROSS et al. (1954)

Heat of vaporization: BARROW (1951)

t°	at 760 mm	cal/mol		t°	at 361 mm	cal/mol
125.3		8263		100.5		8691

2-METHYLHEPTANE C_8H_{18}

Critical temperature: 286.42° AMBROSE, COX and TOWNSEND (1960)

Vapour pressure

t°	p mm	
35	78.24	WEISSMAN and WOOD (1960)
45	119.80	
55	178.08	
65	256.87	
75	361.89	

Boiling temp.: 99.0° HAMMOND and STOKES (1955)
            99.2° EVANS (1938)

Density

t°	d	
20	0.6978	QUAYLE, DAY and BROWN (1944)
30	0.6897	,,
40	0.6816	,,
50	0.6733	,,
25	0.68777	HAMMOND and STOKES (1955)

Viscosity

t°	$\eta \cdot 10^5$	
25	477	HAMMOND and STOKES (1955)

Surface tension

t°	γ	
20	20.81	QUAYLE, DAY and BROWN (1944)
30	19.72	,,
40	18.80	,,
50	17.87	,,

3-ETHYLHEXANE C_8H_{18}

Boiling point: 118.534 FORZIATI, GLASGOW Jr. *et al.* (1946)

Density

t°	d	
20	0.71358	FORZIATI, GLASGOW Jr. *et al.* (1946)
25	0.70948	,,
20	0.7134	QUAYLE, DAY and BROWN (1944)
30	0.7051	,,
40	0.6969	,,
50	0.6887	,,

Surface tension: QUAYLE, DAY and BROWN (1944)

t°	γ	
20	21.62	
30	20.61	
40	19.65	
50	18.71	

Refractive index: FORZIATI, GLASGOW Jr. *et al.* (1946)

t°	n_D	
20	1.40162	
25	1.39919	

Specific heat: BARROW (1951)

t°	cal/mol	
123.94	58.71	
189.54	65.07	
249.54	71.47	

Heat of vaporization at 25°   82.951 cal./gr. OSBORNE and GINNINGS (1947)
      118.2°   8032   cal/mol BARROW (1951)

2,3-DIMETHYLHEXANE C_8H_{18}

Specific heat: BARROW (1951)

t°	cal/mol	
124.24	58.56	
190.54	65.90	
249.04	71.76	

Heat of vaporization: BARROW (1951)

t°	cal/mol	
115.2	7935	

For 2,3 and 2,4-DIMETHYLHEXANE, see also: FORZIATI, GLASGOW Jr. *et al.* (1946)

3,3-DIMETHYLHEXANE C_8H_{18}

Boiling point: 111.969° *dt/dp (10 mm):* 0.4741 FORZIATI, GLASGOW Jr. *et al.* (1946)

Freezing point: −126.13° FORZIATI, GLASGOW Jr. *et al.* (1946)

Density: FORZIATI, GLASGOW Jr. *et al.* (1946)

t°	d	
20	0.71000	
25	0.70596	

Refractive index: FORZIATI, GLASGOW Jr. *et al.* (1946)

t°	n_D	
20	1.40009	
25	1.39782	

Heat of vaporization at 25°: 78.538 cal/gr OSBORNE and GINNINGS (1947)

3,4-DIMETHYLHEXANE   C$_8$H$_{18}$

N.B. (p. 89): Instead of VOGEL (1946): FORZIATI, GLASGOW Jr. *et al.* (1946)

Specific heat

t°	cal/mol	
133.54	59.59	BARROW (1951)
189.14	65.65	
249.44	71.86	

Heat of vaporization at 117.3°: 7952 cal/mol BARROW (1951)

2,2,4-TRIMETHYLPENTANE   C$_8$H$_{18}$

Critical temperature: 270.46 AMBROSE, COX and TOWNSEND (1960)
           270.676 KAY and WARZEL (1951)

Critical pressure: 25.308 atm. KAY and WARZEL (1951)

Critical density: 0.243 g/ml *ibid.*

Saturated vapour pressure and coexisting densities: (ibid.)

t°	P atm	d		t°	P atm	d	
		Liq.	Vap.			Liq.	Vap.
50	—	0.6673	—	215	11.320	0.4847	0.0458
60	—	0.6586	—	220	12.238	0.4760	0.0505
70	—	0.6496	—	225	13.214	0.4667	0.0555
80	—	0.6408	—	230	14.249	0.4570	0.0611
90	—	0.6316	—	235	15.342	0.4462	0.0676
99.239	1.000	0.6228	—	240	16.500	0.4350	0.0747
120	1.736	0.6027	—	245	17.724	0.4222	0.0828
140	2.783	0.5821	—	250	19.022	0.4084	0.0929
160	4.253	0.5602	—	255	20.406	0.3920	0.1049
180	6.245	0.5360	—	260	21.873	0.3720	0.1200
190	7.479	0.5229	—	263	22.793	0.3575	0.1321
200	8.867	0.5088	—	266	23.746	0.3400	0.1484
205	9.635	0.5011	0.0380	269	24.735	0.3130	0.1749
210	10.452	0.4929	0.0418	—	—	—	—

t°	p mm	t°	p.mm	t°	p mm	
23.40	47.9	40.60	102.2	58.15	200.9	NICOLINI (1951)
29.70	63.6	43.40	114.3	60.60	219.4	,,
31.30	68.1	46.10	127.2	63.20	241.1	,,
33.40	74.8	48.35	138.7	65.25	258.7	,,
35.10	80.7	50.65	151.6	67.00	274.9	,,
37.25	88.5	52.10	160.5	70.70	311.9	,,
38.85	94.8	55.35	180.9	75.00	358.7	,,

Boiling point: 99.5° at 766 mm NICOLINI (1951)

                99.239 at 760 mm KAY and WARZEL (1951)

                99.236 at 760 mm *dt/dp (10 mm):* 0.462 POMERANTZ (1952)

Freezing point: −107.393 STREIFF, ZIMMERMAN *et al.* (1948)

                −107.396 FORZIATI, GLASGOW Jr. *et al.* (1946)

                −107.388 POMERANTZ (1952)

                −107.398 KAY and WARZEL (1951)

Density 20°: 0.69188 25°: 0.68783 POMERANTZ (1952)

           25°: 0.68778 BROWN and FOCH (1955)

           27°: 0.6862 KAY and WARZEL (1951)

Refractive index

t°	n_D	
25	1.38908	BROWN and FOCH (1955)
−25	1.4123	BENOLIEL (1941)
+20	1.3915	,,
20	1.39142	POMERANTZ (1952)
25	1.38893	,,

2,2,3,3-TETRAMETHYLBUTANE or
HEXAMETHYLETHANE C_8H_{18}

Saturated vapour pressure: SCOTT, DOUSLIN *et al.* (1952)

t°	p mm	t°	p mm
0.00	4.10	40.00	48.06
15.00	11.25	45.00	62.18
20.00	15.40	50.00	79.81
25.00	20.85	55.00	101.41
30.00	27.85	60.00	127.91
35.00	36.74	65.00	160.13

Melting point: 100.63° SEYER, BENNETT and WILLIAMS (1949)
　　　　　　　100.81° SCOTT, DOUSLIN *et al.* (1952)

Transition points: 99.65° and 74.25° SEYER, BENNETT and WILLIAMS (1949)
　　　　　　　　　−120.66°　　　　　　SCOTT, DOUSLIN *et al.* (1952)

Density (liquid)

t°	d	t°	d	
100.71	0.6568	101.92	0.6557	SEYER, BENNETT and WILLIAMS
100.84	0.6566	102.28	0.6553	,,　　　　　　(1949)
101.18	0.6563	102.81	0.6549	,,

For the *density* of the *solid phases:* see SEYER, BENNETT and WILLIAMS (1949)

Heat of melting: 1802.2 cal/mol SCOTT, DOUSLIN *et al.* (1952)

Heat of transition: 477.9 cal/mol at −120.66° SCOTT, DOUSLIN *et al.* (1952)

n-NONANE　　　　　C_9H_{20}

Critical temperature: 321.41° AMBROSE, COX and TOWNSEND (1960)

Saturated vapour pressure: FORZIATI, NORRIS and ROSSINI (1949)

t°	p mm	t°	p mm	t°	p mm
70.343	48.04	98.545	149.63	143.751	628.22
74.546	57.73	103.072	176.11	149.409	732.45
78.219	67.47	109.136	217.40	150.017	744.37
81.548	77.52	114.712	262.00	150.579	755.57
84.658	87.94	121.433	325.27	151.222	768.57
88.864	103.86	128.357	402.81	151.786	780.11
93.661	124.80	135.741	501.05	—	—

Compressibility of the vapour: See also: CARMICHAEL, SAGE and LACEY (1953)

Boiling point: 150.798° *dt/dp (10 mm):* 0.4967 FORZIATI and ROSSINI (1949)
　　　　　　150.770° *dt/dp (10 mm):* 0.483　MEARS, FOOKSON *et al.* (1950)

Freezing point: −53.528 MEARS, FOOKSON *et al.* (1950)
　　　　　　　−53.539 FINKE, GROSS *et al.* (1954)
　　　　　　　−53.54　DOOLITTLE and PETERSON (1951)

Transition point: −55.95 FINKE, GROSS *et al.* (1954)

Density: N.B. (p. 98): Correct: 0.71398 instead of 0.71328

t°	d	
20	0.71763	FORZIATI and ROSSINI (1949)
25	0.71381	,,
30	0.70994	,,
−10	0.7408	DOOLITTLE and PETERSON (1951)
+20	0.7177	,,
50	0.6942	,,
100	0.6532	,,
150	0.6086	,,
20	0.71758	MEARS, FOOKSON *et al.* (1950)
25	0.71367	,,

Viscosity

t°	$\eta \cdot 10^6$	
−10.10	11518	DOOLITTLE and PETERSON (1951)
+20	7165	,,
50	4968	,,

Surface tension: JASPER and KRING (1955)

t°	γ	t°	γ
0	24.72	60	19.12
10	23.79	70	18.18
20	22.85	80	17.24
30	21.92	90	16.31
40	20.98	100	15.37
50	20.05	—	—

Refractive index

t°	n_D	
25	1.40338	CARMICHAEL, SAGE and LACEY (1953)
20	1.40541	MEARS, FOOKSON *et al.* (1950)
25	1.40305	,,

t°	He$_{red}$	H$_C$	Na$_D$	Hg$_{gr}$	He$_{blue}$	H$_F$	Hg$_v$	
20	1.40314	1.40342	1.40542	1.40715	1.40954	1.41041	1.41437	FORZIATI (1950)
25	1.40084	1.40112	1.40311	1.40482	1.40710	1.40806	1.41199	and FORZIATI
30	1.39854	1.39882	1.40080	1.40249	1.40475	1.40571	1.40961	and ROSSINI (1949)

Specific heat: FINKE, GROSS *et al.* (1954)

Crystals I

t°	cal/mol	t°	cal/mol	t°	cal/mol	t°	cal/mol
−261.23	0.837	−243.18	6.774	−193.72	22.240	−137.55	32.801
259.36	1.278	239.78	8.096	187.79	23.665	132.81	33.531
257.41	1.790	235.79	9.541	181.70	24.963	130.51	33.915
257.22	1.863	231.40	11.141	175.39	26.202	123.78	34.939
255.40	2.378	226.60	12.802	169.38	27.339	123.15	35.062
253.86	2.893	222.05	14.360	163.17	28.466	114.58	36.377
252.85	3.226	217.41	15.843	156.74	29.617	105.72	37.805
250.42	4.082	216.95	15.990	154.86	29.911	97.15	39.274
249.59	4.380	212.07	17.466	150.64	30.678	88.87	40.833
247.22	5.250	211.07	17.750	148.91	30.887	80.86	42.504
246.19	5.637	205.31	19.322	144.28	31.716	72.72	44.569
−243.59	6.613	−199.55	20.798	−141.30	32.175	−64.92	47.487

Crystals II   Liquid

t°	cal/mol	t°	cal/mol	t°	cal/mol
−54.51	167	−48.13	63.264	+1.07	65.607
−54.30	233	43.07	63.193	4.09	65.889
		40.31	63.227	9.13	66.319
		35.23	63.309	10.43	66.453
		30.47	63.467	13.43	66.778
		25.78	63.641	19.22	67.360
		20.70	63.960	19.66	67.439
		15.08	64.354	22.65	67.739
		11.03	64.621	28.78	68.364
		5.44	65.062	31.75	68.693
		−1.08	65.480	+40.72	69.699

Heat of melting at −53.539°: 3697 cal/mol FINKE, GROSS *et al.* (1954)

Heat of transition at −55.95°: 1501 cal/mol FINKE, GROSS *et al.* (1954)

3-3-DIMETHYLHEPTANE C_9H_{20}

Boiling point: 137.012 *dt/dp (10 mm):* 0.489 MEARS, FOOKSON *et al.* (1950)

Density: MEARS, FOOKSON *et al.* (1950)

t°	d	
20	0.72560	
25	0.72163	

Refractive index: MEARS, FOOKSON *et al.* (1950)

t°	n_D	
20	1.40878	
25	1.40631	

2,2,5-TRIMETHYLHEXANE C_9H_{20}

Saturated vapour pressure: FORZIATI, NORRIS and ROSSINI (1949)

t°	p mm	t°	p mm	t°	p mm
46.141	48.03	73.381	149.62	117.225	628.22
50.208	57.72	77.756	176.11	122.731	732.45
53.743	67.46	83.624	217.39	123.324	744.37
56.968	77.51	95.539	325.27	123.868	755.57
59.973	87.94	102.256	402.81	124.497	768.58
68.655	124.80	109.434	501.05	125.050	780.12

Boiling point: 124.084° *dt/dp (10 mm):* 0.4838 FORZIATI and ROSSINI (1949)

Melting point: —105.834° STREIFF, MURPHY, CAHILL *et al.* (1947)

N.B. (p. 102): STREIFF, MURPHY, CAHILL *et al.* (1947) instead of: (1946)

Density: FORZIATI and ROSSINI (1949)

t°	d	
20	0.70721	
25	0.70322	
30	0.69905	

Refractive index: FORZIATI and ROSSINI (1949) and FORZIATI (1950)

t°	He$_{red}$	H$_C$	Na$_D$	Hg$_{gr}$	He$_{blue}$	H$_F$	Hg$_v$	
20	1.39743	1.39771	1.39972	1.40143	1.40373	1.40470	1.40866	
25	1.39500	1.39528	1.39728	1.39899	1.40128	1.40224	1.40618	
30	1.39257	1.39285	1.39484	1.39655	1.39883	1.39978	1.40370	

2,4,4-TRIMETHYLHEXANE C_9H_{20}

Saturated vapour pressure: FORZIATI, NORRIS and ROSSINI (1949)

t°	p mm	t°	p mm	t°	p mm
50.648	48.02	73.786	124.79	115.621	501.05
54.826	57.72	78.631	149.62	129.260	732.45
58.467	67.46	83.123	176.10	129.869	744.37
61.776	77.51	89.149	217.39	130.429	755.57
64.862	87.93	101.368	325.27	131.070	768.57
69.023	103.85	108.264	402.81	131.636	780.11

Boiling point: 130.648 *dt/dp (10 mm):* 0.4960 FORZIATI and ROSSINI (1949)

Density: FORZIATI and ROSSINI (1949)

t°	d	
20	0.72381	
25	0.72007	
30	0.71612	

Refractive index

t°	He$_{red}$	H$_C$	Na$_D$	Hg$_{gr}$	He$_{blue}$	H$_F$	Hg$_v$	
20	1.40510	1.40540	1.40745	1.40920	1.41153	1.41251	1.41650	FORZIATI (1950)
25	1.40282	1.40311	1.40515	1.40689	1.40921	1.41018	1.41415	,,
30	1.40054	1.40082	1.40285	1.40458	1.40689	1.40785	1.41180	,,

2,2,3,3-TETRAMETHYLPENTANE C_9H_{20}

Saturated vapour pressure: FORZIATI, NORRIS and ROSSINI (1949)

t°	p mm	t°	p mm	t°	p mm
57.834	48.10	86.602	149.68	133.015	628.26
62.087	57.79	91.242	176.17	138.844	732.49
65.828	67.52	97.450	217.46	139.471	744.43
69.236	77.57	103.154	262.06	140.051	755.65
72.414	87.99	110.054	325.33	140.713	768.61
76.705	103.91	117.168	402.86	141.295	780.16
81.609	124.86	124.767	501.10	—	—

Boiling point: 140.274 dt/dp *(10 mm):* 0.5124 FORZIATI, NORRIS and ROSSINI (1949)

Density: FORZIATI and ROSSINI (1949)

t°	d	
20	0.75666	
25	0.75299	
30	0.74925	

Refractive index

t°	He_red	Hc	Na_D	Hg_gr	He_blue	H_F	Hg_v	
20	1.42122	1.42152	1.42360	1.42540	1.42778	1.42879	1.43291	FORZIATI (1950)
25	1.41903	1.41933	1.42140	1.42318	1.42555	1.42655	1.43065	,,
30	1.41684	1.41714	1.41920	1.42096	1.42332	1.42431	1.42839	,,

2,2,3,4-TETRAMETHYLPENTANE C_9H_{20}

Saturated vapour pressure: FORZIATI, NORRIS and ROSSINI (1949)

t°	p mm	t°	p mm	t°	p mm
52.028	48.07	80.311	149.66	125.886	628.25
56.243	57.76	84.871	176.15	131.611	732.48
59.913	67.50	90.965	217.43	132.227	744.41
63.262	77.55	96.574	262.04	132.798	755.62
66.381	87.97	103.343	325.31	133.446	768.60
70.587	103.89	110.331	402.85	134.021	780.14
75.418	124.84	117.787	501.08	—	—

Boiling point: 133.016 *dt/dp (10 mm):* 0.5030 FORZIATI, NORRIS and ROSSINI (1949)

Density: FORZIATI and ROSSINI (1949)

$t°$	d
20	0.73895
25	0.73524
30	0.73144

Refractive index

$t°$	He_{red}	H_C	Na_D	Hg_{gr}	He_{blue}	H_F	Hg_v	
20	1.41236	1.41266	1.41472	1.41648	1.41883	1.41981	1.42386	FORZIATI (1950)
25	1.41012	1.41041	1.41246	1.41421	1.41655	1.41753	1.42156	,,
30	1.40788	1.40816	1.41020	1.41194	1.41427	1.41525	1.41926	,,

2,2,4,4-TETRAMETHYLPENTANE C_9H_{20}

Saturated vapour pressure: FORZIATI, NORRIS and ROSSINI (1949)

$t°$	p mm	$t°$	p mm	$t°$	p mm
42.956	48.09	70.625	149.68	115.289	628.27
47.079	57.78	75.085	176.17	120.906	732.49
50.671	67.52	81.052	217.45	121.510	744.43
53.944	77.56	86.549	262.06	122.072	755.65
56.991	87.99	93.183	325.33	122.709	768.61
61.117	103.91	100.031	402.86	123.267	780.16
65.828	124.86	107.342	501.10	—	—

Boiling point: 122.284 *dt/dp (10 mm):* 0.4937 FORZIATI, NORRIS and ROSSINI (1949)

Density: FORZIATI and ROSSINI (1949)

$t°$	d	
20	0.71947	
25	0.71563	
30	0.71167	

Refractive index: FORZIATI (1950)

$t°$	He_{red}	H_C	Na_D	Hg_{gr}	He_{blue}	H_F	Hg_v	
20	1.40457	1.40487	1.40694	1.40874	1.41111	1.41212	1.41623	
25	1.40222	1.40252	1.40459	1.40638	1.40875	1.40975	1.41385	
30	1.39987	1.40017	1.40224	1.40402	1.40639	1.40738	1.41147	

2,3,3,4-TETRAMETHYLPENTANE C_9H_{20}

Saturated vapour pressure: FORZIATI, NORRIS and ROSSINI (1949)

t°	p mm	t°	p mm	t°	p mm
59.010	48.02	82.872	124.78	134.294	628.20
63.320	57.71	87.881	149.61	140.120	732.44
67.037	67.45	98.732	217.38	140.746	744.36
70.491	77.50	111.345	325.26	141.326	755.56
73.670	87.93	118.461	402.80	141.987	768.57
77.969	103.84	126.053	501.04	142.571	780.10

Boiling point: 141.551 *dt/dp (10 mm):* 0.4223 FORZIATI and ROSSINI (1949)

Density: FORZIATI and ROSSINI (1949)

t°	d	
20	0.75473	
25	0.75113	
30	0.74740	

Refractive index: FORZIATI (1950)

t°	He_red	H_C	Na_D	Hg_gr	He_blue	H_F	Hg_v	
20	1.41984	1.42016	1.42222	1.42402	1.42638	1.42737	1.43144	
25	1.41766	1.41798	1.42003	1.42182	1.42417	1.42515	1.42920	
30	1.41548	1.41580	1.41784	1.41962	1.42196	1.42293	1.42696	

3,3-DIETHYLPENTANE C_9H_{20}
(See also Addenda, p. 433)

Saturated vapour pressure: FORZIATI, NORRIS and ROSSINI (1949)

t°	p mm	t°	p mm	t°	p mm
62.882	48.02	92.048	149.62	138.862	628.21
67.240	57.71	96.737	176.10	144.725	732.44
71.026	67.46	103.002	217.38	145.356	744.36
74.484	77.50	115.727	325.26	145.942	755.56
77.699	87.93	122.903	402.80	146.606	768.57
82.043	103.84	130.558	501.04	147.194	780.10
87.000	124.79	—	—	—	—

N.B. (p. 101): Instead of 31.6° and 33.110°: write −31.6° and −33.110°

Boiling point: 146.168° *dt/dp (10 mm):* 0.5109° FORZIATI, NORRIS and ROSSINI (1949)

Density: FORZIATI and ROSSINI (1949)

t°	d	
20	0.75359	
25	0.75000	
30	0.74634	

Refractive index: FORZIATI (1950)

t°	He_red	H_C	Na_D	Hg_gr	He_blue	H_F	Hg_v	
20	1.41816	1.41845	1.42051	1.42226	1.42460	1.42558	1.42957	
25	1.41604	1.41633	1.41837	1.42011	1.42243	1.42340	1.42737	
30	1.41392	1.41421	1.41623	1.41796	1.42026	1.42122	1.42517	

n-DECANE $C_{10}H_{22}$

Critical temperature: 344.4° AMBROSE, COX and TOWNSEND (1960)

Boiling point: 174.119 *dt/dp (10 mm):* 0.514 MEARS, FOOKSON *et al.* (1950)

Freezing point: −29.669 MEARS, FOOKSON *et al.* (1950)
      −29.6645 FINKE, GROSS *et al.* (1954)

Density: MEARS, FOOKSON *et al.* (1950)

t°	d	
20	0.72987	
25	0.72608	

Surface tension: JASPER and KRING (1955)

t°	γ	t°	γ
0	25.67	60	20.15
10	24.75	70	19.23
20	23.83	80	18.31
30	22.91	90	17.39
40	21.99	100	16.47
50	21.07	—	—

Refractive index: MEARS, FOOKSON *et al.* (1950)

t°	n_D	
20	1.41184	
25	1.40943	

Specific heat: FINKE, GROSS *et al.* (1954)

Liquid

t°	cal/mol	t°	cal/mol	t°	cal/mol	t°	cal/mol
−26.14	70.978	−16.63	71.441	−2.68	72.426	+16.28	74.219
21.46	71.173	12.55	71.709	+6.30	73.179	25.43	75.222
20.86	71.202	12.13	71.739	6.66	73.242	26.15	75.299
−20.53	71.261	−3.08	72.411	+15.93	74.171	35.88	76.416
						+45.46	77.588

Crystals

t°	cal/mol	t°	cal/mol	t°	cal/mol	t°	cal/mol
−260.88	0.873	−225.82	13.995	−146.95	33.520	−87.08	43.572
259.09	1.303	221.45	15.597	139.97	34.721	85.31	43.874
258.71	1.399	218.61	16.571	132.68	35.930	83.71	44.234
257.34	1.784	213.78	18.180	124.07	37.168	82.80	44.326
256.93	1.912	208.40	19.863	117.69	38.348	82.65	44.403
255.51	2.353	202.76	21.472	115.09	38.752	80.40	44.884
254.37	2.749	196.65	23.140	110.03	39.545	77.12	45.277
253.23	3.156	190.56	24.764	107.05	40.045	77.02	45.207
251.19	3.920	186.72	25.650	102.08	40.839	75.92	45.420
250.38	4.225	184.48	26.230	101.63	40.875	73.87	45.847
247.59	5.306	181.00	26.958	97.80	41.577	73.39	45.869
247.37	5.408	178.13	27.578	97.45	41.529	69.35	46.670
243.87	6.845	174.68	28.306	93.94	42.172	68.97	46.750
243.17	7.146	171.88	28.864	93.83	42.250	63.84	47.732
238.70	8.987	167.98	29.632	92.05	42.566	55.02	49.741
234.73	10.578	161.19	30.915	90.49	42.893	46.90	51.858
−230.30	12.308	−154.20	32.230	−89.54	42.871	39.46	54.448
						−33.89	60.440

Heat of melting at −29.6645: 6863 cal/mol FINKE, GROSS *et al.* (1954)

4-METHYLNONANE $C_{10}H_{22}$

N.B. (p. 106): Replace: *Freezing point:* −98.46° by: −99.0°

Boiling point: 165.7° CALINGAERT and SOROOS (1936)

Transition point: −101.62° *ibid.*

Critical solution point in aniline: 78.3 *ibid.*

Density at 20°: 0.73234 *ibid.*

Refractive index: $n_D^{20°}$: 1.4123 *ibid.*

2,3-DIMETHYLOCTANE $C_{10}H_{22}$

Boiling point: 164.31° *dt/dp (10 mm):* 0.51 MEARS, FOOKSON *et al.* (1950)

Density: MEARS, FOOKSON *et al.* (1950)

t°	d	
20	0.73793	
25	0.73414	

Refractive index: MEARS, FOOKSON *et al.* (1950)

t°	n_D	
20	1.41491	
25	1.41266	

n-UNDECANE $C_{11}H_{24}$

Critical temperature: 365.58° AMBROSE, COX and TOWNSEND (1960)

Saturated vapour pressure: CAMIN and ROSSINI (1955)

t°	p mm	t°	p mm	t°	p mm	t°	p mm
197.272	786.23	188.431	630.45	150.437	214.14	122.607	82.16
196.511	771.68	179.802	503.12	143.585	171.68	118.963	71.54
195.794	758.17	171.724	403.38	138.713	145.87	115.522	62.53
195.242	747.91	164.039	322.76	132.757	118.79	110.962	52.16
194.595	736.05	156.841	261.22	127.467	98.29	104.458	41.55

Boiling point: 195.890° *dt/dp (10 mm):* 0.5356 CAMIN and ROSSINI (1955)

Freezing point: −25.5712 FINKE, GROSS *et al.* (1954)
  −25.597 STREIFF, HULME *et al.* (1955)
  −25.61 DOOLITTLE and PETERSON (1951)

Transition point: −36.55 FINKE, GROSS *et al.* (1954)

Density: DOOLITTLE and PETERSON (1951)

t°	d	
−10	0.7623	
+20	0.7402	
50	0.7180	
100	0.6800	
150	0.6393	
200	0.5947	

Viscosity: DOOLITTLE and PETERSON (1951)

t°	$\eta \cdot 10^6$	
−10.10	21717	
+20.00	11855	
50.00	7609	

Surface tension: JASPER and KRING (1955)

t°	γ	t°	γ
0	26.46	60	21.05
10	25.56	70	20.15
20	24.66	80	19.25
30	23.76	90	18.35
40	22.86	100	17.45
50	21.96	—	—

Refractive index

t°	He_r	$H\alpha$	Na_D	Hg_{gr}	He_{blue}	H_F	Hg_v	
20	1.41483	1.41513	1.41725	1.41906	1.42144	1.42244	1.42647	CAMIN and ROSSINI
25	1.41266	1.41296	1.41507	1.41687	1.41924	1.42023	1.42424	,, (1955)
30	1.41049	1.41079	1.41289	1.41468	1.41704	1.41801	1.42201	,,
20	—	—	1.4170	—	—	—	—	DOOLITTLE and PETERSON (1951)

Heat of melting at −25.5712°: 5301 cal/mol FINKE, GROSS *et al.* (1954)

Heat of transition at −36.55: 1639 cal/mol FINKE, GROSS *et al.* (1954)

Specific heat: FINKE, GROSS *et al.* (1954)

Crystals I

t°	cal/mol	t°	cal/mol	t°	cal/mol	t°	cal/mol
−261.01	0.967	−244.29	7.049	−196.52	25.117	−153.01	35.375
259.42	1.380	241.18	8.398	192.25	26.350	146.35	36.620
258.60	1.616	237.30	10.095	188.24	27.526	143.65	37.246
257.78	1.844	233.33	11.777	185.56	28.202	143.52	37.223
256.65	2.204	229.30	13.479	179.64	29.683	136.06	38.588
255.85	2.455	225.04	15.226	178.47	29.915	133.96	39.009
254.29	3.008	220.99	17.175	171.18	31.612	125.32	40.536
253.51	3.290	216.38	18.559	170.51	31.701	113.63	42.597
251.40	4.114	214.72	19.174	163.41	33.109	101.99	44.766
250.83	4.327	210.80	20.593	162.81	33.414	90.85	46.904
248.39	5.320	205.27	22.406	161.15	33.553	80.16	49.116
247.79	5.568	204.20	22.778	155.78	34.729	69.89	51.424
−244.92	6.774	−199.11	24.289	−153.65	35.286	− 59.09	54.216

Crystals II

−32.34	83.068	−30.91	83.992	−29.34	86.517		

Liquid

−21.42	78.838	−10.40	79.275	5.91	80.439	16.36	81.521
−18.08	78.892	−3.70	79.661	6.84	80.524	24.82	82.461
−13.40	79.085	−2.09	79.758	15.42	81.394	25.76	82.515

n-DODECANE $C_{12}H_{26}$

Critical temperature: 385.1° AMBROSE, COX and TOWNSEND (1960)

Freezing point: −9.5840 FINKE, GROSS *et al.* (1954)
               −9.599 STREIFF, HULME *et al.* (1955)

Density at 20°: 0.7490   VAN DER WAALS (1951)

Surface tension

t°	γ	t°	γ	
0	27.12	60	21.81	JASPER and KRING (1955)
10	26.24	70	20.93	,,
20	25.35	80	20.05	,,
30	24.47	90	19.16	,,
40	23.58	100	18.28	,,
50	22.70	—	—	,,
20	25.42	30.0	24.52	KOEFOED and VILLADSEN (1958)

Refractive index: $n_D^{20°} = 1.4216$ VAN DER WAALS (1951)

Heat of melting at −9.5840°: 8804 cal/mol FINKE, GROSS *et al.* (1954)

Specific heat: FINKE, GROSS *et al.* (1954)

Crystals

t°	cal/mol	t°	cal/mol	t°	cal/mol	t°	cal/mol
−261.34	0.850	−232.76	12.761	−178.43	31.911	−119.95	44.052
259.82	1.235	228.54	14.664	176.73	32.300	118.12	44.326
258.27	1.667	224.22	16.584	172.21	33.408	110.66	45.741
258.12	1.716	219.98	18.393	168.00	34.131	108.44	46.135
256.76	2.158	218.16	19.099	165.92	34.845	101.68	47.418
255.95	2.417	215.35	20.241	161.20	35.893	98.33	48.034
255.19	2.692	212.53	21.344	159.57	36.243	92.52	49.175
253.52	3.327	211.36	21.742	153.76	37.492	88.37	49.958
253.44	3.377	210.77	21.998	152.67	37.702	78.20	51.968
251.49	4.170	207.49	23.170	146.21	39.044	67.79	54.149
250.39	4.631	204.84	24.085	145.56	39.156	57.64	56.394
248.93	5.256	202.13	24.983	138.52	40.580	48.01	58.729
247.24	6.026	198.51	26.142	138.30	40.601	38.63	61.282
246.11	6.534	196.44	26.805	134.75	41.084	29.57	63.994
243.93	7.544	191.82	28.263	130.68	42.076	21.30	66.932
243.19	7.894	190.75	28.588	129.60	42.260	−14.75	70.340
240.24	9.280	184.71	30.350	−127.12	42.761		
−236.48	11.050	−184.42	30.393				

Liquid

t°	cal/mol	t°	cal/mol	t°	cal/mol	t°	cal/mol
−6.47	86.984	8.04	88.040	20.45	89.340	34.97	91.085
−0.77	87.249	9.90	88.198	26.09	89.999	44.25	92.282
−0.34	87.377	17.12	88.960	30.87	90.585	—	—

n-TRIDECANE $\qquad$ C₁₃H₂₈

Saturated vapour pressure: CAMIN and ROSSINI (1955)

t°	p mm	t°	p mm	t°	p mm
236.065	771.28	209.788	403.29	157.603	82.01
235.316	757.97	201.634	323.69	150.011	62.45
234.052	735.86	187.176	214.10	145.160	51.99
227.524	630.35	174.699	145.63	139.300	41.48
218.367	503.00	162.749	98.10	—	—

Boiling point: 235.434 *dt/dp (10 mm):* 0.5679 CAMIN and ROSSINI (1955)

Freezing point: −5.3786 *transit. point:* −18.15 FINKE, GROSS *et al.* (1954)
             −5.402   STREIFF, HULME *et al.* (1955)
             −5.42   DOOLITTLE and PETERSON (1951)

Density

t°	d	t°	d	
−5.4	0.7745	100	0.6985	DOOLITTLE and PETERSON (1951)
0	0.7706	150	0.6604	,,
20	0.7563	200	0.6201	,,
50	0.7349	—	—	,,
20	0.75622	30	0.74907	CAMIN and ROSSINI (1955)
25	0.75270	—	—	,,

Viscosity: DOOLITTLE and PETERSON (1951)

t°	$\eta \cdot 10^6$
−5.48	34460
0.0	29710
20.00	18834
50.00	11177

Surface tension: JASPER and KRING (1955)

t°	γ	t°	γ
0	27.73	60	22.50
10	26.86	70	21.63
20	25.99	80	20.75
30	25.11	90	19.88
40	24.24	100	19.01
50	23.37	—	—

Refractive index: CAMIN and ROSSINI (1955)

$t°$	He_r	$H\alpha$	Na_D	Hg_{gr}	He_{blue}	H_F	Hg_v
20	1.42314	1.42345	1.42560	1.42744	1.42987	1.43088	1.43501
25	1.42100	1.42131	1.42346	1.42530	1.42773	1.42874	1.43287
30	1.41886	1.41917	1.42132	1.42316	1.42559	1.42660	1.43073

n_D 20° = 1.4254 DOOLITTLE and PETERSON (1951)

Heat of melting at −5.3786°: 6812 cal/mol FINKE, GROSS *et al.* (1954)

Heat of transition at −18.15°: 1831 cal/mol FINKE, GROSS *et al.* (1954)

Specific heat: FINKE, GROSS *et al.* (1954)

$t°$	cal/mol	$t°$	cal/mol	$t°$	cal/mol
Crystals I				**Crystals II**	
— 261.38	0.950	— 193.19	29.906	— 14.85	104.0
260.23	1.263	186.19	32.181	12.47	107.9
269.93	1.356	178.95	34.236	11.77	109.3
258.49	1.780	171.24	36.274	— 9.14	114.6
258.53	1.790	162.52	38.458	**Liquid**	
256.81	2.319	153.37	40.632		
256.60	2.357	146.88	42.060		
254.95	2.999	144.68	42.574	— 0.50	94.950
254.77	3.062	148.07	43.993	+ 3.37	95.132
252.93	3.854	138.01	44.452	4.95	95.223
252.40	4.003	138.76	45.953	10.08	95.646
252.56	4.790	121.35	47.887	12.10	95.828
249.64	5.240	110.26	49.692	18.23	96.487
247.77	6.090	105.21	50.675	25.95	97.320
246.67	6.600	101.07	51.439	+ 33.17	98.298
244.98	7.396	100.53	51.744		
243.36	8.192	97.06	52.412		
242.25	8.733	92.03	53.445		
239,45	10.130	90.65	53.840		
235.20	12.224	88.22	54.341		
230.58	14.519	82.37	55.605		
225.48	16.952	81.58	55.842		
220.19	19.418	72.27	57.975		
217.28	20.700	62.21	60.572		
214.77	21.810	49.17	64.438		
212.18	22.884	39.98	67.741		
209.23	24.084	31.65	71.580		
207.90	25.026	28.19	76.324		
— 240.42	27.368				

n-TETRADECANE $C_{14}H_{30}$

Saturated vapour pressure: CAMIN and ROSSINI (1955)

t°	p mm	t°	p mm	t°	p mm
254.165	771.44	236.013	503.00	173.637	81.97
253.401	758.02	218.840	323.71	165.911	62.44
252.104	735.86	204.019	214.11	154.860	41.49
245.408	630.36	191.234	145.64	—	—
				—	—

Boiling point: 253.515 dt/dp *(10 mm):* 0.5824 CAMIN and ROSSINI (1955)

Freezing point: +5.857 FINKE, GROSS *et al.* (1954)
    +5.853 STREIFF, HULME *et al.* (1955)

Density: CAMIN and ROSSINI (1955)

t°	d
20	0.76275
25	0.75917
30	0.75566

Surface tension: JASPER and KRING (1955)

t°	γ	t°	γ
10	27.43	60	23.09
20	26.56	70	22.22
30	25.69	80	21.35
40	24.82	90	20.48
50	23.96	100	19.61

Refractive index: CAMIN and ROSSINI (1955)

t°	He_r	H_C	Na_D	Hg_{gr}	He_{blue}	H_F	Hg_v
20	1.42644	1.42676	1.42892	1.43078	1.43324	1.43427	1.43849
25	1.42439	1.42470	1.42685	1.42870	1.43115	1.43217	1.43637
30	1.42234	1.42264	1.42478	1.42662	1.42906	1.43007	1.43425

Heat of melting: 10,772 cal/mol FINKE, GROSS *et al.* (1954)

Specific heat: FINKE, GROSS *et al.* (1954)

Crystals

t°	cal/mol	t°	cal/mol	t°	cal/mol	t°	cal/mol
−261.07	1.004	−228.61	16.322	−142.34	45.284	−82.13	58.273
260.97	1.026	223.83	18.763	134.89	46.978	79.50	58.861
259.33	1.492	218.97	21.084	127.31	48.619	78.14	59.107
259.11	1.557	218.77	21.185	119.26	50.317	75.88	59.633
257.53	2.062	214.06	23.361	111.13	52.049	74.11	60.092
257.23	2.167	213.89	23.429	105.21	53.139	71.10	60.796
255.77	2.707	209.29	25.431	103.25	53.723	67.98	61.510
255.29	2.890	204.28	27.443	98.91	54.558	64.22	62.297
253.87	3.474	198.94	29.469	98.72	54.635	59.23	63.652
253.22	3.759	193.17	31.582	98.24	54.394	49.96	66.074
251.65	4.461	186.99	33.720	97.39	54.968	40.02	68.554
250.74	4.887	184.83	34.362	95.58	55.344	32.37	71.174
250.02	5.712	180.80	35.587	92.29	55.995	28.64	72.390
247.68	6.364	179.12	36.026	91.21	56.275	23.98	74.064
246.14	7.140	174.60	37.343	91.02	56.188	23.49	73.741
244.69	7.884	172.59	37.850	89.91	56.565	19.06	75.835
243.18	8.680	168.33	39.017	87.66	57.057	15.87	77.002
240.06	10.349	165.19	39.813	85.36	57.530	13.58	77.818
236.59	12.192	157.68	41.758	83.90	57.896	9.84	79.501
−232.85	14.156	−150.07	43.543	−83.56	57.887	−4.95	81.923

Liquid

t°	cal/mol	t°	cal/mol	t°	cal/mol	t°	cal/mol
9.55	103.186	15.32	103.760	22.49	104.484	29.61	105.352
12.72	103.490	18.58	104.122	25.44	104.841	—	—

N.B. p. 111, suppress Specific heat of PARKS and LIGHT (1934)

n-PENTADECANE $\qquad$ $C_{15}H_{32}$

Saturated vapour pressure: CAMIN and ROSSINI (1955)

t°	p mm	t°	p mm	t°	p mm
270.499	758.08	235.150	323.72	188.905	81.96
269.164	735.86	219.982	214.11	180.919	62.44
262.310	630.36	206.886	145.64	169.686	41.49
252.703	503.00	—	—	—	—

Boiling point: 91.5° (1 mm) CUTLER, MCMICKLE *et al.* (1958)

270.614° *dt/dp (10 mm):* 0.5956 CAMIN and ROSSINI (1955)

Freezing point: +9.9371° FINKE, GROSS *et al.* (1954)

+9.916° STREIFF, HULME *et al.* (1955)

Density: CAMIN and ROSSINI (1955)

t°	d	t°	d	t°	d
20	0.76830	25	0.76488	30	0.76140

CUTLER, MCMICKLE *et al* (1958)

P (atm)	37.8°	60.0°	79.4°	98.9°	115.0°	135.0°
1	0.7562	0.7408	0.7272	0.7135	0.7011	0.6861
340.1	0.7769	0.7635	0.7525	0.7414	0.7311	0.7191
680.2	0.7940	0.7811	0.7715	0.7615	0.7522	0.7416
1020.2	—	0.7962	0.7872	0.7780	0.7694	0.7600
1360.3	—	0.8091	0.8008	0.7920	0.7841	0.7780
1700.4	—	0.8207	0.8113	0.8046	0.7968	0.7888
2040.5	—	—	0.8238	0.8157	0.8081	0.8003
2380.4	—	—	0.8336	0.8256	0.8184	0.8103
2720.6	—	—	0.8422	0.8345	0.8277	0.8195
3070.7	—	—	—	0.8427	0.8360	0.8280
3400.0	—	—	—	0.8506	0.8437	0.8361
3740.7	—	—	—	0.8580	0.8514	0.8436
4080.3	—	—	—	0.8651	0.8586	0.8508
4421.1	—	—	—	0.8719	0.8654	0.8576
4761.0	—	—	—	—	0.8719	0.8642
5101.1	—	—	—	—	0.8780	0.8704
5441.2	—	—	—	—	0.8837	0.8762
5781.3	—	—	—	—	—	0.8820
6121.3	—	—	—	—	—	0.8876
6461.3	—	—	—	—	—	0.8932

Surface tension: JASPER and KRING (1955)

t°	γ	t°	γ	t°	γ
20	27.07	50	24.50	80	21.93
30	26.21	60	23.64	90	21.07
40	25.35	70	22.78	100	20.21

Refractive index: CAMIN and ROSSINI (1951)

t°	He$_{red}$	H$_C$	Na$_D$	Hg$_{gr}$	He$_{blue}$	H$_F$	Hg$_v$
20	1.42940	1.42971	1.43188	1.43375	1.43623	1.43726	1.44153
25	1.42732	1.42736	1.42979	1.43165	1.43412	1.43515	1.43940
30	1.42524	1.42555	1.42770	1.42955	1.43201	1.43304	1.43727

Heat of melting: 8268 cal/mol FINKE, GROSS *et al.* (1954)

Heat of transition at −2.26°: 2191 cal/mol FINKE, GROSS *et al.* (1954)

Specific heat: FINKE, GROSS *et al.* (1954)
Crystals I

t°	cal/mol	t°	cal/mol	t°	cal/mol	t°	cal/mol
−261.32	1.031	−223.97	19.715	−143.65	48.226	−95.29	59.509
260.84	1.170	218.91	22.305	140.29	48.939	92.54	60.196
259.82	1.460	216.39	23.551	135.90	50.108	90.02	60.766
259.00	1.680	213.39	25.034	135.67	50.164	88.63	61.048
258.30	1.967	211.05	26.121	131.13	50.934	87.01	61.438
257.19	2.412	207.80	27.644	130.93	51.267	81.11	62.940
256.66	2.546	205.69	28.547	128.81	51.801	77.32	63.843
255.31	3.108	200.34	30.737	127.05	52.185	67.61	66.387
254.88	3.260	194.51	33.050	123.74	52.919	58.23	68.900
253.42	3.908	188.29	35.445	121.98	53.365	50.58	71.357
252.92	4.126	186.32	36.122	118.32	54.191	48.67	71.936
251.31	4.867	181.85	37.609	115.64	54.801	41.44	74.429
250.50	5.267	179.83	38.230	114.48	55.011	38.95	75.249
248.76	6.119	175.06	39.697	112.35	55.632	31.21	78.291
247.49	6.770	173.46	40.169	108.90	56.375	29.60	78.952
245.92	7.601	167.66	41.866	107.36	56.483	28.65	79.327
244.52	8.329	167.06	42.015	104.89	57.114	20.92	83.055
243.27	8.991	160.03	43.995	104.71	57.314	20.63	83.178
240.37	10.627	159.72	44.061	102.37	57.909	18.45	84.394
236.83	12.637	152.41	46.020	99.37	58.591	11.59	88.805
233.04	14.761	151.71	46.195	97.83	58.842	10.90	89.389
−228.77	17.094	−144.28	48.051	−96.25	59.207	−5.85	94.862

Crystals II

t°	cal/mol	t°	cal/mol	t°	cal/mol	t°	cal/mol
+0.14	130.1	3.12	138.7	4.85	143.6	6.63	150.7
3.11	138.7	3.97	141.4	—	—	—	—

Liquid

t°	cal/mol	t°	cal/mol	t°	cal/mol	t°	cal/mol
+12.35	111.161	18.46	111.689	25.31	112.366	39.62	114.233
16.60	111.464	22.93	112.089	31.32	113.074	—	—

n-HEXADECANE $C_{16}H_{34}$

Saturated vapour pressure: CAMIN, FORZIATI and ROSSINI (1954)

t°	p mm	t°	p mm	t°	p mm
286.704	758.50	242.432	261.15	208.962	98.24
285.337	736.32	235.145	214.20	203.437	82.14
278.333	630.54	227.336	171.66	199.273	71.49
268.540	503.11	221.780	145.87	195.301	62.48
259.336	403.36	215.000	118.69	190.054	52.09
250.605	323.81	—	—	—	—

Freezing point: 18.1626° FINKE, GROSS *et al.* (1954)

18.149° STREIFF, HULME *et al.* (1955)

Density

t°	d	
20	0.7736	WIBAUT and BRAND (1961)
25	0.7703	,,
20	0.77344	CAMIN, FORZIATI and ROSSINI (1954)
25	0.76996	,,
30	0.76643	,,
20	0.7737	HARDY (1958)

Viscosity

t°	$\eta \cdot 10^5$	
20	3454	HARDY (1958)
20	3453	SCHIESSLER and WHITMORE (1955)

Surface tension

t°	γ	
20	27.47	JASPER and KRING (1955)
30	26.62	,,
40	25.76	,,
50	24.91	,,
60	24.06	,,
70	23.20	,,
80	22.35	,,
90	21.49	,,
100	20.64	,,
20	27.42	KOEFOED and VILLADSEN (1958)
30	26.62	,,

Refractive index: CAMIN, FORZIATI and ROSSINI (1954)

t°	He$_r$	H$_C$	D	Hg$_{gr}$	He$_{blue}$	H$_F$	Hg$_v$
20	1.43204	1.43235	1.43453	1.43640	1.43888	1.43993	1.44419
25	1.43001	1.43032	1.43250	1.43436	1.43684	1.43788	1.44213
30	1.42798	1.42829	1.43047	1.43232	1.43480	1.43583	1.44007

t°	Hα	Na$_D$	Hβ	Hγ	
20	1.4322	1.4345	1.4398	1.4442	WIBAUT and BRAND (1961)
25	1.4303	1.4325	1.4378	1.4422	,,

Heat of melting: 12753 cal/mol FINKE, GROSS et al. (1954)

Specific heat: FINKE, GROSS et al. (1954)

Crystals

t°	cal/mol	t°	cal/mol	t°	cal/mol	t°	cal/mol
−261.26	1.052	−235.95	13.752	−177.20	41.024	−102.77	60.294
260.29	1.348	232.26	15.944	174.08	41.951	100.29	60.905
259.72	1.506	227.56	18.658	171.51	42.761	94.63	62.148
258.56	1.896	222.37	21.577	167.16	44.027	92.40	62.808
258.15	2.016	218.88	23.502	165.72	44.497	90.47	63.298
256.79	2.545	217.49	24.237	161.24	45.703	86.77	64.252
256.60	2.580	213.96	26.068	160.10	46.058	81.24	65.562
255.00	3.251	212.62	26.790	159.05	46.397	80.52	65.739
254.81	3.348	209.20	28.421	154.44	47.596	77.97	66.427
253.29	4.014	206.43	29.630	152.03	48.289	70.47	68.319
252.40	4.491	204.18	30.685	151.00	48.600	68.32	68.929
251.23	5.062	200.04	32.416	146.14	49.794	57.91	71.749
249.53	5.938	198.95	32.910	143.14	50.632	47.31	74.811
248.63	6.405	193.75	35.059	137.77	51.974	37.08	77.959
246.48	7.609	193.70	35.081	133.26	53.068	26.71	81.361
245.77	7.986	188.28	37.261	129.42	53.995	16.24	85.252
243.10	9.518	187.54	37.511	120.03	56.239	−5.75	89.709
242.94	9.640	182.78	39.222	112.68	57.885	+4.73	95.164
−239.33	11.755	−180.98	39.804	−109.98	58.590	—	—

Liquid

t°	cal/mol	t°	cal/mol	t°	cal/mol	t°	cal/mol
+22.25	119.622	29.34	120.389	34.97	121.204	39.61	121.859
25.77	119.945	32.72	120.832	35.54	121.176	47.12	123.091
28.57	120.282	—	—	—	—	—	—

OTHER PARAFFINS IN $C_{16}H_{34}$

WIBAUT and BRAND (1961)

Compound	Boiling points			Melting point	Densities	
	15 mm	20 mm	25 mm		20°	25°
2-Methylpentadecane	153.10	159.93	165.37	−9.24	0.7708	0.7673
3- „	153.76	160.63	166.12	−17.3	0.7749	0.7715
4- „	151.97	158.78	164.24	−20.22	0.7743	0.7708
5- „	151.02	157.98	163.57	−28.90	0.7742	0.7707
6- „	150.59	157.53	163.09	−30.61	0.7740	0.7705
7- „	150.45	157.33	162.87	−29.39	0.7739	0.7704
8- „	150.23	157.20	162.79	−25.55	0.7739	0.7705
3-Ethyltetradecane	152.63	159.41	164.85	−30.70	0.7790	0.7756
4-Propyltridecane	147.02	153.78	159.23	−33.58	0.7764	0.7730
5-Butyldodecane	143.98	150.72	156.19	−47.38	0.7762	0.7728
6-Pentylundecane	142.91	149.61	154.97	−41.76	0.7756	0.7721

Refractive index

Compound	H_α		Na_D	
	20°	25°	20°	25°
2-Methylpentadecane	1.4307	1.4288	1.4331	1.4310
3- „	1.4325	1.4306	1.4348	1.4328
4- „	1.4323	1.4303	1.4345	1.4325
5- „	1.4323	1.4302	1.4345	1.4324
6- „	1.4321	1.4302	1.4344	1.4324
7- „	1.4322	1.4301	1.4343	1.4324
8- „	1.4321	1.4301	1.4343	1.4323
3-Ethyltetradecane	1.4342	1.4323	1.4366	1.4344
4-Propyltridecane	1.4329	1.4311	1.4352	1.4333
5-Butyldodecane	1.4328	1.4310	1.4350	1.4332
6-Pentylundecane	1.4325	1.4306	1.4347	1.4328

Compound	H_β		H_γ	
	20°	25°	20°	25°
2-Methylpentadecane	1.4384	1.4364	1.4427	1.4408
3- „	1.4401	1.4382	1.4446	1.4426
4- „	1.4400	1.4379	1.4445	1.4424
5- „	1.4400	1.4378	1.4444	1.4424
6- „	1.4397	1.4378	1.4442	1.4423
7- „	1.4398	1.4377	1.4442	1.4421
8- „	1.4398	1.4377	1.4443	1.4421
3-Ethyltetradecane	1.4419	1.4398	1.4465	1.4442
4-Propyltridecane	1.4405	1.4386	1.4450	1.4429
5-Butyldodecane	1.4405	1.4385	1.4450	1.4429
6-Pentylundecane	1.4401	1.4381	1.4445	1.4423

n-HEPTADECANE $C_{17}H_{36}$

Freezing point: 21.7 *trans. point:* 10.5 SCHAERER, BUSSO *et al.* (1955)
                   21.95   DOOLITTLE and PETERSON (1951)
                   21.964 STREIFF, HULME *et al.* (1955)

Surface tension: JASPER and KRING (1955)

t°	γ	t°	γ
30	27.06	70	23.68
40	26.22	80	22.83
50	25.38	90	22.00
60	24.52	100	21.14

Refractive index $n_D^{70°} = 1.4170$ SCHAERER, BUSSO *et al.* (1955)

n-OCTADECANE $C_{18}H_{38}$

Freezing point: 28.20   HOFFMAN and DECKER (1953)
                   28.2   SCHAERER, BUSSO *et al.* (1955)
                   28.168 STREIFF, HULME *et al.* (1955)

Surface tension: JASPER and KRING (1955)

t°	γ	t°	γ
30	27.45	70	24.08
40	26.61	80	23.24
50	25.77	90	22.39
60	24.92	100	21.55

Refractive index: $n_D^{70°} = 1.4191$ SCHAERER, BUSSO *et al.* (1955)
Heat of melting: 14670 cal/mol *ibid.*

n-NONADECANE $C_{19}H_{40}$

Freezing point: 32.0   SCHAERER, BUSSO *et al.* (1955)
Transition point: 22.8   ,,
Refractive index: $n_D^{70°}$: 1.4211   ,,
Heat of melting: 10950 cal/mol   ,,
Heat of transition: 3300 cal/mol   ,,

n-EICOSANE $C_{20}H_{42}$

Saturated vapour pressure: WATERMAN, LEENDERTSE and VAN KREVELEN (1939)

t°	p mm	
137.0	0.50	
149.5	1.00	
162.5	2.00	
181.0	5.00	
196.5	10.00	

Critical solution point: Aniline point: 106.1° *Furfural point:* 138.1° SCHIESSLER and WHITMORE (1955)

Freezing point: 36.6 SCHIESSLER and WHITMORE (1955); SCHAERER, BUSSO *et al.* (1955)

Transition point: 36.2 SCHAERER, BUSSO *et al.* (1955)

Density

t°	d	
70	0.7550	SCHAERER, BUSSO *et al.* (1955)
37.8	0.7769	SCHIESSLER and WHITMORE (1955)
60.0	0.7621	,,
99.0	0.7361	,,

Viscosity: SCHIESSLER and WHITMORE (1955)

t°	$\eta \cdot 10^5$	
37.8	4290	
60.0	2664	
99.0	1424	

Refractive index

t°	n_D	
70	1.4230	SCHAERER, BUSSO *et al.* (1955)
30	1.4385	SCHIESSLER and WHITMORE (1955)
40	1.4346	,,

Heat of melting: 16700 cal/mol SCHAERER, BUSSO *et al.* (1955)

n-PARAFFINS　　　　　$C_{21}-C_{24}$

SCHAERER, BUSSO *et al.* (1955)

Formula	Freezing point	Transition point	Density 70°	n_D 70°	Heat of melting cal/mol	Heat of transition cal/mol
$C_{21}H_{44}$	40.2	32.5	0.7583	1.4247	11400	3700
$C_{22}H_{46}$	44.0	43.0	0.7631	1.4260	11700	6740
$C_{23}H_{48}$	47.5	40.5	0.7641	1.4276	12900	5200
$C_{24}H_{50}$	50.6	48.1	0.7657	1.4286	13120	7480

n-PENTACOSANE　　　　　$C_{25}H_{52}$

Freezing point: 53.5° SCHAERER, BUSSO *et al.* (1955)

Transition point: 47.0° *ibid.*

Density at 70°: 0.7693 *ibid.*

Refractive index: n_D at 70°: 1.4302 *ibid.*

Heat of melting: 53.8 cal/g; 18960 cal/mol *ibid.*

Heat of transition: 6230 cal/mol *ibid.*

Specific heat: SPAGHT, THOMAS *et al.* (1932)

t°	cal/gr	t°	cal/gr	
30	0.453	80	0.569	
40	0.468	90	0.578	
60	0.553	100	0.586	
70	0.561			

n-PARAFFINS　　　　　C_{26} and C_{27}

SCHAERER, BUSSO *et al.* (1955)

Formula	Freezing point	Transition point(s)	Density 70°	n_D 70°	Heat of melting cal/mol	Heat of transition cal/mol
$C_{26}H_{54}$	56.3	53.3	0.7704	1.4310	14220	7700
$C_{27}H_{56}$	58.8	47.1, 53.0	0.7732	1.4321	14440	6920

n-OCTACOSANE $C_{28}H_{58}$

Freezing point: 61.4° DOOLITTLE and PETERSON (1951)
61.2° SCHAERER, BUSSO *et al.* (1955)

Transition point: 58.0° *ibid.*

Density

t°	d	t°	d	
62	0.7799	200	0.6910	DOOLITTLE and PETERSON (1951)
100	0.7555	250	0.6578	,,
150	0.7235	300	0.6226	,,
70	0.7750	—	—	SCHAERER, BUSSO *et al.* (1955)

Refractive index: n_D at 62°: 1.4359 DOOLITTLE and PETERSON (1951)
n_D at 70°: 1.4330 SCHAERER, BUSSO *et al.* (1955)

Viscosity: $\eta \cdot 10^5$ at 62°: 5965 DOOLITTLE and PETERSON (1951)

Heat of melting: 15450 cal/mol *ibid.*

Heat of transition: 8470 cal/mol *ibid.*

n-PARAFFINS C_{29} and C_{30}

SCHAERER, BUSSO *et al.* (1955)

	Freezing point	Transition point	Density 70°	n_D 70°	Heat of melting cal/mol	Heat of transition cal/mol
$C_{29}H_{60}$	63.4	58.2	0.7755	1.4340	15800	7100
$C_{30}H_{62}$	65.4	62.0	—	1.4348	—	—

n-TRITRIACONTANE $C_{33}H_{68}$

SPAGHT, THOMAS *et al.* (1932)

Melting point: 71.0°

Heat of melting: 54.0 cal/gr

Specific heat

t°	cal/gr	t°	cal/gr
30	0.464	80	0.572
40	0.483	90	0.579
50	0.501	100	0.586
60	0.520	110	0.592

n-HEXATRIACONTANE $C_{36}H_{74}$

Melting point: 75.73° DOOLITTLE and PETERSON (1951)
  75.9° *Transition points:* 72.1 and 73.8° SCHAERER, BUSSO *et al.* (1955)
  76.0° WATERMAN, LEENDERTSE and VAN KREVELEN (1939)

Critical solution point with aniline: 132.8° WATERMAN, LEENDERTSE and VAN KREVELEN (1939)

Density

t°	d	
82	0.7795	WATERMAN *et al.* (1939)
100	0.7671	,,
100	0.7667	DOOLITTLE and PETERSON (1951)
150	0.7357	,,
200	0.7048	,,
250	0.6730	,,
300	0.6399	,,

Refractive index

t°	n$_D$	
77.0	1.4360	DOOLITTLE and PETERSON (1951)
77	1.4359	WATERMAN, LEENDERTSE and VAN KREVELEN (1939)
80	1.4349	,,
82	1.4341	,,
88	1.4316	,,
89	1.4313	,,

Heat of melting: 21230 cal/mol at 75.9° SCHAERER, BUSSO *et al.* (1955)

Heat of transition: 7300 cal/mol at 73.8°   ,,
  and 2370 cal/mol at 72.1°   ,,

For 5,14-DI-n-BUTYLOCTADECANE and other complex HYDROCARBONS of all series, see: SCHIESSLER and WHITMORE (1955)
7-n-HEXYLTRIDECANE, 13-n-DODECYLHEXACOSANE, 9-n-OCTYLHEPTADECANE, 11-n-DECYLHENEICOSANE: *viscosities under high pressure* see: LOWITZ, SPENCER *et al.* (1959)

B. ETHYLENIC HYDROCARBONS

ETHYLENE C_2H_4

Critical constants: cr. temperature: $+9.2°$ *cr. pressure:* 49.90   VAN GUNST (1950)
                                    $+9.26°$ *cr. density:* 0.2098 WHITEWAY and
                                                                MASON (1953)

Boiling point: $-103.86°$ CLARK and DIN (1950)
                $-103.78°$ MICHELS and WASSENAAR (1950)

N.B. (p. 115): In the last table replace -188.51 by -18.851
Saturated vapour pressure: CLUSIUS and KONNERTZ (1949)

t°	P atm.	t°	P atm.
-129.75	0.1575	-63.35	6.54
-103.65	1.002	-37.15	15.62
-81.25	3.16	-19.15	25.51

MICHELS and WASSENAAR (1950)

t°	P atm.	t°	P atm.	t°	P atm.
-123.783	0.25690	-103.441	1.02032	-49.818	10.5481
-117.037	0.42477	-103.443	1.02036	-40.044	14.3118
-113.407	0.54541	-100.704	1.19428	-30.078	19.0615
-109.549	0.70186	-93.376	1.77476	-23.476	22.7850
-106.531	0.84771	-89.182	2.19056	-17.881	26.3283
-104.112	0.98059	-84.581	2.72991	-11.252	31.0273
-104.113	0.98069	-76.546	3.9058	-5.308	35.7569
-104.106	0.98078	-68.912	5.3379	$+0.448$	40.8129
-104.109	0.98078	-59.538	7.5778	$+4.155$	44.3586
-103.437	1.02032	—	—	$+6.467$	46.6873
—	—	—	—	$+7.395$	47.6481

Viscosity: RONDENKO (1944)

t°	$\eta \cdot 10^4$
−103.85	16.7
−67.05	9.6
−39.25	7.75
−32.25	7.50
−30.05	6.50
+7.75	6.25

Refractive index: (vapour) ASHTON and HALBERSTADT (1958)

t°	10^6 (n–1)
26.65	658.52
50.19	609.57
50.37	609.32
63.9	584.17

Heat of vaporization: CLUSIUS and KONNERTZ (1949)

t°	cal/mol
−129.75	3424
−103.65	3201
−81.25	2993
−63.35	2787
−37.15	2313
−19.15	1877

PROPENE C_3H_6

Saturated vapour pressure: MICHELS, WASSENAAR *et al.* (1953)

t°	P atm.	t°	P atm.
24.785	11.344	87.872	42.349
44.134	17.866	88.284	42.708
66.335	28.359	88.411	42.801
74.757	33.314	89.983	44.043
82.783	38.627		

t°	kg/cm²	t°	kg/cm²	
−141.38	4.1	−117.33	14.0	EUCKEN and BERGER (1934)
137.01	5.0	115.88	15.0	,,
133.29	6.0	113.11	16.9	,,
132.48	7.0	111.54	19.0	,,
127.74	8.0	107.31	21.2	,,
126.66	9.1	104.14	23.8	,,
124.75	10.1	99.77	27.7	,,
123.15	11.0	96.93	30.5	,,
121.40	12.1	94.05	33.5	,,
−119.08	13.1	93.15	34.6	,,
		−91.25	35.2	,,

Compressibility: MICHELS, WASSENAAR *et al.* (1953)

d in Amagat units	t°			
	25	45	50	75
	P atm.			
6.4976	6.4994	7.0393	7.1728	7.8365
8.3409	8.0810	8.7941	8.9703	9.8430
10.1832	9.5481	10.4444	10.6654	11.7558
12.1074	10.9607	12.0596	12.3293	13.6579
14.3997	—	13.8413	14.1728	15.7973
16.6494	—	15.4418	15.8382	17.7674
18.3557	—	—	—	19.1775
19.5100	—	17.2712	17.7551	20.0937
23.0078	—	—	—	22.6744
27.6638	—	—	—	25.6809
32.1907	—	—	—	28.1611
36.9366	—	—	—	30.3249
41.6597	—	—	—	32.0613

d in Amagat units	t°		
	100	125	150
	P		
6.4976	8.4920	9.1415	9.7866
8.3409	10.7020	11.5514	12.3940
10.1832	12.8257	13.8818	14.9285
12.1074	14.9562	16.2349	17.5010
14.3997	17.3793	18.9330	20.4685
16.6494	19.6391	21.4729	23.2824
18.3557	21.2770	23.3297	25.3542
19.5100	22.3483	24.5522	26.7238
23.0078	25.4271	28.1038	30.7336
27.6638	29.1347	32.4745	35.7472
32.1907	32.3417	36.3613	40.2915
36.9366	35.3143	40.0840	44.7339
41.6597	37.9045	43.4519	48.8506
42.4108	38.2855	43.9626	49.4773
46.1992	40.0797	46.4052	52.5530
47.3154	40.5730	47.0935	53.4215
50.9531	42.0618	49.2283	56.1855
52.6441	42.6970	50.1746	57.4131
57.7422	44.4147	52.8358	60.9798
63.2257	45.9607	55.4262	64.5705
66.2871	46.7032	56.7583	66.4826
68.2506	47.1373	57.5776	67.6739
73.5555	48.1715	59.6557	70.7847
73.9529	48.2417	59.8050	71.0088
78.9146	49.0320	61.5897	73.7796
82.2813	49.4889	62.7263	75.6033
90.2497	50.3702	65.2397	79.7843
95.7646	50.8558	66.8667	82.6190
98.8200	51.0919	67.7431	84.1867
106.6739	51.6323	69.9599	88.2417
106.8394	51.6419	70.0065	88.3305
114.9653	52.1356	72.3235	92.6758
118.8718	52.3749	73.4842	94.8597
123.3417	52.6595	74.8573	97.4572
130.3844	53.1538	77.1993	101.837
142.7671	54.3229	82.0668	110.730
144.9426	54.5970	83.0565	112.502
154.1153	56.0656	87.8858	120.837
161.7072	57.9025	92.8474	129.067
162.8614	58.2327	93.7056	130.429
166.0968	59.2833	96.2680	134.515
178.2029	65.0066	108.290	152.827
179.9245	66.1205	110.357	155.879
181.7025	67.3280	112.616	159.170
197.3615	83.1958	138.883	195.631
202.1815	90.3731	149.734	210.012
210.4000	106.075	172.141	238.880
216.1284	119.943	191.092	262.836

d in Amagat units	t°		
	100	125	150
	P		
221.7928	136.482	212.999	289.828
233.3462	181.014	269.468	357.890
234.7870	187.679	277.734	367.557
242.9190	231.133	330.603	429.527
251.5578	289.196	399.431	508.796
261.3570	372.781	496.241	618.781
262.3302	382.254	507.092	630.846
270.0093	465.207	601.232	735.616
282.9071	641.744	798.265	952.316
286.9120	707.347	870.514	1030.912
303.8279	1052.080	1245.603	1435.353
314.6450	1339.551	1554.516	1764.007
340.4340	2296.792	2568.932	2832.465

BUTENE-1 C_4H_8

BEATTIE and MARPLE (1950)

Critical constants: cr. temperature: 146.4° *cr. pressure:* 39.7 atm. *cr. density:* 4.15 mol/litre (0.233 g/ml)

Isotherms

t°	d (mol/litre)										
	1.0	1.5	2.0	2.5	3.0	3.5	4.0	5.0	6.0	7.0	8.0
	P atm.										
150	25.60	32.76	37.21	39.74	41.02	41.63	41.95	42.66	46.22	63.13	117.33
175	28.35	37.34	43.86	48.60	52.16	55.04	57.69	64.04	76.69	108.07	183.55
200	31.03	41.76	50.24	57.11	62.94	68.23	73.51	86.32	108.30	153.70	248.94
225	33.65	46.08	56.47	65.42	73.51	81.29	89.32	108.98	140.68	199.98	—
250	36.20	50.27	62.48	73.50	83.84	94.11	104.93	131.47	172.72	245.26	—

Vapour pressure and orthobaric liquid density

t°	P atm.	d	
30	3.410	—	
50	5.889	0.561	
75	10.613	0.523	
100	17.675	0.477	
125	27.784	0.411	

Boiling point: −6.32 BENOLIEL (1941)

Density: at −20°: 0.5952 *dd/dt:* 0.00113

Refractive index: $n_D^{-25°}$ = 1.3777 *dn/dt:* 0.000600

Heat of vaporization: 5540 cal/mol

Heat of combustion at 25°: 649.33 kcal/mol PROSEN, MARON and ROSSINI (1951)

Cis-BUTENE-2 C_4H_8

Critical temp.: 162.40° AMBROSE, COX and TOWNSEND (1960)

Boiling temp.: +3.64° BENOLIEL (1941)

Density: at −20°: 0.6213 *dd/dt:* 0.00110

Refractive index: at −25°: n_D = 1.3932 *dn/dt:* 0.000603

Heat of vaporization: 5830 cal/mol

Heat of combustion at 25°: 647.65 kcal/mol PROSEN, MARON and ROSSINI (1951)

Trans-BUTENE-2 C_4H_8

Critical temp.: 155.46° AMBROSE, COX and TOWNSEND (1960)

Boiling temp.: +0.86° BENOLIEL (1941)

Density: at −20°: 0.6042 *dd/dt:* 0.00108

Refractive index: at −25°: n_D = 1.3842 *dn/dt:* 0.000608

Heat of vaporization: 5725 cal/mol

Heat of combustion at 25°: 646.90 kcal/mol PROSEN, MARON and ROSSINI (1951)

Iso-BUTENE C_4H_8

Boiling temp.: −6.93° BENOLIEL (1941)

Density: at −20°: 0.5942 *dd/dt:* 0.00112

Refractive index: −25° = 1.3796 *dn/dt:* 0.000606

Heat of vaporization: 5535 cal/mol

Heat of combustion at 25°: 645.19 kcal/mol PROSEN, MARON and ROSSINI (1951)

N.B. (pp. 121, 122, 123), suppress the *melting points* of GLASGOW Jr., KROUSKOF *et al.* (1948)

PENTENE-1 C_5H_{10}

Critical temp.: 191.59° AMBROSE, COX and TOWNSEND (1960)

Saturated vapour pressure

t°	p mm	t°	p mm	
12.834	402.81	29.362	744.27	FORZIATI, CAMIN and ROSSINI (1950)
18.468	501.02	29.796	755.52	,,
24.584	628.21	30.289	768.46	,,
28.900	732.40	30.723	779.98	,,
−0.159	233.78	35.142	906.17	SCOTT, WADDINGTON *et al.* (1949)
+4.751	289.11	40.359	1074.8	,,
9.706	355.14	45.614	1268.2	,,
14.706	433.45	50.914	1489.3	,,
19.750	525.75	56.253	1740.6	,,
24.834	633.86	61.641	2025.7	,,
29.967	759.98	—	—	,,

Boiling point: 30.3° GELDOF (1951)

Compressibility of the vapour: see DAY and FELSING (1951)

Density:

t°	d	
20	0.64050	FORZIATI, CAMIN and ROSSINI (1950)
25	0.63533	,,
15	0.64577	GELDOF (1951)
20	0.64057	,,

Refractive index: FORZIATI, CAMIN and ROSSINI (1950)

t°	He$_{red}$	H$_C$	Na$_D$	Hg$_{gr}$	He$_{blue}$	H$_F$	Hg$_v$
20	1.36883	1.36916	1.37148	1.37348	1.37614	1.37725	1.38183
25	1.36573	1.36605	1.36835	1.37032	1.37295	1.37405	1.37858

— 25° : n_D = 1.3974 + 20° : n_D = 1.3714 BENOLIEL (1941)

N.B. (p. 125): The purity of the samples of PENTENE-1 by TODD, OLIVER and HUFFMAN (1947) is not sure.

Cis-PENTENE-2   C$_5$H$_{10}$

Saturated vapour pressure: SCOTT and WADDINGTON (1950)

t°	p mm	t°	p mm
1.595	187.58	36.944	760.03
6.522	233.74	42.161	906.11
11.486	289.12	47.423	1074.7
16.494	355.21	52.724	1268.1
21.541	433.50	58.070	1489.3
26.633	525.81	63.456	1740.8
31.766	633.94	68.882	2025.6

Boiling point: 36.94° *ibid.*

Trans-PENTENE-2   C$_5$H$_{10}$

Saturated vapour pressure: SCOTT and WADDINGTON (1950)

t°	p mm	t°	p mm
1.026	187.56	36.354	760.03
5.956	233.74	41.561	906.09
10.922	289.15	46.813	1074.7
15.927	355.22	52.100	1267.5
20.969	433.49	57.430	1489.2
26.055	525.78	62.803	1740.8
31.183	633.93	68.211	2025.7

Boiling point: 36.35° SCOTT and WADDINGTON (1950)

2-METHYLBUTENE-1   C$_5$H$_{10}$

N.B. (p. 127): *Saturated vapour pressure:* SCOTT, WADDINGTON *et al.* (1949)

t°	p mm	t°	p mm
1.155	233.74	36.308	906.02
6.054	289.13	41.500	1074.7
10.993	355.21	46.728	1268.0
15.973	433.54	52.005	1489.3
20.996	526.86	57.320	1740.9
26.062	634.06	62.675	2025.8
31.162	759.96	—	—

Specific heat: McCULLOUGH and SCOTT (1959)

t°	cal/mol	t°	cal/mol	
47.50	27.76	180.25	36.60	
89.35	30.68	229.05	39.52	
133.95	33.61			

3-METHYLBUTENE-1 C_5H_{10}

Saturated vapour pressure: SCOTT and WADDINGTON (1950)

t°	p mm	t°	p mm
0.218	355.25	30.245	1074.6
5.112	433.53	35.402	1268.1
10.053	525.86	40.602	1489.2
15.033	633.94	45.847	1740.7
20.061	760.00	51.139	2025.9
25.128	906.00	—	—

Boiling point: 20.06° *ibid.*

HEXENE-1 C_6H_{12}

Critical temperature: 230.83° AMBROSE, COX and TOWNSEND (1960)

Boiling point: 63.49 *dt/dp (10 mm):* 0.42 MEARS, FOOKSON *et al.* (1950)
      63.5 GELDOF (1951)

Saturated vapour pressure: FORZIATI, CAMIN and ROSSINI (1950)

t°	p mm	t°	p mm
15.890	124.85	50.914	501.03
19.950	149.61	62.323	732.42
23.720	176.15	62.827	744.29
28.762	217.44	63.299	755.54
33.399	262.04	63.837	768.49
38.993	325.27	64.311	780.03
44.763	402.82	—	—

Freezing point: —139.7743 McCULLOUGH, FINKE, GROSS *et al.* (1957)
       —139.9 MEARS, FOOKSON *et al.* (1950)

Density

t°	d	
20	0.67356	GELDOF (1951)
25	0.66887	,,
20	0.6732	MEARS, FOOKSON *et al.* (1950)
25	0.6684	,,
20	0.67317	FORZIATI, CAMIN and ROSSINI (1950)
25	0.66848	,,
30	0.66374	,,

Surface tension: JASPER and KRING (1955)

$t°$	0	10	20	30	40	50	60
γ	20.47	19.44	18.42	17.39	16.36	15.33	14.31

Refractive index

$t°$	He_{red}	H_α	Na_D	Hg_{gr}	He_{blue}	H_β	Hg_v	
20	1.38519	1.38552	1.38788	1.38991	1.39261	1.39373	1.39837	FORZIATI,
25	1.38235	1.38268	1.38502	1.38703	1.38971	1.39083	1.39543	CAMIN and
30	1.37951	1.37984	1.38216	1.38415	1.38681	1.38793	1.39249	ROSSINI (1950)
20			1.3879					MEARS, FOOKSON
25			1.3850					*et al.* (1950)

Specific heat: MCCULLOUGH, FINKE, GROSS *et al.* (1957)

Crystals   **Liquid**

$t°$	cal/mol	$t°$	cal/mol	$t°$	cal/mol	$t°$	cal/mol	$t°$	cal/mol
−261.89	0.566	−248.37	3.830	−198.39	15.258	−136.97	36.88	−63.60	38.27
261.63	0.611	246.44	4.378	192.92	16.145	132.56	36.85	53.65	38.71
260.50	0.817	245.53	4.642	187.39	17.015	130.28	36.85	43.80	39.21
260.32	0.858	243.59	5.190	181.79	17.798	126.21	36.86	33.66	39.76
258.95	1.121	242.54	5.502	176.55	18.430	124.40	36.89	27.40	40.13
258.70	1.180	239.79	6.283	176.09	18.536	117.45	36.93	17.05	40.78
257.33	1.468	236.13	7.296	170.63	19.230	113.75	36.95	−6.87	41.46
256.92	1.567	231.95	8.392	168.70	19.458	109.78	37.00	+3.55	42.20
255.55	1.886	228.07	9.354	168.58	19.474	104.18	37.09	+14.22	42.99
254.98	2.029	223.47	10.443	163.00	20.173	94.22	37.28	+24.70	43.78
253.57	2.396	219.32	11.357	160.83	20.455	83.89	37.54	+35.00	44.63
252.84	2.582	218.14	11.607	152.90	21.454	−73.68	37.88	—	—
251.89	2.961	214.46	12.366	−145.75	22.578	—	—	—	—
250.67	3.188	208.99	13.443	—	—	—	—	—	—
−249.12	3.616	−203.70	14.374	—	—	—	—	—	—

4-METHYLPENTENE-1 C_6H_{12}

MEARS, FOOKSON et al. (1950)

Boiling point: 53.89 *dt/dp (10 mm):* 0.42

Freezing point: −153.95

Density

t°	d	
20	0.6638	
25	0.6589	

Refractive index

t°	n_D	
20	1.3826	
25	1.3797	

3-METHYLPENTENE-2 C_6H_{12}

Freezing point: −134.866 STREIFF, SOULE et al. (1950)

N.B. (p. 131): Suppress: 2,3-DIMETHYLBUTENE-2 and TETRAMETHYL-ETHYLENE, and replace by:

2,3-DIMETHYLBUTENE-2
or TETRAMETHYLETHYLENE C_6H_{12}

Saturated vapour pressure: SCOTT, FINKE et al. (1955)

t°	p mm	t°	p mm	t°	p mm
29.026	149.41	45.278	289.13	61.909	525.86
34.404	187.57	50.778	355.22	67.535	633.99
39.820	233.72	56.321	433.56	73.208	760.00

t°	p mm	t°	p mm	
12.98	78.3	24.89	132.2	CUMMINGS and McLAUGHLIN (1955)
13.99	81.9	29.83	162.8	,,
15.94	89.4	34.93	199.8	,,
16.99	93.6	39.88	242.4	,,
19.04	102.6	74.1	781.0	,,

Boiling point:

73.206 *dt/dp (10 mm)* 0.424 HOWARD, MEARS et al. (1947)
73.24 *dt/dp (10 mm)* 0.414 BROOKS, HOWARD and CRAFTON (1940)
73.39 KISTIAKOWSKY, RUHOFF et al. (1936)

Freezing point: —74.2   KISTIAKOWSKY, RUHOFF *et al.* (1936)
              —74.2596 SCOTT, FINKE *et al.* (1955)
              —74.3   HOWARD, MEARS *et al.* (1947)
              —74.304 STREIFF, HULME *et al.* (1955)
              —74.6   PARKS, TODD and SHOMATE (1936)

Transition point: —76.34 SCOTT, FINKE *et al.* (1955)

Density: HOWARD, MEARS *et al.* (1947)

t°	d	
20	0.70795	
25	0.70336	

Refractive index

t°	n_D	
20	1.41221	HOWARD, MEARS *et al.* (1947)
25	1.40944	,,
20	1.4124	KISTIAKOWSKY, RUHOFF *et al.* (1936)

Specific heat: SCOTT, FINKE *et al.* (1955)

Crystals

t°	cal/mol	t°	cal/mol	t°	cal/mol
—261.56	0.525	—235.56	7.697	—170.64	22.035
261.36	0.551	231.39	8.930	170.09	22.064
260.11	0.760	227.12	10.148	168.66	22.344
260.09	0.771	222.59	11.412	164.92	22.883
258.53	1.065	217.85	12.620	162.62	23.198
258.22	1.119	215.48	13.217	161.06	23.457
256.61	1.463	213.25	13.765	158.28	23.841
255.98	1.616	210.18	14.493	154.65	24.339
254.32	2.028	204.91	15.706	149.05	24.945
253.61	2.216	199.67	16.806	145.56	25.518
251.65	2.756	195.36	17.683	136.02	26.710
251.13	2.908	194.35	17.901	126.89	27.853
248.84	3.631	189.33	18.916	123.18	28.331
248.30	3.796	188.82	19.012	118.10	28.984
246.03	4.429	187.90	19.159	113.07	29.658
245.31	4.652	182.69	20.124	109.24	30.156
243.24	5.297	182.43	20.085	97.12	32.063
242.38	5.558	176.61	21.095	87.68	33.864
—239.30	6.541	—176.01	21.206	—79.69	37.220

Liquid

t°	cal/mol	t°	cal/mol	t°	cal/mol
−68.91	36.86	−44.71	37.70	+13.94	40.99
64.17	36.99	35.91	38.10	22.41	41.58
61.67	37.08	26.36	38.56	24.05	41.69
61.40	37.07	16.06	39.11	29.53	42.08
53.60	37.34	−5.91	39.71	34.40	42.43
−50.75	37.46	+4.09	40.34	+44.98	43.23

Heat of vaporization

t°	cal/mol	
18.97	7856	SCOTT, FINKE *et al.* (1955)
34.71	7641	,,
52.63	7386	,,
73.21	7083	,,

Heat of fusion: 1542 cal/mol SCOTT, FINKE *et al.* (1955)

Heat of transition: 844.0 cal/mol *ibid.*

HEPTENE-1 C_7H_{14}

Critical temperature: 264.08 AMBROSE, COX and TOWNSEND (1960)

Saturated vapour pressure: FORZIATI, CAMIN and ROSSINI (1950)

t°	p mm	t°	p mm
21.609	47.89	67.366	325.27
25.492	57.69	73.563	402.82
28.768	67.44	80.179	501.05
34.525	87.91	92.391	732.44
38.281	103.85	92.941	744.31
42.564	124.84	93.444	755.56
46.923	149.60	94.022	768.53
50.970	176.13	94.531	780.08
56.384	217.43	—	—

Boiling point: 93.4 (755 mm) GELDOF (1951)

Freezing point: −119.313 McCULLOUGH, FINKE, GROSS *et al.* (1957)

Density

t°	d	
20	0.69698	FORZIATI, CAMIN and ROSSINI (1950)
25	0.69267	,,
30	0.68815	,,
20	0.69720	GELDOF (1951)
25	0.69286	,,

Surface tension

t°	0	10	20	30	40	50	60	70	80	
γ	22.28	21.29	20.30	19.31	18.32	17.33	16.34	15.34	14.35	JASPER and KRING (1955)

Refractive index: FORZIATI, CAMIN and ROSSINI (1950)

t°	He_{red}	H_α	Na_D	Hg_{gr}	He_{blue}	H_γ	Hg_v	
20	1.39711	1.39744	1.39980	1.40183	1.40455	1.40569	1.41042	
25	1.39446	1.39479	1.39713	1.39914	1.40184	1.40297	1.40766	
30	1.39181	1.39214	1.39446	1.39645	1.39913	1.40025	1.40490	

GELDOF (1951)

t°	He_{red}	H_α	Na_D	He_{gr}	He_v	H_β	He_c	He_i	H_γ
20	1.39715	1.39751	1.39988	1.39994	1.40463	1.40578	1.40708	1.40940	1.41077
25	1.39461	1.39495	1.39727	1.39733	1.40205	1.40319	1.40451	1.40680	1.40819

Specific heat: McCULLOUGH, FINKE, GROSS *et al.* (1957)

Liquid

t°	cal/mol	t°	cal/mol	t°	cal/mol
−116.03	43.38	−70.51	44.27	−24.80	46.73
111.97	43.35	62.22	44.62	15.60	47.37
110.40	43.37	54.02	44.99	−6.52	48.02
105.80	43.41	45.90	45.44	+2.44	48.74
103.51	43.42	37.87	45.89	11.27	49.44
95.81	43.54	33.35	46.17	19.98	50.17
87.30	43.73	−29.53	46.42	+26.45	50.76
−78.87	43.96	—	—	—	—

Crystals I

t°	cal/mol	t°	cal/mol	t°	cal/mol
−261.81	0.651	−244.68	5.301	−188.43	18.871
261.07	0.775	243.09	5.801	186.08	19.278
260.51	0.888	240.37	6.656	184.47	19.524
259.90	1.015	237.50	7.554	182.23	19.871
259.03	1.212	234.29	8.518	180.04	20.201
258.39	1.353	230.55	9.614	177.26	20.604
257.46	1.566	226.22	10.814	176.35	20.738
256.75	1.746	221.58	12.020	170.28	21.614
255.74	1.999	218.78	12.681	164.02	22.471
255.08	2.173	218.19	12.838	161.80	22.720
253.81	2.528	217.03	13.126	158.00	23.310
253.17	2.709	213.82	13.865	156.26	23.537
251.89	3.087	211.67	14.358	151.73	24.169
251.03	3.349	208.34	15.095	150.03	24.382
249.83	3.705	205.86	15.593	144.51	25.167
248.60	4.083	200.13	16.694	142.01	25.470
247.46	4.444	194.39	17.768	−131.90	27.249
−245.86	4.962	−191.13	18.366	—	—

Crystals II

t°	cal/mol	t°	cal/mol	t°	cal/mol
−261.76	0.629	−246.70	4.481	−184.81	19.320
261.55	0.661	244.53	5.128	178.35	20.303
260.55	0.857	243.93	5.311	171.75	21.287
260.23	0.906	240.81	6.282	170.11	21.326
258.99	1.174	237.37	7.332	165.74	22.124
258.59	1.259	234.11	8.305	165.45	22.180
257.25	1.556	230.62	9.318	160.57	22.851
256.26	1.645	226.52	10.441	158.99	23.083
255.35	2.002	221.77	11.710	156.27	23.464
254.67	2.187	219.67	12.459	155.57	23.547
253.28	2.555	217.16	12.842	152.38	24.011
252.34	2.819	210.13	13.780	150.71	24.218
251.27	3.119	207.68	14.990	149.63	24.394
249.77	3.563	202.22	16.079	146.02	24.919
249.14	3.746	196.77	17.121	143.63	25.363
−246.80	4.444	−190.90	18.239	−135.09	26.549

OCTENE-1 C_8H_{16}

Critical temperature: 293.4° AMBROSE, COX and TOWNSEND (1960)

Saturated vapour pressure: FORZIATI, CAMIN and ROSSINI (1950)

t°	p mm	t°	p mm	t°	p mm
44.893	47.87	67.096	124.84	106.997	501.09
48.975	57.68	71.736	149.60	119.967	732.50
52.410	67.46	76.022	176.13	120.539	744.38
55.581	77.48	81.779	217.44	121.075	755.64
58.557	87.91	87.053	262.03	121.685	768.62
62.557	103.84	93.428	325.27	122.223	780.21

Boiling point: 121.26°   POMERANTZ, FOOKSON *et al.* (1954)

Freezing point: —101.7119 McCULLOUGH, FINKE, GROSS *et al.* (1957)
                  —101.84° POMERANTZ, FOOKSON *et al.* (1954)

Density

t°	d	
20	0.71492	FORZIATI, CAMIN and ROSSINI (1950)
25	0.71085	,,
30	0.70658	,,
20	0.71486	POMERANTZ, FOOKSON *et al.* (1954)

Surface tension: JASPER and KRING (1955)

t°	0	10	20	30	40	50	60	70	80	90	100
γ	23.68	22.72	21.76	20.81	19.85	18.89	17.93	16.97	16.02	15.06	14.10

Refractive index: FORZIATI, CAMIN and ROSSINI (1950)

t°	He$_{red}$	H$_C$	Na$_D$	Hg$_{gr}$	He$_{blue}$	H$_F$	Hg$_v$
20	1.40594	1.40629	1.40870	1.41077	1.41351	1.41465	1.41933
25	1.40346	1.40380	1.40620	1.40825	1.41097	1.41210	1.41675
30	1.40098	1.40131	1.40370	1.40573	1.40843	1.40955	1.41417

n$_D$ at 20°: 1.40875 POMERANTZ, FOOKSON *et al.* (1954)

N.B. (p. 134): The data of GELDOF are not very sure.

Specific heat: McCULLOUGH, FINKE, GROSS *et al.* (1957)

Liquid

t°	cal/mol	t°	cal/mol	t°	cal/mol
−97.73	50.86	−50.04	51.82	5.11	55.82
92.66	50.76	40.93	52.35	9.48	56.24
90.26	50.76	31.49	52.94	13.96	56.63
85.55	50.75	22.16	53.60	19.02	57.12
76.58	50.85	12.95	54.30	27.64	57.91
67.66	51.09	−3.86	55.06	35.37	58.67
−58.81	51.41	+0.22	55.41	—	—

Crystals

t°	cal/mol	t°	cal/mol	t°	cal/mol
−261.89	0.783	−237.83	8.410	−173.75	23.153
261.68	0.831	234.13	9.617	165.76	24.336
260.64	1.073	230.12	10.862	157.47	25.566
260.41	1.124	225.51	12.227	154.47	26.000
259.19	1.422	220.59	13.609	153.98	26.070
258.81	1.495	218.14	14.236	148.69	26.814
257.53	1.853	217.88	14.289	148.64	26.814
257.20	1.942	215.42	14.945	147.96	26.914
255.70	2.367	212.66	15.619	147.37	26.990
255.18	2.532	212.39	15.730	141.52	27.825
253.52	3.049	206.81	16.996	140.88	27.901
252.96	3.231	206.54	17.066	140.35	27.992
251.26	3.755	201.04	18.197	132.84	29.032
250.70	3.975	200.78	18.264	132.30	29.096
249.23	4.470	195.28	19.365	131.19	29.246
248.15	4.833	189.47	20.528	124.85	30.148
247.79	5.302	187.05	20.941	122.17	30.493
246.30	5.817	183.66	21.565	−121.69	32.459
245.17	6.210	180.92	21.999	—	—
−241.79	7.042	−177.36	22.573	—	—

ISOMERIC OCTENES C_8H_{16}

	Boil. p.	dt/dp	$n_D\,20°$	dn/dt	$d^{20°}$	dd/dt	$\eta \cdot 10^3$		
							20°	30°	40°
5,5-Dimethyl-1-hexene	103.1	0.47	1.4043	0.00049	0.7060	0.00086	469	417	373
5,5-Dimethyl-2-hexene low	104.1	0.46	1.4055	0.00050	0.7066	0.00086	493	437	391
„ high	106.9	0.47	1.4113	0.00050	0.7169	0.00088	525	466	417
2,4-Dimethyl-3-hexene low	107.6	0.46	1.4126	0.00050	0.7145	0.00087	434	391	353
„ high	109.0	0.45	1.4140	0.00051	0.7178	0.00086	458	411	370
2,4-Dimethyl-2-hexene	110.6	0.47	1.4118	0.00049	0.7213	0.00085	455	407	367
3-Ethyl-4-methylpentene-1	107.5	0.47	1.4097	0.00049	0.7200	0.00083	452	405	365
3-Ethyl-4-methylpentene-2 low	114.3	0.47	1.4210	0.00049	0.7350	0.00085	477	427	385
„ high	116	0.47	1.4240	0.00049	0.7390	0.00085	45	41	37

NONENE-1 C_9H_{18}

Saturated vapour pressure: FORZIATI, CAMIN and ROSSINI (1950)

$t°$	p mm	$t°$	p mm	$t°$	p mm
66.607	47.89	94.829	149.60	145.488	732.50
70.874	57.69	99.341	176.13	146.091	744.38
74.517	67.46	110.935	262.03	146.653	755.63
77.861	77.49	117.622	325.26	147.289	768.62
81.001	87.92	124.521	402.84	147.860	780.22
85.202	103.85	131.881	501.09	—	—
89.942	124.84	139.859	628.33	—	—

Boiling point: 147.2 GELDOF (1951)

Density:

$t°$	d	
20	0.72931	GELDOF (1951)
25	0.72531	„
20	0.72922	FORZIATI, CAMIN and ROSSINI (1950)
25	0.72531	„
30	0.72134	„

Surface tension: JASPER and KRING (1955)

$t°$	0	10	20	30	40	50	60	70	80	90	100
γ	24.90	23.96	23.82	22.09	21.15	20.21	19.27	18.33	17.40	16.46	15.52

Refractive index: GELDOF (1951)

$t°$	He_r	H_α	Na_D	He_{gr}	He_{bl}	H_β	He_c	He_i	H_γ
20	1.41291	1.41327	1.41570	1.41575	1.42047	1.42156	1.42288	1.42523	1.42667
25	1.41053	1.41084	1.41329	1.41335	1.41810	1.41913	1.42049	1.42281	1.42426

DECENE-1 $C_{10}H_{20}$

Saturated vapour pressure: FORZIATI, CAMIN and ROSSINI (1950)

$t°$	p mm	$t°$	p mm	$t°$	p mm
86.774	47.98	111.213	124.86	154.939	501.12
91.308	57.71	116.283	149.64	169.134	732.53
95.134	67.48	120.995	176.14	169.762	744.42
98.604	77.51	127.265	217.44	170.345	755.67
101.844	87.93	140.063	325.22	171.012	768.65
106.223	103.87	147.265	402.86	171.605	780.26

Boiling point: 170.9 (753 mm) GELDOF (1951)

Freezing point: —66.2979 McCULLOUGH, FINKE, GROSS *et al.* (1957)
　　　　　　　　—66.326 STREIFF, SOULE *et al.* (1950)

Density:

$t°$	d	
20	0.74079	GELDOF (1951)
25	0.73695	,,
20	0.74081	FORZIATI, CAMIN and ROSSINI (1950)
25	0.73693	,,
30	0.73304	,,

Surface tension: JASPER and KRING (1955)

$t°$	0	10	20	30	40	50	60	70	80	90	100
γ	25.84	24.92	24.00	23.08	22.16	21.24	20.33	19.41	18.49	17.57	16.65

Refractive index: FORZIATI, CAMIN and ROSSINI (1950)

t°	He$_r$	H$_\alpha$	Na$_D$	Hg$_{gr}$	He$_{bl}$	H$_\beta$	Hg$_v$	
20	1.41870	1.41904	1.42146	1.42352	1.42627	1.42741	1.43213	
25	1.41639	1.41673	1.41913	1.42118	1.42391	1.42505	1.42974	
30	1.41408	1.41442	1.41680	1.41884	1.42155	1.42269	1.42735	

GELDOF (1951)

t°	He$_{red}$	H$_\alpha$	Na$_D$	He$_{gr}$	He$_v$	H$_\beta$	He$_c$	He$_i$	H$_\gamma$
20	1.41849	1.41889	1.42132	1.42138	1.42610	1.42721	1.42851	1.43084	1.43235
25	1.41622	1.41662	1.41902	1.41908	1.42379	1.42487	1.42621	1.42851	1.42997

Specific heat: McCULLOUGH, FINKE, GROSS *et al.* (1957)

Crystals II

t°	cal/mol	t°	cal/mol	t°	cal/mol
−260.92	1.064	−233.95	10.836	−168.54	28.797
259.63	1.406	229.31	12.385	162.03	29.854
258.41	1.755	225.24	14.036	157.37	30.929
257.00	1.881	219.96	15.815	151.37	32.025
256.38	2.150	217.85	16.520	145.56	33.075
255.41	2.663	214.20	17.689	139.58	34.126
254.63	2.924	211.89	18.419	133.26	35.274
253.74	3.231	205.07	20.118	127.12	36.356
252.52	3.668	200.27	21.654	121.15	37.448
251.80	3.933	194.91	23.015	115.35	38.523
249.98	4.620	190.65	23.353	107.21	40.016
249.41	4.830	188.31	24.707	101.21	41.304
247.19	5.681	186.81	25.028	95.37	42.599
246.72	5.856	181.30	26.232	89.69	43.911
244.27	6.801	179.78	26.571	84.16	45.429
243.88	6.944	176.04	27.282	79.49	46.617
241.17	8.037	174.28	27.666	79.39	46.831
−237.70	9.405	−170.51	28.392	−77.40	47.808

Crystals IA		Crystals IB		Liquid	
t°	cal/mol	t°	cal/mol	t°	cal/mol
−72.84	69.109	−71.94	68.641	−61.74	66.03
71.74	70.375	71.76	68.615	56.88	65.86
70.93	71.654	71.61	68.743	56.69	65.85
70.29	73.528	70.81	69.706	52.10	65.83
69.89	74.519	70.58	69.908	49.97	65.85
−69.32	77.732	70.53	70.084	41.61	66.06
		69.88	71.013	32.48	66.50
		69.80	71.523	22.61	67.16
		−69.58	71.556	12.44	67.98
				−2.00	68.97
				+8.29	69.99
				18.43	71.06
				28.36	72.16
				28.44	72.17
				38.63	73.40
				50.12	74.68
				60.95	76.08
				71.85	77.37
				81.59	78.68

UNDECENE-1 $C_{11}H_{22}$

Saturated vapour pressure: FORZIATI, CAMIN and ROSSINI (1950)

t°	p mm	t°	p mm	t°	p mm
105.866	47.99	136.350	149.65	185.091	628.38
110.423	57.72	141.240	176.14	191.179	732.55
114.388	67.48	147.780	217.45	191.832	744.43
117.997	77.51	153.780	262.05	192.441	755.69
121.355	87.94	161.031	325.28	193.130	768.66
125.902	103.87	168.501	402.87	193.742	780.26
131.081	124.86	176.462	501.13		

Freezing point: −49.206 STREIFF, SOULE *et al.* (1950)

               −49.1865 McCULLOUGH, FINKE, GROSS *et al.* (1957)

Density: FORZIATI, CAMIN and ROSSINI (1950)

t°	d	
20	0.75032	
25	0.74655	
30	0.74276	

Surface tension: JASPER and KRING (1955)

t°	0	10	20	30	40	50	60	70	80	90	100
γ	26.67	25.77	24.86	23.96	23.05	22.15	21.24	20.34	19.43	18.53	17.62

Refractive index: FORZIATI, CAMIN and ROSSINI (1950)

t°	He$_r$	H$_\alpha$	Na$_D$	Hg$_{gr}$	He$_{bl}$	H$_\gamma$	Hg$_g$
20	1.42332	1.42366	1.42609	1.42816	1.43093	1.43208	1.43682
25	1.42108	1.42142	1.42383	1.42589	1.42864	1.42978	1.43449
30	1.41884	1.41918	1.42157	1.42362	1.42635	1.42748	1.43216

Specific heat: McCULLOUGH, FINKE, GROSS et al. (1957)

Crystals II

t°	cal/mol	t°	cal/mol	t°	cal/mol
−261.26	0.957	−230.33	13.124	−141.42	36.548
260.38	1.157	226.00	14.854	134.91	37.771
259.54	1.386	221.05	16.720	129.80	38.686
258.51	1.688	218.48	17.653	128.09	38.994
257.53	1.983	216.26	18.447	121.74	40.225
256.30	2.386	214.01	19.247	120.98	40.386
255.46	2.675	208.99	20.941	113.61	41.804
254.17	3.143	203.68	22.560	110.65	42.388
253.50	3.398	197.90	24.202	105.98	43.306
252.22	3.890	191.73	25.910	103.23	43.865
251.30	4.261	185.95	27.427	101.90	44.158
249.82	4.860	180.86	28.603	98.59	44.831
248.51	5.388	175.65	29.734	94.41	45.705
247.14	5.976	173.36	30.212	93.02	46.061
246.47	6.659	170.31	30.854	91.42	46.373
244.12	7.240	167.10	31.519	84.45	47.957
240.88	8.647	160.65	32.838	76.00	50.024
237.58	10.079	154.45	34.079	68.69	52.081
−234.05	11.578	−148.07	35.303	− 62.65	54.116

Crystals I		**Liquid**			
$t°$	cal/mol	$t°$	cal/mol	$t°$	cal/mol
− 54.71	79.34	− 45.92	73.75	− 11.28	75.08
52.62	81.75	42.29	73.65	− 1.71	75.97
52.10	82.74	40.97	73.58	+ 8.48	77.00
− 50.64	90.22	35.27	73.64	18.53	78.09
		28.47	73.87	28.44	79.28
		− 20.21	74.39	+ 38.21	80.49

DODECENE-1 $C_{12}H_{24}$

Saturated vapour pressure: FORZIATI, CAMIN and ROSSINI (1950)

$t°$	p mm	$t°$	p mm	$t°$	p mm
123.703	48.02	155.208	149.72	196.624	501.21
128.424	57.78	160.266	176.24	205.542	628.45
136.258	77.59	167.019	217.54	211.823	732.62
139.736	88.03	173.214	262.14	212.497	744.57
144.428	103.97	180.699	325.41	213.125	755.81
149.773	124.95	188.406	402.97	213.826	768.75
				214.472	780.36

Boiling point: 96.8 (15 mm) GELDOF (1951)

Freezing point: −35.2510 McCULLOUGH, FINKE, GROSS *et al.* (1957)

Density

$t°$	d	
20	0.75894	GELDOF (1951)
25	0.75526	,,
20	0.75836	FORZIATI, CAMIN and ROSSINI (1950)
25	0.75474	,,
30	0.75103	,,

Surface tension: JASPER and KRING (1955)

$t°$	0	10	20	30	40	50	60	70	80	90	100
γ	27.38	26.49	25.63	24.71	23.82	22.92	22.03	21.14	20.25	19.36	18.47

Refractive index: FORZIATI, CAMIN and ROSSINI (1950)

$t°$	He_r	H_α	Na_D	Hg_{gr}	He_{blue}	H_γ	Hg_g
20	1.42727	1.42761	1.43002	1.43210	1.43486	1.43601	1.44077
25	1.42508	1.42542	1.42782	1.42988	1.43262	1.43377	1.43850
30	1.42289	1.42323	1.42562	1.42766	1.43038	1.43153	1.43623

$t°$	He_r	H_α	D	He_y	He_{gr}	H_β	He_{bl}	He_v	H_γ	
20	1.42733	1.42769	1.43009	1.43016	1.43491	1.43602	1.43767	1.43967	1.44108	GELDOF (1951)
25	1.42515	1.42552	1.42790	1.42796	1.43272	1.43379	1.43513	1.43745	1.43887	,,

Specific heat: McCULLOUGH, FINKE, GROSS *et al.* (1957)

Crystals II

$t°$	cal/mol	$t°$	cal/mol	$t°$	cal/mol
−261.31	1.199	−205.24	24.093	89.89	53.124
260.49	1.477	199.20	26.014	88.23	53.687
260.21	1.549	193.19	27.873	85.89	54.548
259.09	1.945	187.21	29.661	82.62	55.640
258.84	1.989	181.21	31.246	81.75	56.098
257.44	2.476	179.93	31.563	77.39	58.062
257.34	2.502	175.31	32.709	75.52	59.036
255.83	3.054	173.91	33.046	72.66	60.531
255.63	3.130	168.99	34.224	72.36	60.860
254.07	3.732	162.49	35.714	69.57	62.781
253.74	3.850	158.17	36.736	68.26	63.865
252.15	4.547	155.84	37.241	−65.23	66.769
252.06	4.758	152.94	37.886		
249.92	5.455	149.02	38.755	**Crystals I**	
248.77	5.964	142.45	40.171	−59.44	84.42
247.77	6.402	135.53	41.666	57.94	81.22
245.70	7.329	127.25	43.271	56.42	81.08
245.49	7.415	122.01	44.679	54.91	81.25
242.49	8.777	121.23	44.859	54.44	81.40
238.97	10.420	116.14	46.029	53.40	81.89
235.19	12.138	110.77	47.293	51.04	82.43
230.94	14.060	110.42	47.403	50.73	83.07
226.16	16.126	105.16	48.757	50.54	83.29
220.12	18.207	99.70	50.232	48.17	84.98
217.78	19.518	95.49	51.292	46.73	86.20
216.26	20.117	94.95	51.570	44.42	88.65
−211.42	21.944	−91.90	52.502	−42.06	90.21

Liquid

t°	cal/mol	t°	cal/mol	t°	cal/mol
− 32.83	81.67	− 20.09	81.76	+ 1.70	83.52
28.62	81.58	17.15	81.98	12.07	84.62
25.80	81.64	− 7.04	82.61	22.30	85.87
− 24.03	81.71			+32.39	87.12

TRIDECENE-1 $C_{13}H_{26}$

Saturated vapour pressure: CAMIN and ROSSINI (1955)

t°	p mm	t°	p mm	t°	p mm
232.663	758.08	207.152	403.30	160.170	98.22
231.393	735.83	198.998	323.78	147.442	62.44
224.865	630.35	184.559	214.16	142.603	51.91

Boiling point: 232.780 *dt/dp (10 mm):* 0.5680 CAMIN and ROSSINI (1955)

Density: CAMIN and ROSSINI (1955)

t°	d	
20	0.76527	
25	0.76168	
30	0.75801	

Refractive index: CAMIN and ROSSINI (1955)

t°	H_{er}	H_α	D	Hg_{gr}	He_{bl}	H_γ	Hg_v
20	1.43060	1.43094	1.43336	1.43544	1.43820	1.43936	1.44409
25	1.42843	1.42877	1.43118	1.43325	1.43599	1.43714	1.44185
30	1.42626	1.42660	1.42900	1.43106	1.43378	1.43492	1.43961

TETRADECENE-1 $C_{14}H_{28}$

Saturated vapour pressure: CAMIN and ROSSINI (1955)

t°	p mm	t°	p mm	t°	p mm
251.750	771.36	224.822	403.31	188.869	145.81
250.984	758.09	216.455	323.78	163.516	62.44
249.689	735.82	201.642	214.15	158.464	51.91
242.996	630.35				

Boiling point: 251.100 *dt/dp (10 mm):* 0.5820 CAMIN and ROSSINI (1955)

Density: CAMIN and ROSSINI (1955)

t°	d	
20	0.77127	
25	0.76767	
30	0.76416	

Surface tension: JASPER and KRING (1955)

t°	0	10	20	30	40	50	60	70	80	90	100
γ	28.56	27.68	26.80	25.92	25.04	24.16	23.29	22.41	21.53	20.65	19.77

Refractive index: CAMIN and ROSSINI (1955)

t°	He_r	H_α	Na_D	Hg_{gr}	He_{blue}	H_γ	Hg_v
20	1.43354	1.43388	1.43631	1.43839	1.44116	1.44232	1.44707
25	1.43140	1.43174	1.43415	1.43622	1.43897	1.44012	1.44484
30	1.42926	1.42960	1.43199	1.43405	1.43678	1.43792	1.44261

PENTADECENE-1 $C_{15}H_{30}$

Saturated vapour pressure: CAMIN and ROSSINI (1955)

t°	p mm	t°	p mm	t°	p mm
268.273	758.10	250.494	503.04	232.940	323.78
266.940	735.79	241.504	403.34	173.613	51.91
260.094	630.35				

Boiling point: 268.394 *dt/dp (10 mm):* 0.5956 CAMIN and ROSSINI (1955)

Density: CAMIN and ROSSINI (1955)

t°	d	
20	0.77641	
25	0.77290	
30	0.76939	

Refractive index: CAMIN and ROSSINI (1955)

$t°$	He_r	$H\alpha$	Na_D	Hg_{gr}	He_{bl}	H_γ	Hg_v
20	1.43607	1.43642	1.43883	1.44089	1.44365	1.44481	1.44957
25	1.43395	1.43429	1.43669	1.43875	1.44150	1.44265	1.44739
30	1.43183	1.43216	1.43455	1.43661	1.43935	1.44049	1.44521

HEXADECENE-1 $C_{16}H_{32}$

Saturated vapour pressure: CAMIN, FORZIATI and ROSSINI (1954)

$t°$	p mm	$t°$	p mm	$t°$	p mm
284.768	758.24	248.690	323.84	206.981	98.06
283.402	736.10	233.203	214.17	197.257	71.56
266.590	503.01	225.397	171.68	188.152	52.06
257.440	403.38	219.806	145.81		

139.2 at 6 mm GELDOF (1951)

Freezing point: +4.1 GELDOF (1951)

Density

$t°$	d	
20	0.78116	GELDOF (1951)
25	0.77770	,,
20	0.78112	CAMIN, FORZIATI and ROSSINI (1954)
25	0.77759	,,
30	0.77409	,,

Surface tension: JASPER and KRING (1955)

$t°$	10	20	30	40	50	60	70	80	90	100
γ	28.61	27.75	26.89	26.03	25.16	24.30	23.44	22.58	21.72	20.86

Refractive index: GELDOF (1951)

$t°$	He_r	H_α	Na_D	He_y	He_{gr}	H_β	He_{bl}	He_v	H_γ
20	1.43827	1.43860	1.44100	1.44106	1.44585	1.44700	1.44827	1.45063	1.45199
25	1.43621	1.43656	1.34898	1.43900	1.44379	1.44491	1.44620	1.44851	1.44987

t°	He$_r$	H$_\alpha$	Na$_D$	Hg$_{gr}$	He$_{bl}$	H$_\beta$	Hg$_v$	
20	1.43845	1.43879	1.44120	1.44326	1.44601	1.44715	1.45188	CAMIN, FORZIATI and
25	1.43633	1.43667	1.43907	1.44113	1.44387	1.44501	1.44973	ROSSINI (1954)
30	1.43421	1.43455	1.43694	1.43900	1.44173	1.44287	1.44758	,,

Specific heat: McCULLOUGH, FINKE, GROSS *et al.* (1957)

Crystals

t°	cal/mol	t°	cal/mol	t°	cal/mol
−261.24	1.383	−188.83	37.267	−90.61	66.703
260.57	1.617	182.97	39.318	86.73	68.000
259.91	1.863	182.71	39.424	79.84	70.289
258.90	2.244	182.12	39.602	77.42	71.302
258.35	2.458	176.91	41.253	72.49	72.999
256.93	3.032	176.04	41.531	67.72	75.060
256.87	3.059	175.07	41.835	64.54	76.372
255.35	3.738	169.64	43.537	57.94	79.30
254.85	3.954	168.76	43.805	55.27	80.25
253.60	4.558	167.94	44.044	48.64	84.30
252.34	5.196	161.85	46.004	46.06	85.83
251.60	5.561	160.94	46.262	41.33	89.38
249.66	6.599	160.72	46.272	39.84	90.82
249.12	6.873	153.61	48.587	37.46	94.02
246.98	8.058	153.23	48.683	37.15	94.06
246.05	8.565	145.56	50.861	33.19	101.97
244.01	9.719	145.48	50.886	31.88	106.40
240.63	11.710	137.53	53.120	29.59	118.50
237.11	13.781	129.30	55.389	22.64	133.12
234.00	15.595	121.38	57.577	22.26	132.32
230.50	17.636	119.24	58.134	20.88	129.96
226.49	19.889	116.07	59.035	19.16	129.20
222.28	22.199	113.28	59.901	18.92	129.20
217.61	24.590	111.80	60.231	16.62	130.84
217.26	24.812	108.61	61.208	16.05	131.32
211.54	27.694	104.59	62.353	12.94	135.82
205.95	30.277	104.55	62.388	10.06	142.10
200.37	32.617	100.53	63.604	− 7.23	150.13
194.80	34.896	97.61	64.485	+ 0.31	186.24
−189.04	37.166	− 95.68	65.103		

Liquid

t°	cal/mol	t°	cal/mol	t°	cal/mol
+ 6.22	114.15	+ 10.95	114.50	+18.51	115.03
6.27	114.05	11.82	114.41	24.60	115.85
6.93	114.17	12.22	114.48	30.31	116.62
7.19	113.96	12.38	114.38	30.65	116.61
10.43	114.45	12.54	114.48		

OCTADECENE-1 $C_{18}H_{36}$

Boiling point: 162.98° GELDOF (1951)

Freezing point: 18.0° GELDOF (1951)

Density: GELDOF (1951)

t°	d	
20	0.78908	
25	0.78569	

Refractive index: GELDOF (1951)

t°	He_r	H_α	Na_D	He_y	He_{gr}	H_β	He_{bl}	He_v	H_γ
20	1.44205	1.44239	1.44473	1.44489	1.44965	1.45071	1.35204	1.45436	1.45579
25	1.44003	1.44039	1.44281	1.44286	1.44460	1.44871	1.44999	1.45030	1.45371

C. DIENES

BUTADIENE-1,3 C_4H_6

Boiling point: —4.54 BENOLIEL (1941)

Freezing point: —108.71 GARNER, ADAMS and STUCHELL (1942)
        —108.937 PROSEN, SOULE *et al.* (1930) and STREIFF, SOULE *et al.* (1950)
        —108.966 GLASGOW, KROUSKOP and ROSSINI (1950)

Density: at 20°: 0.6206 *dd/dt:* 0.00114 BENOLIEL (1941)

Refractive index: at —25°: 1.4292 BENOLIEL (1941) *dn/dt:* 0.000660

Heat of vaporization: 5610 cal/mol BENOLIEL (1941)

Heat of combustion at 25° 607.16 kcal/mol PROSEN, MARON and ROSSINI (1951)

PENTADIENE-1,2 C_5H_8

Density: FORZIATI, CAMIN and ROSSINI (1950)

t°	d	
20	0.69257	
25	0.68760	
30	0.68260	

Refractive index: FORZIATI, CAMIN and ROSSINI (1950)

t°	He$_r$	H$_\alpha$	Na$_D$	Hg$_{gr}$	He$_{blue}$	H$_\beta$	Hg$_v$
20	1.41724	1.41769	1.42091	1.42372	1.42750	1.42910	1.43579
25	1.41409	1.41454	1.41773	1.42052	1.42428	1.42586	1.43251
30	1.41094	1.41139	1.41455	1.41732	1.42106	1.42262	1.42923

Heat of combustion: 777.14 kcal/mol FRASER and PROSEN (1955)

PENTADIENE-1,3   C$_5$H$_8$

cis   *trans*

STREIFF, SOULE *et al.* (1950)

Freezing point: −140.836   −87.483

Density: FORZIATI, CAMIN and ROSSINI (1950)

t°		d		d	
20		0.69102		0.67603	
25		0.68592		0.67102	
30		0.68082		0.66592	

Refractive index (ibid.)

t°	20	25	30	20	25	30
He$_r$	1.43103	1.42765	1.42427	1.42483	1.42148	1.41813
H$_\alpha$	1.43168	1.42829	1.42490	1.42547	1.42212	1.41877
Na$_D$	1.43634	1.43291	1.42948	1.43008	1.42669	1.42330
Hg$_{gr}$	1.44046	1.43699	1.43352	1.43415	1.43073	1.42731
He$_{bl}$	1.44612	1.44261	1.43910	1.43972	1.43625	1.43278
H$_\beta$	1.44854	1.44501	1.44148	1.44209	1.43861	1.43513
Hg$_v$	1.45887	1.45526	1.45165	1.45219	1.44863	1.44507

Heat of combustion: 763.30 kcal/mol   761.64 kcal/mol FRASER and PROSEN (1955)
                    (cis)   *(trans)*

PENTADIENE-1,4   C$_5$H$_8$

Freezing point: −148.287 STREIFF, SOULE *et al.* (1950)

Refractive index: FORZIATI, CAMIN and ROSSINI (1950)

t°	He$_r$	H$_\alpha$	Na$_D$	Hg$_{gr}$	He$_{blue}$	H$_\beta$	Hg$_v$
20	1.38550	1.38591	1.38876	1.39125	1.39461	1.39603	1.40199

Heat of combustion: 768.94 kcal/mol FRASER and PROSEN (1955)

PENTADIENE-2,3 C_5H_8

Boiling point: 48.2 POMERANTZ, FOOKSON *et al.* (1954)

Freezing point: −125.680 STREIFF, SOULE *et al.* (1950)
           −125.72   POMERANTZ, FOOKSON *et al.* (1954)

Density at 20°: 0.6957 POMERANTZ, FOOKSON *et al.* (1954)

t°	d	
20	0.69502	FORZIATI, CAMIN and ROSSINI (1950)
25	0.69000	,,
30	0.68479	,,

Refractive index: FORZIATI, CAMIN and ROSSINI (1950)

t°	He$_r$	H$_\alpha$	Na$_D$	Hg$_{gr}$	He$_{blue}$	H$_\beta$	Hg$_v$
20	1.42450	1.42498	1.42842	1.43140	1.43542	1.43711	1.44415
25	1.42120	1.42168	1.42509	1.42805	1.43204	1.43372	1.44071
30	1.41790	1.41838	1.42176	1.42470	1.42866	1.43033	1.43727

Heat of combustion: 775.32 kcal/mol FRASER and PROSEN (1955)

ISOPRENE or 2-METHYLBUTADIENE-1,3 C_5H_8

Freezing point: −145.962 STREIFF, SOULE *et al.* (1950)
           −146.016 GLASGOW, KROUSKOP and ROSSINI (1950)

Density: FORZIATI, CAMIN and ROSSINI (1950)

t°	d	
20	0.68095	
25	0.67587	
30	0.67076	

Refractive index: FORZIATI, CAMIN and ROSSINI (1950)

t°	He$_r$	H$_\alpha$	Na$_D$	Hg$_{gr}$	He$_{blue}$	H$_\beta$	Hg$_v$
20	1.41708	1.41768	1.42194	1.42570	1.43081	1.43300	1.44221
25	1.41370	1.41429	1.41852	1.42224	1.42731	1.42948	1.43862
30	1.41032	1.41090	1.41510	1.41878	1.42381	1.42596	1.43503

Heat of combustion: 761.62 kcal/mol FRASER and PROSEN (1955)

HEXADIENE-1,5 C_6H_{10}

Saturated vapour pressure: CUMMINGS and McLAUGHLIN (1955)

t°	p mm	t°	p mm	t°	p mm
0.04	71.9	14.83	144.8	17.83	164.9
12.96	133.3	15.64	149.9	31.00	282.6
13.90	138.9	16.52	156.5	38.22	370.3
				59.2	750.8

Boiling point: 59.2 CUMMINGS and McLAUGHLIN (1955)
59.46 POMERANTZ, FOOKSON *et al.* (1954)

Freezing point: −140.698 STREIFF, SOULE *et al.* (1950)

Density at 20°: 0.69115 POMERANTZ, FOOKSON *et al.* (1954)
n_D at 20°: 1.40386 POMERANTZ, FOOKSON *et al.* (1954)

2,3-DIMETHYLBUTADIENE-1,3 C_6H_{10}

Saturated vapour pressure: CUMMINGS and McLAUGHLIN (1955)

t°	p mm	t°	p mm	t°	p mm
0.04	46.0	15.42	98.4	19.86	120.4
12.00	83.7	16.96	105.9	25.74	156.2
13.46	89.6	17.24	106.8	31.35	197.8
				68.40	757.0

Boiling point: 68.4 CUMMINGS and McLAUGHLIN (1955)

Freezing point: −76.020 STREIFF, SOULE *et al.* (1950)

D. ACETYLENES

ACETYLENE C_2H_2

Saturated vapour pressure: AMBROSE and TOWNSEND (1963)

t°	P (atm)	t°	P (atm.)	t°	P (atm.)
− 58.513	3.708	− 36.083	8.837	− 20.032	14.897
52.794	4.718	30.676	10.824	14.848	17.386
47.195	5.889	25.353	12.643	14.824	17.400
41.610	7.260	25.321	12.657	+ 13.618	26.285
36.117	8.825	− 20.665	14.891	+ 13.518	60.386

BUTYNE-1 C_4H_6

Triple point: -125.73 ASTON, MASTRANGELO and MOESSEN (1950)

Saturated vapour pressure: ASTON, MASTRANGELO and MOESSEN (1950)

t°	p mm	t°	p mm	t°	p mm
−78.758	3.92	−29.761	131.04	−1.838	513.10
68.911	9.24	23.857	179.82	+2.725	613.55
58.723	20.54	18.745	233.07	6.161	704.87
48.679	41.64	14.437	287.38	8.063	759.84
41.225	67.08	10.344	349.64	+9.553	805.16
−36.414	89.65	− 5.738	426.39		

Freezing point: -125.87 POMERANTZ, FOOKSON *et al.* (1954)

Specific heat: ASTON, MASTRANGELO and MOESSEN (1950)

t°	c_p cal/mol	t°	c_p	t°	c_p
−259.86	0.736	−207.11	10.39	−97.13	27.55
258.51	0.988	202.96	10.900	91.33	27.66
256.44	1.363	201.92	11.005	85.78	27.74
254.00	1.921	200.52	11.21	80.31	27.80
253.87	1.961	196.41	11.659	74.49	27.96
251.47	2.473	194.20	11.92	69.06	28.17
248.42	3.199	190.12	12.281	63.44	28.28
248.33	3.210	189.22	12.38	57.55	28.43
244.73	4.048	183.43	12.906	52.23	28.51
240.98	4.924	178.09	13.43	46.88	28.71
239.70	5.169	173.04	13.88	44.69	28.97
235.91	5.941	167.70	14.36	34.13	29.32
233.82	6.320	162.09	14.88	27.05	29.76
231.42	6.807	157.48	15.34	19.78	30.23
228.00	7.452	152.22	15.84	13.01	30.42
226.71	7.673	146.88	16.24	7.63	30.89
222.60	8.330	141.20	16.81	− 2.58	31.08
222.06	8.401	135.85	17.29	+ 1.85	31.14
217.12	9.088	130.80	17.89		
212.43	9.678	123.28	27.31		
211.91	9.742	117.23	27.31		
207.66	10.349	110.15	27.33		
−207.12	10.374	−103.69	27.42		

Heat of vaporization: ASTON, MASTRANGELO and MOESSEN (1950)

t°	cal/mol	t°	cal/mol	t°	cal/mol
−10.63	6166.5	+ 3.79	5928.0	+8.30	5849.6
−10.45	6161.7	+8.15	5863.7	+9.36	5844.2

Heat of melting: 1441.03 cal/mol ASTON, MASTRANGELO and MOESSEN (1950)

Heat of combustion at 25°: 620.64 kcal/mol PROSEN, MARON and ROSSINI (1951)

BUTYNE-2　　　　　C_4H_6

Boiling point: 26.97 POMERANTZ, FOOKSON *et al.* (1954)

Freezing point: −32.33 POMERANTZ, FOOKSON *et al.* (1954)

Density: at 20°: 0.6906 POMERANTZ, FOOKSON *et al.* (1954)

Refractive index: n_D 20°: 1.3918 POMERANTZ, FOOKSON *et al.* (1954)

Heat of combustion at 25°: 615.84 kcal/mol PROSEN, MARON and ROSSINI (1951)

N.B. (p. 139): In the note at the end of the table of *Specific heat* of YOST, OSBORNE and GARNER (1941), instead of: 130° and 110°: −130° and −100°.

N.B. (p. 140): The data of HEXYNE-1, taken from VAN RISSEGHEM (1926), do not very well agree with those from POMERANTZ, FOOKSON *et al.* (1954).

E.　AROMATIC HYDROCARBONS

BENZENE　　　　　C_6H_6

Purification: EVANS, ORMROD *et al.* (1950) have studied a new method of purification of benzene, as a nickel complex: $Ni(CN)_2,NH_3,C_6H_6$.

SWIETOSLAWSKI and USAKIEWICZ (1933) have found that by careful distillation of moist benzene it could be dehydrated to 0.0001 %; see also the work of THOMPSON and UBBELOHDE (1950).

Constants

Critical temperature: 288.94° AMBROSE, COX and TOWNSEND (1960); correct the value of AMBROSE and GRANT (1957).

Saturated vapour pressure

t°	p mm	t°	p mm	
10.983	47.98	49.084	261.95	FORZIATI, NORRIS and ROSSINI(1949)
14.575	57.68	54.852	325.21	,,
17.697	67.42	60.803	402.76	·,
20.628	77.47	67.148	501.00	,,
23.271	87.90	74.035	628.15	,,
26.908	103.81	78.903	732.38	,,
31.013	124.75	79.424	744.29	,,
35.207	149.58	79.909	755.48	,,
39.095	176.06	80.461	768.51	,,
44.294	217.34	80.948	780.04	,,

t°	p mm	t°	p mm	
79.74	749.6	51.85	290.4	Dreyer, Martin and Von Weber
72.22	590.1	47.63	247.3	(1954–1955)
67.51	505.6	35.72	151.9	
59.62	385.4	15.76	60.8	

t°	p mm	t°	p mm	
35	148.28	65	466.10	Weissman and Wood (1960)
45	223.50	75	648.17	,,
55	327.05	—	—	,,

t°	p mm	
40.20	183.80	Marechal (1952)
50.00	271.03	,,
60.00	390.56	,,

t°	p mm	t°	p mm	
40.00	182.93	60.00	391.74	Brown and Smith (1955)
45.00	223.66	70.00	551.25	,,
50.00	271.52	80.00	758.44	,,

t°	p mm	
15.0	182.5	Rybicka and Wynne-Jones (1950)
25.0	93.5	,,
40.0	57.4	,,

t°	p mm	t°	p mm	
121	2260.16	240	19395.00	Griswold, Andres and Klein
162	5275.44	255	24308.40	(1943)
200	10861.20	—	—	,,

t°	p mm	t°	p mm	
77.700	705.49	59.066	378.75	HERINGTON and MARTIN (1953)
73.350	614.46	50.916	280.90	,,
67.286	503.29	—	—	,,
100	1350.5	200	10806	BENDER, FURUKAWA
110	1756	210	12637	and HYNDMAN (1952)
120	2249	220	14702	,,
130	2841	230	17010	,,
140	3544	240	19570	,,
150	4371	250	22420	,,
160	5332	260	25565	,,
170	6440	270	29040	,,
190	9159.2	280	32885	,,

N.B. (p. 142): Suppress values of FIOCK, GINNINGS and HOLTON (1931).

Second virial coefficient: ANDON, COX *et al.* (1957)

Boiling point: 80.110 SWIETOSLAWSKI and USAKIEWICZ (1933)

              80.07 BROWN and EWALD (1951) and BROWN (1937)

              80.10 GRUNBERG (1954)

              80.099 FORZIATI, NORRIS and ROSSINI (1949)

Freezing point: 5.5165 MATHIEU (1953)

              5.525 RYBICKA and WYNNE-JONES (1950)

              5.528 THOMPSON and UBBELOHDE (1950)

              5.53   NECKEL and VOLK (1958)

              5.535 EVANS, ORMROD *et al.* (1950)

N.B. The *triple point* of 100% C_6H_6, resulting from a short extrapolation, has been found to be: 5.524 MATHIEU (1953)

              5.5241 WICHERS, SAYLOR and GLASGOW (1961).

              5.525 OLIVER, EATON and HUFFMAN (1948)

Constants of state

Density

t°	d	
9.25	0.8907	KETELAAR and VAN MEURS (1957)
20.38	0.8789	,,
31.25	0.8674	,,
20	0.87903	DONALDSON and QUAYLE (1950)
30	0.86833	,,
40	0.85763	,,
20	0.87904	NYVLT and ERDOS (1961)
25	0.87363	,,
30	0.86825	,,
35	0.86296	,,
40	0.85760	,,
20	0.87889	NECKEL and VOLK (1958)
20	0.8789	KAZANSKII, ROZENGART et al. (1953)
20	0.87896	RYBICKA and WYNNE-JONES (1950)
20	0.87904	EVANS, ORMROD et al. (1950)
25	0.87359	BROWN and FOCH (1950), BROWN and EWALD (1951)
25	0.87364	WOOD, LANGER and BATTINO (1960)
25	0.87366	WOOD and MASLAND (1960)
25	0.87369	BROWN and SMITH (1955)
30	0.8685	KURMANADHARAO, KRISHNAMURTY and VENKATARAO (1957)
25	0.87350	MARECHAL (1952)
60	0.83566	,,
70	0.82486	,,

Compressibility: at $24.40°$ $\pi \cdot 10^6$: 97.61

Viscosity at $25°$: $\eta \cdot 10^5 = 599.6$ GRUNBERG (1954)

Surface tension

t°	γ	
20	28.87	DONALDSON and QUAYLE (1950)
30	27.49	,,
40	26.14	,,
30	27.59	KOEFOED and VILLADSEN (1958)
60	23.72	MARECHAL (1952)

Refractive index: FORZIATI, NORRIS and ROSSINI (1949)

t°	He_red	H_C	Na_D	Hg_gr	He_blue	H_F	Hg_v
20	1.49578	1.49643	1.50112	1.50521	1.51077	1.51313	1.52302
25	1.49262	1.49327	1.49792	1.50197	1.50748	1.50982	1.51964
30	1.48950	1.49015	1.49478	1.49881	1.50429	1.50662	1.51640

t°	H_α	D	H_β	H_γ	
20	1.49622	1.50089	1.51298	1.52306	VOGEL, CRESSWELL *et al.* (1952)
20	1.49635	1.50100	1.51305	—	KAZANSKII, ROZENGART *et al.* (1953)
9.25	—	1.50783			KETELAAR and VAN MEURS (1957)
20.38	—	1.50076			,,
31.25	—	1.49364			,,
20	—	1.5009			GRUNBERG (1954)
20	—	1.50114			NECKEL and VOLK (1958)
20	—	1.5011			EVANS, ORMROD *et al.* (1950)
20	—	1.50110			KORTÜM and FREIHER (1954)
25	—	1.49792			WOOD and MASLAND (1960)
25	—	1.49793			WOOD, LANGER and BATTINO (1960)
25	—	1.49803			BROWN and SMITH (1955)
25	—	1.4979			BROWN and EWALD (1951)

WAXLER and WEIR (1963)

t°	P (atm.)	d	n_D	t°	P (atm.)	d	n_D
24.80	0.99	0.87387	1.49859	54.34	0.99	0.84206	1.47910
	246.8	0.89307	1.51031		270.9	0.86693	1.49422
	482.5	0.90862	1.51982		477.9	0.88257	1.50382
	657.2	0.91888	1.52593		759.9	0.90079	1.51478
					1109.5	0.91992	1.52633
34.50	0.99	0.86352	1.49221				
	242.9	0.88349	1.50438				
	478.3	0.89978	1.51445				
	747.1	0.91581	1.52418				
	1093.0	0.93360	1.53489				

Polarisability: 9.25° = 9.823 20.38°= 9.824 31.25°= 9.823 KETELAAR and VAN MEURS (1957)

N.B. (p. 148): Replace LUNT and RAN (1930) by LUNT and RAU (1930) and MOURADOFF (unp.) by MOURADOFF (1948)

Dielectric constant

t°	ε	t°	ε	
33.10	2.262	−40.1	2.281	PHILIPPE and PIETTE (1955)
22.25	2.279	−12.0	2.308	
17.10	2.288	−0.3	2.324	
8.85	2.302	3.55	2.330	
4.95	2.308	5.40	2.333	
− 6.0	2.315	6.90	2.306	
−18.0	2.301	13.60	2.293	
−26.9	2.293	15.75	2.291	
−60.4	2.271	25.95	2.273	
		39.90	2.251	
		47.80	2.239	
20	2.283			STAUDHAMMER and SEYER (1958)
20	2.2816			MECKE, JOECKLE and
				KLINGENBERG (1962)
20	2.2832			MECKE and JOECKLE (1962)

Specific magnetic susceptibility at $20°$: $− 0.699 \cdot 10^{-6}$ VON RAUTENFELD and STEURER (1941)

TOLUENE C_7H_8

Critical temperature: $318.57°$ AMBROSE, COX and TOWNSEND (1960); AMBROSE and GRANT (1957)

Saturated vapour pressure

t°	p mm	
138	1784.34	GRISWOLD, ANDRES and KLEIN (1943)
189	4628.94	,,
227	9051.00	,,
253	13188.60	,,
295	23377.44	,,

t°	p mm	t°	p mm	t°	p mm	
35.504	47.99	66.107	176.06	104.052	628.16	FORZIATI, NORRIS and
39.437	57.68	71.758	217.34	109.328	732.39	ROSSINI (1949)
45.997	77.47	76.965	261.95	109.894	744.30	,,
48.894	87.90	83.230	325.22	110.420	755.49	,,
52.848	103.81	89.695	402.76	111.018	768.52	,,
57.315	124.75	96.580	501.00	111.545	780.05	,,
61.869	149.58	—	—	—	—	,,

t°	p mm	t°	p mm	
110.25	750.4	69.58	201.0	DREYER, MARTIN and VON WEBER
99.01	540.8	60.41	141.0	(1954–1955)
90.26	410.7	49.76	91.5	,,
79.45	286.2	39.73	58.2	,,

Second virial coefficient: ANDON, COX et al. (1957)

Boiling point: 110.626 *dt/dp (10 mm):* 0.4630 FORZIATI and ROSSINI (1949)

Density

t°	d	
20	0.8672	KAZANSKII, ROZENGART et al. (1953)
20	0.8669	HAMMOND, HOWARD and MCALLISTER (1958)
20	0.86696	DONALDSON and QUAYLE (1950)
30	0.85766	,,
40	0.84836	,,
20	0.86694	FORZIATI and ROSSINI (1949)
25	0.86230	,,
30	0.85770	,,
25	0.86232	KYLE and REED (1958)

Surface tension

t°	γ	
20	28.53	DONALDSON and QUAYLE (1950)
30	27.32	,,
40	26.15	,,

Refractive index

t°	He$_{red}$	H$_C$	Na$_D$	Hg$_{gr}$	He$_{blue}$	H$_F$	Hg$_v$	
20	1.49180	1.49243	1.49693	1.50086	1.50620	1.50847	1.51800	FORZIATI (1950)
25	1.48903	1.48966	1.49413	1.49803	1.50334	1.50559	1.51506	,,
30	1.48619	1.48682	1.49126	1.49514	1.50041	1.50265	1.51206	,,

t°	n_D	
25	1.4939	JONES, SCHOENBORN and COLBURN (1943)
25	1.49405	HAMMOND, HOWARD and McALLISTER (1958)
+20	1.4970	BENOLIEL (1941)
−25	1.5216	,,

Dielectric constant: ALTSHULLER (1954)

t°	ε	
20	2.385	
30	2.364	

ETHYLBENZENE C_8H_{10}

Critical temperature: 343.97° AMBROSE, COX and TOWNSEND (1960)

Saturated vapour pressure: FORZIATI, NORRIS and ROSSINI (1949)

t°	p mm	t°	p mm	t°	p mm
56.689	47.99	84.619	149.59	129.234	628.17
60.887	57.68	89.090	176.07	134.815	732.40
64.510	67.43	95.074	217.35	135.413	744.32
67.827	77.48	100.576	261.96	135.969	755.50
70.891	87.91	107.210	325.23	136.602	768.53
75.054	103.81	114.046	402.77	137.160	780.06
79.791	124.76	121.331	501.01		

t°	p mm	
136.4	760	YANG and VAN WINKLE (1955)
114.0	400	,,
92.8	200	,,
74.2	100	,,
57.8	50	,,

t°	p mm	t°	p mm	t°	p mm	
136.27	755.2	104.07	293.5	37.85	18.3	DREYER, MARTIN and VON WEBER
120.22	480.7	73.12	95.5	33.24	14.5	,, (1954–55)
112.97	386.9	55.24	44.4	29.67	11.6	,,

Boiling point: 136.4 YANG and VAN WINKLE (1955)

   136.186 *dt/dp (10 mm):* 0.4898 FORZIATI and ROSSINI (1949)

Density

t°	d	
20	0.86696	DONALDSON and QUAYLE (1950)
30	0.85820	,,
40	0.84944	,,
25	0.8621	YANG and VAN WINKLE (1955)
20	0.86702	FORZIATI and ROSSINI (1949)
25	0.86264	,,
30	0.85828	,,

Surface tension: DONALDSON and QUAYLE (1950)

t°	γ	
20	29.04	
30	27.93	
40	26.79	

Refractive index: FORZIATI (1950) and FORZIATI and ROSSINI (1949)

t°	He_{red}	H_C	Na_D	Hg_{gr}	He_{blue}	H_F	Hg_v
20	1.49102	1.49162	1.49588	1.49960	1.50465	1.50678	1.51575
25	1.44837	1.48896	1.49320	1.49689	1.50191	1.50403	1.51295
30	1.48569	1.48628	1.49050	1.49418	1.49918	1.50129	1.51018

Dielectric constant: ALTSHULLER (1954)

t°	ε	
20	2.403	
30	2.381	

n-PROPYLBENZENE C_9H_{12}

Critical temperature: 365.21° AMBROSE, COX and TOWNSEND (1960)

Saturated vapour pressure: FORZIATI, NORRIS and ROSSINI (1949)

$t°$	p mm	$t°$	p mm	$t°$	p mm
75.818	48.02	105.085	149.61	151.921	628.20
80.181	57.71	109.781	176.09	157.779	732.43
83.993	67.45	116.060	217.38	158.408	744.35
87.457	77.50	128.794	325.26	158.991	755.54
90.688	87.93	135.972	402.80	159.654	768.55
95.049	103.84	143.625	501.03	160.239	780.09
100.020	124.78				

Boiling point: 159.218 *dt/dp (10 mm)* 0.5143 FORZIATI and ROSSINI (1949)

N.B. (p. 157): *Freezing point:* Add to the quotation of GLASGOW JR. *et al.* the following: FORZIATI, GLASGOW JR. *et al.* (1946).

Density: FORZIATI and ROSSINI (1949)

$t°$	d
20	0.86204
25	0.85780
30	0.85370

Refractive index

$t°$	He_{red}	H_C	Na_D	Hg_{gr}	He_{blue}	H_F	Hg_v	
20	1.48742	1.48799	1.49202	1.49555	1.50033	1.50235	1.51083	FORZIATI (1950)
25	1.48494	1.48550	1.48951	1.49301	1.49776	1.49977	1.50820	and FORZIATI
30	1.48248	1.48303	1.48702	1.49051	1.49523	1.49723	1.50562	and ROSSINI (1949)

Dielectric constant: ALTSHULLER (1954)

$t°$	ε
20	2.372
30	2.351

Iso-PROPYLBENZENE C_9H_{12}

Critical temperature: 357.9° AMBROSE, COX and TOWNSEND (1960) and AMBROSE and GRANT (1957)

Saturated vapour pressure: DREYER, MARTIN and VON WEBER (1954–55)

$t°$	p mm	$t°$	p mm	$t°$	p mm	$t°$	p mm
151.89	747.2	125.98	362.6	97.45	140.9	79.31	70.5
148.31	679.4	121.30	313.9	95.23	130.0	75.26	59.9
143.53	601.3	116.52	270.1	93.08	120.3	71.20	50.7
138.61	523.7	111.18	227.0	90.84	110.5	67.65	43.2
134.21	461.7	105.81	189.2	88.28	99.9	64.01	36.8
129.74	405.8	99.97	154.6	85.77	90.8	59.94	30.3
—	—	—	—	82.58	80.2	56.39	25.2

$t°$	p mm	$t°$	p mm	$t°$	p mm	
70.16	48.01	99.00	149.61	145.19	628.19	FORZIATI, NORRIS and ROSSINI
74.47	57.70	103.64	176·09	150.97	732.43	,, (1949)
78.23	67.45	109.82	217.37	151.59	744.34	,,
81.64	77.49	115.52	261.98	152.17	755.54	,,
84.82	87.92	122.38	325.25	152.82	768.55	,,
89.11	103.83	129.46	402.79	153.40	780.09	,,
94.01	124.78	137.01	501.03	—	—	,,

Boiling point: 152.48   DREYER, MARTIN and VON WEBER (1954–55)
152.392 *dt/dp (10 mm):* 0.5074 FORZIATI and ROSSINI (1949)

Density

$t°$	d	
20	0.86179	FORZIATI and ROSSINI (1949)
25	0.85751	,,
30	0.85335	,,
20	0.86175	DONALDSON and QUAYLE (1950)
30	0.85321	,,
40	0.84467	,,

Surface tension

t°	γ	
20	28.20	DONALDSON and QUAYLE (1950)
30	27.17	,,
40	26.09	,,

Refractive index

t°	He$_{red}$	H$_C$	Na$_D$	Hg$_{gr}$	He$_{blue}$	H$_F$	Hg$_v$	
20	1.48688	1.48744	1.49145	1.49498	1.49970	1.50171	1.51018	FORZIATI (1950)
25	1.48436	1.48492	1.48890	1.49239	1.49711	1.49911	1.50753	,,
30	1.48194	1.48250	1.48646	1.48993	1.49462	1.49661	1.50499	,,

$n_D^{20°}$: 1.4915 DREYER, MARTIN and VON WEBER (1954–55)

Dielectric constant: ALTSHULLER (1954)

t°	ε	
20	2.384	
30	2.363	

n-BUTYLBENZENE $C_{10}H_{14}$

Critical temperature: 387.3° AMBROSE, COX and TOWNSEND (1960)

Saturated vapour pressure: FORZIATI, NORRIS and ROSSINI (1949)

t°	p mm	t°	p mm	t°	p mm
96.233	48.12	121.506	124.82	175.666	628.20
100.814	57.73	126.797	149.60	181.767	732.40
104.778	67.44	138.300	217.36	182.429	744.40
108.403	77.47	151.541	325.17	183.036	755.57
111.762	87.92	159.032	402.73	183.725	768.48
116.322	103.81	167.011	500.99	184.329	779.98

Boiling point: 183.270 *dt/dp (10 mm):* 0.5358 FORZIATI and ROSSINI (1949)
          183.35   BIRCH, DEAN *et al.* (1949)

Freezing point: −87.54 *ibid.*

Density

t°	d	
20	0.86013	DONALDSON and QUAYLE (1950)
30	0.85201	,,
40	0.84389	,,
20	0.8603	BIRCH, DEAN *et al.* (1949)
20	0.86013	FORZIATI and ROSSINI (1949)
25	0.85607	,,
30	0.85218	,,

Surface tension: DONALDSON and QUAYLE (1950)

t°	γ	
20	29.23	
30	28.19	
40	27.18	

Refractive index: FORZIATI (1950)

t°	He_{red}	H_C	Na_D	Hg_{gr}	He_{blue}	H_F	Hg_v
20	1.48537	1.48591	1.48979	1.49315	1.49770	1.49963	1.50770
25	1.48303	1.48357	1.48742	1.49076	1.49529	1.49721	1.50523
30	1.48064	1.48118	1.48502	1.48836	1.49288	1.49480	1.50281

at 20°: 1.4897 BIRCH, DEAN *et al.* (1949)

Dielectric constant: ALTSHULLER (1954)

t°	ε	
20	2.359	
30	2.338	

N.B. (p. 160): Instead of STREIFF, CAHILL *et al.*, read STREIFF, MURPHY, CAHILL *et al.*

Iso-BUTYLBENZENE $C_{10}H_{14}$

Critical temperature: 384.72° AMBROSE, COX and TOWNSEND (1960)

Saturated vapour pressure: FORZIATI, NORRIS and ROSSINI (1949)

$t°$	p mm	$t°$	p mm	$t°$	p mm
86.637	48.12	116.808	149.60	165.217	628.21
91.118	57.73	121.659	176.07	171.270	732.41
95.026	67.44	128.149	217.36	171.920	744.41
98.620	77.47	134.112	261.91	172.526	755.59
101.946	87.92	141.301	325.17	173.209	768.49
106.450	103.81	148.724	402.73	173.814	779.99
111.582	124.82	156.632	500.99		

Boiling point: 172.759 *dt/dp (10 mm):* 0.5319 FORZIATI and ROSSINI (1949)
172.85 BIRCH, DEAN *et al.* (1949)

Freezing point: −51.59 *ibid.*

Density

$t°$	d	
20	0.85321	FORZIATI and ROSSINI (1949)
25	0.84907	,,
30	0.84512	,,
20	0.8535	BIRCH, DEAN *et al.* (1949)

Refractive index: FORZIATI (1950)

$t°$	He_{red}	H_C	Na_D	Hg_{gr}	He_{blue}	H_F	Hg_v
20	1.48206	1.48260	1.48646	1.48983	1.49438	1.49631	1.50437
25	1.47962	1.48016	1.48400	1.48735	1.49187	1.49379	1.50181
30	1.47721	1.47774	1.48157	1.48490	1.48941	1.49132	1.49931

$t°$	n_D	
20	1.48646	FORZIATI and ROSSINI (1949)
25	1.48400	,,
30	1.48157	,,
20	1.4865	BIRCH, DEAN *et al.* (1949)

Dielectric constant: ALTSHULLER (1954)

$t°$	ε	
20	2.319	
30	2.298	

Sec.-BUTYLBENZENE　　　$C_{10}H_{14}$

Saturated vapour pressure: FORZIATI, NORRIS and ROSSINI (1949)

t°	p mm	t°	p mm	t°	p mm
87.118	48.12	117.387	149.60	165.768	628.21
91.684	57.72	122.232	176.08	171.820	732.41
95.620	67.43	128.715	217.36	172.468	744.40
99.179	77.47	134.683	261.90	173.068	755.59
102.523	87.92	141.867	325.17	173.754	768.49
107.009	103.81	149.288	402.73	174.358	779.99
112.151	124.82	157.194	500.99		

Boiling point: 173.305 *dt/dp (10 mm):* 0.5313 FORZIATI and ROSSINI (1949)
173.30 BIRCH, DEAN *et al.* (1949)

Freezing point: − 75.30 *ibid.*

Density

t°	d	
20	0.86207	FORZIATI and ROSSINI (1949)
25	0.85797	,,
30	0.85405	,,
20	0.8622	BIRCH, DEAN *et al.* (1949)

Refractive index: FORZIATI (1950)

t°	He$_{red}$	H$_C$	Na$_D$	Hg$_{gr}$	He$_{blue}$	H$_F$	Hg$_v$
20	1.48580	1.48633	1.49020	1.49356	1.49812	1.50004	1.50810
25	1.48342	1.48395	1.48779	1.49113	1.49566	1.49757	1.50559
30	1.48102	1.48154	1.48537	1.48870	1.49322	1.49512	1.50312

20° : n_D = 1.4898 BIRCH, DEAN *et al.* (1949)

Dielectric constant: ALTSHULLER (1954)

t°	ε	
20	2.364	
30	2.345	

Tert.-BUTYLBENZENE $C_{10}H_{14}$

Saturated vapour pressure: FORZIATI, NORRIS and ROSSINI (1949)

$t°$	p mm	$t°$	p mm	$t°$	p mm
83.877	48.20	113.720	149.60	161.649	628.21
88.312	57.72	118.524	176.08	167.646	732.41
92.194	67.43	124.936	217.36	168.287	744.41
95.715	77.50	137.968	325.18	168.886	755.59
99.017	87.92	145.315	402.72	169.565	768.50
103.471	103.81	153.149	500.99	170.165	780.00
108.546	124.82				

Boiling point: 169.119 *dt/dp (10 mm):* 0.5269 FORZIATI and ROSSINI (1949)
169.5 BIRCH, DEAN et al. (1949)

Freezing point: — 58.09 *ibid.*

Density

$t°$	d	
20	0.86650	FORZIATI and ROSSINI (1949)
25	0.86240	,,
30	0.85834	,,
20	0.8666	BIRCH, DEAN et al. (1949)
20	0.86650	DONALDSON and QUAYLE (1950)
30	0.85830	,,
40	0.85010	,,

Surface tension: DONALDSON and QUAYLE (1950)

$t°$	γ
20	28.13
30	27.14
40	26.16

Refractive index: FORZIATI (1950) and FORZIATI and ROSSINI (1949)

$t°$	He_{red}	H_C	Na_D	Hg_{gr}	He_{blue}	H_F	Hg_v
20	1.48822	1.48877	1.49266	1.49604	1.50062	1.50256	1.51066
25	1.48583	1.48637	1.49024	1.49360	1.49816	1.50009	1.50815
30	1.48338	1.48392	1.48776	1.49110	1.49564	1.49755	1.50557

$20° : n_D = 1.4926$ BIRCH, DEAN et al. (1949)

Dielectric constant: ALTSHULLER (1954)

t°	ε	
20	2.366	
30	2.346	

n-DECYLBENZENE $C_{16}H_{26}$

Saturated vapour pressure: CAMIN, FORZIATI and ROSSINI (1954)

t°	p mm	t°	p mm	t°	p mm
297.799	758.41	260.372	323.82	217.156	98.17
296.370	736.16	244.331	214.18	211.392	82.04
278.950	503.12	230.476	145.83	202.987	62.47

Freezing point: —14.403 STREIFF, HULME *et al.* (1955)

Density: CAMIN, FORZIATI and ROSSINI (1954)

t°	d	
20	0.85553	
25	0.85189	
30	0.84833	

Surface tension: JASPER and KRING (1955)

t°	γ	t°	γ	
0	32.73	60	27.44	
10	31.85	70	26.55	
20	30.97	80	25.67	
30	30.08	90	24.79	
40	29.21	100	23.91	
50	28.32	—	—	

Refractive index: CAMIN, FORZIATI and ROSSINI (1954)

t°	He_r	H_C	D	Hg_gr	He_bl	Hβ	Hg_v
20	1.47939	1.47986	1.48319	1.48607	1.48994	1.49158	1.49836
25	1.47735	1.47782	1.48112	1.48398	1.48782	1.48944	1.49617
30	1.47523	1.47570	1.47899	1.48184	1.48567	1.48729	1.49400

POLYSUBSTITUTED AROMATIC HYDROCARBONS

Ortho-XYLENE C_8H_{10}

Critical temperature: 357.1° AMBROSE and GRANT (1957); AMBROSE *et al.* (1960)

Second virial coefficient: ANDON, COX *et al.* (1957)

Saturated vapour pressure: FORZIATI, NORRIS and ROSSINI (1949)

t°	p mm	t°	p mm	t°	p mm
63.608	48.01	92.015	149.60	137.356	628.18
67.852	57.70	96.568	176.08	143.019	732.41
71.548	67.44	102.657	217.36	143.626	744.33
74.916	77.49	108.250	261.97	144.190	755.52
78.048	87.92	114.988	325.24	144.832	778.54
82.285	103.83	121.935	402.78	145.400	780.07
87.101	124.77	129.333	501.02		

Boiling point: 144.411 *dt/dp (10 mm):* 0.4969 FORZIATI and ROSSINI (1949)

Density

t°	d	
20	0.88020	FORZIATI and ROSSINI (1949)
25	0.87596	,,
30	0.87186	,,
20	0.88005	DONALDSON and QUAYLE (1950)
30	0.87161	,,
40	0.86317	,,

Surface tension: DONALDSON and QUAYLE (1950)

t°	γ	
20	30.03	
30	28.93	
40	27.84	

Refractive index: FORZIATI (1950) and FORZIATI and ROSSINI (1949)

t°	He$_{red}$	H$_C$	Na$_D$	Hg$_{gr}$	He$_{blue}$	H$_F$	Hg$_v$
20	1.50037	1.50100	1.50545	1.50935	1.51463	1.51688	1.52630
25	1.49791	1.49853	1.50295	1.50682	1.51207	1.51430	1.52366
30	1.49531	1.49593	1.50032	1.50417	1.50940	1.51161	1.52093

Dielectric constant

t°	ε	
20	2.574	ALTSHULLER (1954)
30	2.544	,,
24.2	2.553	PYLE (1931)

Meta-XYLENE   C$_8$H$_{10}$

Saturated vapour pressure: FORZIATI, NORRIS and ROSSINI (1949)

t°	p mm	t°	p mm	t°	p mm
59.335	48.00	87.387	149.60	132.144	628.17
63.518	57.69	91.874	176.07	137.731	732.41
67.157	67.44	97.887	217.36	138.329	744.32
70.506	77.48	103.412	261.96	138.887	755.51
73.601	87.91	110.067	325.23	139.520	768.54
77.778	103.82	116.923	402.78	140.078	780.07
81.527	124.76	124.226	501.01		

Boiling point: 139.104 *dt/dp (10 mm):* 0.4903 FORZIATI and ROSSINI (1949)

Second virial coefficient: ANDON, COX et al. (1957)

Density

t°	d	
20	0.86417	FORZIATI and ROSSINI (1949)
25	0.85990	,,
30	0.85565	,,

Refractive index

t°	He$_{red}$	H$_C$	Na$_D$	Hg$_e$	He$_{blue}$	H$_F$	Hg$_g$	
20	1.49221	1.49283	1.49722	1.50105	1.50626	1.50847	1.51777	FORZIATI (1950)
25	1.48968	1.49029	1.49464	1.49844	1.50361	1.50580	1.51503	,,
30	1.48704	1.48765	1.49198	1.49577	1.50092	1.50311	1.51231	,,

Dielectric constant

t°	ε	
24.1	2.371	PYLE (1931)
20	2.367	ALTSHULLER (1954)
30	2.347	,,

Para-XYLENE C_8H_{10}

Second virial coefficient: ANDON, COX et al. (1957)

Saturated vapour pressure: FORZIATI, NORRIS and ROSSINI (1949)

t°	p mm	t°	p mm	t°	p mm
58.419	47.99	81.658	124.76	123.431	501.01
62.619	57.68	86.506	149.59	131.371	628.17
66.280	67.43	91.017	176.07	137.574	744.32
69.605	77.48	97.032	217.35	138.132	755.51
72.684	87.91	102.573	261.96	138.768	768.53
76.885	103.82	109.240	325.22	139.329	780.06

Boiling point: 138.351 *dt/dp (10 mm):* 0.4917 FORZIATI and ROSSINI (1949)

Density

t°	d	
20	0.86105	FORZIATI and ROSSINI (1949)
25	0.85669	,,
30	0.85246	,,
20	0.8611	HEIL (1932)
30	0.8522	,,
40	0.8433	,,
20	0.86100	DONALDSON and QUAYLE (1950)
30	0.85232	,,
40	0.84364	,,
25	0.8567	WILLIAMS and KRCHMA (1927)

Surface tension:

$t°$	γ	
20	28.31	DONALDSON and QUAYLE (1950)
30	27.22	,,
40	26.13	,,

Refractive index: FORZIATI (1950) and FORZIATI and ROSSINI (1949)

$t°$	He_{red}	H_C	Na_D	Hg_{gr}	He_{blue}	H_F	Hg_g
20	1.49079	1.49141	1.49582	1.49966	1.50489	1.50712	1.51644
25	1.48827	1.48888	1.49325	1.49707	1.50226	1.50447	1.51373
30	1.48558	1.48619	1.49054	1.49434	1.49951	1.50172	1.51094

Dielectric constant

$t°$	ε	$t°$	ε	
29.00	2.254	−54.8	2.380	PHILIPPE and PIETTE (1955)
13.95	2.286	−42.2	2.388	,,
12.00	2.290	−20.1	2.414	,,
3.75	2.464	+10.05	2.479	,,
− 4.2	2.446	12.90	2.485	,,
−12.0	2.430	17.10	2.279	,,
−30.0	2.400	24.00	2.265	,,
−70.4	2.372	35.25	2.241	,,
20	2.264			HEIL (1932)
30	2.249			,,
40	2.234			,,
50	2.219			,,
60	2.024			,,
24.3	2.269			PYLE (1931)
25	2.265			WILLIAMS and KRCHMA (1927)

1,2,3-TRIMETHYLBENZENE C_9H_{12}

Critical temperature: 391.35° AMBROSE, COX and TOWNSEND (1960)

Saturated vapour pressure: FORZIATI, NORRIS and ROSSINI (1949)

t°	p mm	t°	p mm	t°	p mm
90.332	48.13	120.504	149.59	168.614	628.18
94.826	57.73	125.333	176.07	174.606	732.39
98.770	67.45	131.800	217.35	175.252	744.34
102.336	77.47	137.737	261.91	175.852	755.55
105.663	87.91	144.882	325.16	176.527	768.46
110.157	103.81	152.260	402.72	177.126	779.95
115.287	124.81	160.106	500.98		

Boiling point: 176.084 *dt/dp (10 mm):* 0.5263 FORZIATI and ROSSINI (1949)

Freezing point −25.381 STREIFF, MURPHY *et al.* (1946)
　　　　　　　　−25.35 TAYLOR, JOHNSON and KILPATRICK (1955)

Transition point I : −42.89 *ibid.*
　　　　　　　II: −54.46 ,,

Density: FORZIATI and ROSSINI (1949)

t°	d	
20	0.89438	
25	0.89044	
30	0.88652	

Refractive index: FORZIATI (1950)

t°	He$_{red}$	H$_C$	Na$_D$	Hg$_{gr}$	He$_{blue}$	H$_F$	Hg$_g$
20	1.50891	1.50952	1.51393	1.51778	1.52303	1.52524	1.53459
25	1.50650	1.50711	1.51150	1.51533	1.52055	1.52276	1.53206
30	1.50412	1.50473	1.50911	1.51293	1.51814	1.52034	1.52962

Dielectric constant: ALTSHULLER (1954)

t°	ε
20	2.636
30	2.609

Specific heat: TAYLOR, JOHNSON and KILPATRICK (1955)

t°	cal/mol	t°	cal/mol	t°	cal/mol	t°	cal/mol
−253.16	3.16	−178.16	19.43	−108.16	29.67	−38.16	40.71
248.16	4.63	173.16	20.20	103.16	30.45	33.16	41.65
243.16	6.04	168.16	20.96	98.16	31.27	28.16	42.59
238.16	7.36	163.16	21.73	93.16	32.13	23.16	47.98
233.16	8.62	158.16	22.46	88.16	33.06	18.16	48.35
228.16	9.82	153.16	23.20	83.16	34.07	13.16	48.73
223.16	10.96	148.16	23.93	78.16	35.20	8.16	49.11
218.16	12.04	143.16	24.65	73.16	36.51	− 3.16	49.49
213.16	13.09	138.16	25.37	68.16	38.06	+ 1.84	49.88
208.16	14.09	133.16	26.07	63.16	39.91	6.84	50.28
203.16	15.05	128.16	26.76	58.16	42.70	11.84	50.66
198.16	15.99	123.16	27.47	53.16	48.96	16.84	51.06
193.16	16.91	118.16	28.18	48.16	50.45	21.84	51.47
188.16	17.79	−113.16	28.92	− 43.16	56.47	+ 26.84	51.89
−183.16	18.63						

Heat of melting: 1955.1 cal/mol TAYLOR, JOHNSON and KILPATRICK (1955)

Heat of transition I: 319.3 cal/mol   *ibid.*
          II: 157.4 cal/mol   ,,

1,2-DIETHYLBENZENE $C_{10}H_{14}$

Saturated vapour pressure: FORZIATI, NORRIS and ROSSINI (1949)

t°	p mm	t°	p mm	t°	p mm
96.729	48.19	127.171	149.76	175.853	628.32
101.263	57.88	132.059	176.26	181.936	732.54
105.223	67.59	138.590	217.54	182.590	744.50
108.822	77.64	144.596	262.13	183.197	755.75
112.191	88.05	151.832	325.42	183.885	768.64
116.728	104.00	159.290	402.93	184.493	780.21
121.906	124.95	167.235	501.16		

Boiling point: 183.423 *dt/dp (10 mm):* 0.5340 FORZIATI and ROSSINI (1949)

Density

t°	d	
20	0.87996	FORZIATI and ROSSINI (1949)
25	0.87592	„
30	0.87197	„
20	0.8805	DONALDSON and QUAYLE (1950)
30	0.8725	„
40	0.8645	„

Surface tension: DONALDSON and QUAYLE (1950)

t°	γ	
20	30.30	
30	29.25	
40	28.24	

Refractive index: FORZIATI (1950), and FORZIATI and ROSSINI (1949)

t°	He_{red}	Hc	Na_D	Hg_{gr}	He_{blue}	H_F	Hg_g
20	1.49877	1.49935	1.50346	1.50706	1.51192	1.51398	1.52265
25	1.49640	1.49698	1.50106	1.50463	1.50946	1.51151	1.52012
30	1.49400	1.49458	1.49865	1.50221	1.50703	1.50908	1.51767

1,3-DIETHYLBENZENE $C_{10}H_{14}$

Saturated vapour pressure: FORZIATI, NORRIS and ROSSINI (1949)

t°	p mm	t°	p mm	t°	p mm
95.092	48.18	125.303	149.75	173.595	628.31
99.573	57.86	130.157	176.25	179.628	732.53
103.524	67.58	136.638	217.53	180.275	744.49
107.096	77.63	142.597	262.12	180.877	755.74
110.436	88.04	149.777	325.41	181.558	768.64
114.946	103.98	157.169	402.92	182.162	780.20
120.082	124.94	165.050	501.15		

Boiling point: 181.25 BIRCH, DEAN *et al.* (1949)

  181.102 *dt/dp (10 mm):* 0.5293 FORZIATI and ROSSINI (1949)

Freezing point: −83.82 BIRCH, DEAN *et al.* (1949)

Density

t°	d	
20	0.86394	FORZIATI and ROSSINI (1949)
25	0.85993	,,
30	0.85590	,,
20	0.8641	BIRCH, DEAN *et al.* (1949)
20	0.8641	DONALDSON and QUAYLE (1950)
30	0.8561	,,
40	0.8481	,,

Surface tension: DONALDSON and QUAYLE (1950)

t°	γ	
20	29.17	
30	28.11	
40	27.08	

Refractive index

t°	$H_{e_{red}}$	H_C	Na_D	Hg_e	He_{blue}	H_F	Hg_g	
20	1.49089	1.49146	1.49552	1.49906	1.50385	1.50588	1.51441	FORZIATI (1950)
25	1.48850	1.48907	1.49310	1.49662	1.50138	1.50340	1.51188	,,
30	1.48609	1.48666	1.49067	1.49417	1.49891	1.50092	1.50936	,,

$n_D^{20°}$ 1.4956 BIRCH, DEAN *et al.* (1949)

Dielectric constant: at 20°: 2.369 at 30°: 2.350 ALTSHULLER (1954)

1,4-DIETHYLBENZENE $\qquad$ $C_{10}H_{14}$

Saturated vapour pressure: FORZIATI, NORRIS and ROSSINI (1949)

t°	p mm	t°	p mm	t°	p mm
96.817	48.17	127.360	149.75	176.164	628.31
101.370	57.86	132.256	176.24	182.260	732.53
105.353	67.58	138.811	217.53	182.916	744.49
108.962	77.63	144.823	262.12	183.524	755.73
112.339	88.04	152.086	325.40	184.212	768.63
116.893	103.98	159.566	402.92	184.821	780.20
122.043	124.94	167.530	501.14		

Boiling point: 183.752 *dt/dp (10 mm):* 0.5351 FORZIATI and ROSSINI (1949)

Density

t°	d	
20	0.86196	FORZIATI and ROSSINI (1949)
25	0.85794	,,
30	0.85402	,,
20	0.8619	DONALDSON and QUAYLE (1950)
30	0.8539	,,
40	0.8459	,,

Surface tension: DONALDSON and QUAYLE (1950)

t°	γ	
20	29.00	
30	27.97	
40	26.94	

Refractive index: FORZIATI (1950) and FORZIATI and ROSSINI (1949)

t°	He_{red}	H_C	Na_D	Hg_{gr}	He_{blue}	H_F	Hg_g
20	1.49017	1.49075	1.49483	1.49838	1.50321	1.50525	1.51384
25	1.48783	1.48840	1.49245	1.49598	1.50077	1.50280	1.51133
30	1.48542	1.48599	1.49003	1.49355	1.49832	1.50035	1.50885

Dielectric constant at 20°: 2.259; 30°: 2.244 ALTSHULLER (1954)

1-METHYL-2-ETHYLBENZENE C_9H_{12}

Saturated vapour pressure: FORZIATI, NORRIS and ROSSINI (1949)

t°	p mm	t°	p mm	t°	p mm
81.146	48.13	110.711	149.59	157.825	628.17
85.618	57.73	115.436	176.06	163.706	732.39
89.448	67.45	121.762	217.35	164.337	744.38
92.949	77.43	127.574	261.92	164.925	755.53
96.200	87.91	134.570	325.16	165.591	768.46
100.584	103.81	141.792	402.73	166.174	779.94
105.598	124.82	149.482	500.98		

Boiling point: 165.153 *dt/dp (10 mm):* 0.5163 FORZIATI and ROSSINI (1949)

Density

t°	d	
20	0.88069	FORZIATI and ROSSINI (1949)
25	0.87657	,,
30	0.87252	,,

Refractive index: FORZIATI and ROSSINI (1949), FORZIATI (1950)

t°	He_{red}	H_C	Na_D	Hg_{gr}	He_{blue}	H_F	Hg_g
20	1.49968	1.50028	1.50456	1.50828	1.51333	1.51546	1.52442
25	1.49723	1.49783	1.50208	1.50578	1.51080	1.51292	1.52183
30	1.49479	1.49539	1.49963	1.50332	1.50833	1.51044	1.51933

1-METHYL-3-ETHYLBENZENE $\quad\quad$ C_9H_{12}

Saturated vapour pressure: FORZIATI, NORRIS and ROSSINI (1949)

t°	p mm	t°	p mm	t°	p mm
78.105	48.13	107.383	149.59	154.053	628.17
82.525	57.73	112.074	176.06	159.871	732.39
86.293	67.45	118.338	217.35	160.498	744.38
89.793	77.47	124.082	261.92	161.080	755.54
93.022	87.91	131.027	325.16	161.735	768.46
97.368	103.81	138.178	402.73	162.316	779.94
102.326	124.82	145.795	500.98		

Boiling point: 161.305 *dt/dp (10 mm):* 0.5111 FORZIATI and ROSSINI (1949)

Density: FORZIATI and ROSSINI (1949)

t°	d	
20	0.86452	
25	0.86040	
30	0.85630	

Refractive index: FORZIATI (1950) and FORZIATI and ROSSINI (1949)

t°	He_{red}	H_C	Na_D	Hg_e	He_{blue}	H_F	Hg_g
20	1.49179	1.49238	1.49660	1.50028	1.50526	1.50738	1.51623
25	1.48928	1.48987	1.49406	1.49771	1.50266	1.50476	1.51356
30	1.48678	1.48737	1.49154	1.49518	1.50011	1.50221	1.51098

1-METHYL-4-ETHYLBENZENE   C$_9$H$_{12}$

Saturated vapour pressure: FORZIATI, NORRIS and ROSSINI (1949)

t°	p mm	t°	p mm	t°	p mm
78.306	48.13	107.710	149.59	154.684	628.18
82.701	57.43	112.422	176.07	160.548	732.39
86.523	67.45	118.727	217.35	161.179	744.39
89.988	77.47	131.499	325.16	161.761	755.55
93.252	87.91	138.701	402.73	162.424	768.46
97.630	103.81	146.368	500.98	163.008	779.95
102.619	124.82				

Boiling point: 161.989 *dt/dp (10 mm):* 0.5148 FORZIATI and ROSSINI (1949)

Density: ibid.

t°	d		
20	0.86118		
25	0.85702		
30	0.85299		

Refractive index: FORZIATI (1950)

t°	He$_{red}$	H$_C$	Na$_D$	Hg$_{gr}$	He$_{blue}$	H$_F$	Hg$_g$
20	1.49021	1.49079	1.49500	1.49866	1.50364	1.50576	1.51463
25	1.48768	1.48826	1.49244	1.49608	1.50104	1.50314	1.51197
30	1.48525	1.48583	1.48999	1.49361	1.49855	1.50064	1.50943

1,2,4-TRIMETHYLBENZENE   C$_9$H$_{12}$

N.B. (p. 170): Suppress p. 170 and replace it as follows:

Critical temperature: 375.87° AMBROSE, COX and TOWNSEND (1960)

Saturated vapour pressure: FORZIATI, NORRIS and ROSSINI (1949)

t°	p mm	t°	p mm	t°	p mm
84.804	48.13	114.572	149.59	161.991	628.18
89.259	57.73	119.328	176.07	167.896	732.39
93.155	67.44	125.694	217.35	168.534	744.34
96.650	77.47	131.556	261.91	169.121	755.55
99.940	87.91	138.599	325.16	169.788	768.47
104.369	103.81	145.867	402.72	170.377	779.96
109.418	124.81	153.603	500.98		

Boiling point: 169.40 *dt/dp(10 mm):* 0.52 TIMMERMANS and HENNAUT-ROLAND (1959)

169.351 *dt/dp(10 mm):* 0.5187 FORZIATI and ROSSINI (1949)

Freezing point: —45.9 TIMMERMANS and HENNAUT-ROLAND (1959)

Density

t°	d	
0	0.89188	TIMMERMANS and HENNAUT-ROLAND (1959)
15	0.87981	,,
30	0.86770	,,
20	0.87582	FORZIATI and ROSSINI (1949)
25	0.87180	,,
30	0.86782	,,

Viscosity

t°	$\eta \cdot 10^5$	
15	894	TIMMERMANS and HENNAUT-ROLAND (1959)
30	730	,,

Surface tension: TIMMERMANS and HENNAUT-ROLAND (1959)

t°	γ	
15	30.21	
20	29.74	
30	28.70	

Refractive index: TIMMERMANS and HENNAUT-ROLAND (1959)

t°	He$_r$	H$_\alpha$	D	He$_y$	He$_{gr}$	H$_\beta$	He$_{viol.}$	H$_\gamma$
15	1.50170	1.50229	1.50685	1.50695	1.51570	1.51787	1.52476	1.52763

t°	He$_{red}$	H$_C$	Na$_D$	Hg$_e$	He$_{blue}$	H$_F$	Hg$_g$	
20	1.49986	1.50047	1.50484	1.50867	1.51386	1.51607	1.52536	FORZIATI (1950)
25	1.49742	1.49803	1.50237	1.50618	1.51134	1.51354	1.52278	and FORZIATI
30	1.49498	1.49559	1.49990	1.50369	1.50892	1.51101	1.52020	and ROSSINI (1949)

Dielectric constant: 20°: 2.383 LAFONTAINE (1958)

20°: 2.378 ALTSHULLER (1954)

30°: 2.359   ,,

Specific heat: PUTNAM and KILPATRICK (1957) (cal/mol)

$t°$	c_p	$t°$	c_p	$t°$	c_p	$t°$	c_p
Series A		Series B		Series C		Series D	
−216.48	12.40	−124.04	27.04	−258.39	1.901	− 42.99	46.22
211.38	13.50	113.16	28.39	257.36	2.188	36.52	46.69
205.56	14.72	102.68	29.66	256.20	2.518	29.99	47.10
199.38	15.76	93.02	30.81	254.76	2.914	23.41	47.57
193.15	16.91	82.95	31.99	252.80	3.472	16.39	48.04
186.38	18.15	73.02	33.12	250.34	4.165	9.66	48.59
178.71	19.38	62.97	34.25	247.70	4.900	− 3.05	49.05
169.92	20.74	− 52.46	35.52	245.00	5.626	+ 3.58	49.60
160.97	22.06			242.25	6.360		
152.46	23.28			239.32	7.123		
143.34	24.53			236.09	7.922		
−133.66	25.85			227.25	10.02		
				221.86	11.25		
				215.62	12.59		
				−209.26	13.90		

$t°$	c_p	$t°$	c_p	$t°$	c_p	$t°$	c_p
Series E		Series F		Series G		Series H	
− 1.51	49.06	−209.97	13.76	−150.83	23.48	−215.46	12.61
+ 5.38	49.69	202.72	15.14	139.78	24.99	208.28	14.10
+ 12.84	50.36	195.48	16.47	129.24	26.38	201.54	15.36
+ 20.32	50.93	188.17	17.82	118.37	27.73	194.26	16.71
+ 27.81	51.63	179.03	19.31	106.80	29.14	185.37	18.21
		−168.89	20.88	95.77	30.45	176.79	19.68
				85.20	31.70	166.82	21.20
				74.46	32.93	156.53	22.71
				66.14	33.76	−146.20	24.15
				60.09	34.50		
				54.71	35.16		
				− 49.97	35.68		

$t°$	c_p	$t°$	c_p	$t°$	c_p	$t°$	c_p
Series J		Series K		Series L		Series M	
−136.76	25.44	− 48.71	45.98	+ 13.88	50.34	− 38.18	46.54
126.17	26.77	42.90	46.27	18.10	50.81	30.94	47.03
115.59	28.08	38.16	46.55	22.24	51.14	23.48	47.50
105.06	29.35	34.46	46.88			16.08	48.04
93.75	30.69	29.81	47.18			8.83	48.59
82.70	31.97	24.21	47.48			− 2.22	49.08
72.04	33.17	19.60	47.83			+ 4.13	49.57
62.59	34.28	15.04	48.14			10.28	50.15
54.70	35.26	10.50	48.43			16.02	50.59
− 48.20	35.94	6.00	48.81			+ 21.55	51.09
		− 1.55	49.19				
		+ 2.82	49.50				
		7.20	49.85				
		11.58	50.20				

Series I		Series II		Series III	
$t°$	c_p	$t°$	c_p	$t°$	c_p
−94.38	30.48	−107.12	28.99	−96.02	30.30
−86.12	31.47	− 98.59	30.01	−85.44	31.57
−77.07	32.43	− 90.33	30.97		

1,3,5-TRIMETHYLBENZENE C_9H_{12}

Critical temperature: 364.14° AMBROSE, COX and TOWNSEND (1960)

Saturated vapour pressure: FORZIATI, NORRIS and ROSSINI (1949)

$t°$	p mm	$t°$	p mm	$t°$	p mm
81.488	48.12	110.789	149.59	157.477	628.19
85.857	57.73	115.489	176.07	163.289	732.39
89.662	67.44	121.765	217.36	163.911	744.39
93.131	77.47	134.464	325.17	164.489	755.56
96.386	87.92	141.618	402.72	165.146	768.47
100.747	103.81	149.228	500.98	165.725	779.97
105.716	124.82				

Boiling point: 164.716 *dt/dp (10 mm):* 0.5100 FORZIATI and ROSSINI (1949)

Freezing points: stable: −44.736 TAYLOR and KILPATRICK (1955)

−44.72   STREIFF, MURPHY *et al.* (1946)

metast. I : −49.814 TAYLOR and KILPATRICK (1955)

II: −51.698

metast. I : −49.79   STREIFF, MURPHY *et al.* (1946)

II: −51.68

Density

$t°$	d	
20	0.86518	FORZIATI and ROSSINI (1949)
25	0.86111	,,
30	0.85707	,,
20	0.8653	DONALDSON and QUAYLE (1950)
30	0.8569	,,
40	0.8485	,,

Surface tension: DONALDSON and QUAYLE (1950)

$t°$	γ	
20	28.83	
30	27.79	
40	26.75	

Refractive index

t°	He$_{red}$	H$_C$	Na$_D$	Hg$_{gr}$	He$_{blue}$	H$_F$	Hg$_g$	
20	1.49446	1.49507	1.49937	1.50314	1.50826	1.51043	1.51957	FORZIATI (1950)
25	1.49195	1.49255	1.49684	1.50059	1.50569	1.50786	1.51697	and FORZIATI
30	1.48951	1.49011	1.49437	1.49810	1.50318	1.50534	1.51440	and ROSSINI (1949)

Specific heat: TAYLOR, JOHNSON and KILPATRICK (1955) (cal/mol)

t°	c_p	t°	c_p	t°	c_p
−253.16	3.77	−158.16	22.54	−63.16	33.18
248.16	5.67	153.16	23.12	58.16	33.75
243.16	7.48	148.16	23.70	53.16	34.31
238.16	9.09	143.16	24.28	48.16	34.86
233.16	10.49	138.16	24.84	43.16	44.36
228.16	11.77	133.16	25.39	38.16	44.68
223.16	12.97	128.16	25.92	33.16	45.04
218.16	14.19	123.16	26.48	28.16	45.42
213.16	15.16	118.16	27.04	23.16	45.82
208.16	15.80	113.16	27.58	18.16	46.23
203.16	16.59	108.16	28.12	13.16	46.66
198.16	17.37	103.16	28.67	8.16	47.08
193.16	18.18	98.16	29.22	− 3.16	47.51
188.16	18.87	93.16	29.78	+ 1.84	47.95
183.16	19.55	88.16	30.34	6.84	48.39
178.16	20.17	83.16	30.90	11.84	48.84
173.16	20.76	78.16	31.48	16.84	49.29
168.16	21.36	73.16	32.05	21.84	49.74
−163.16	21.95	− 68.16	32.62	+26.84	50.20

HEXAMETHYLBENZENE $C_{12}H_{18}$

Melting point: 165.5 SPAGHT, THOMAS *et al.* (1932)

Transition point: 110.6 *ibid.*

Specific heat: ibid.

t°	c cal/gr	t°	c cal/gr	
30	0.380	120	0.466	
40	0.393	130	0.480	
50	0.407	140	0.493	
60	0.420	150	0.507	
70	0.434	170	0.555	
80	0.448	180	0.566	
90	0.463	190	0.576	
100	0.478	200	0.587	

Heat of transition: 2.6 cal/gr *ibid.*

Heat of melting: 30.4 cal/gr   ,,

For 1,3,5-TRI*iso*PROPYLBENZENE see also WIBAUT and PAULUS (1958)

STYRENE (PHENYLETHYLENE) C_8H_8

Saturated vapour pressure: DREYER, MARTIN and VON WEBER (1954–55)

$t°$	p mm	$t°$	p mm	$t°$	p mm
144.77	753.9	120.81	377.5	80.17	90.5
137.23	610.0	113.10	295.4	74.42	72.3
134.83	571.6	110.06	269.1	63.23	44.3
125.41	434.4	99.51	188.3	60.04	38.3
125.38	432.5	85.53	112.5	39.21	13.7
				29.92	8.2

Boiling point: 145.60 DREYER, MARTIN and VON WEBER (1954–55)

Density at 20°: 0.9072 *ibid.*

Refractive index: $n_{20}^{D}°$ = 1.5468 *ibid.*

METHYLSTYRENES C_9H_{10}

CLEMENTS, WISE and JOHNSEN (1953)

Saturated vapour pressure

ortho		meta		para	
$t°$	p mm	$t°$	p mm	$t°$	p mm
32.01	2.90	41.78	5.15	31.82	2.82
40.85	4.97	43.22	5.58	41.76	5.17
58.51	13.15	49.90	8.28	41.83	5.20
58.54	13.24	52.12	9.46	52.17	9.05
70.20	23.35	55.73	11.24	53.94	9.98
82.80	41.47	57.80	12.55	59.58	13.48
82.83	41.51	65.20	18.34	59.91	13.91
100.35	84.83	70.95	23.94	66.62	19.04
112.35	132.75	71.01	24.02	75.40	28.94
		71.02	24.02	76.19	29.81
		71.10	24.36	80.20	35.39
		77.12	31.76	82.44	39.06
		99.33	80.23	90.90	55.80
		111.80	127.66	96.93	71.00

		ortho	meta	para
Boiling point:		169.80	171.60	172.78
Freezing point:		—68.57	—86.34	—34.15
Density:	0°	0.9284	0.9283	0.9383
	25°	0.9077	0.9076	0.9173
	35°	0.8992	0.8992	0.9088
Refractive index:				
$n_D^{20°}$		1.54374	1.54114	1.54202
dn/dt		0.00048	0.00052	0.00051

F. POLYCYCLIC AROMATIC HYDROCARBONS

BIPHENYL $\quad$ $C_{12}H_{10}$

Satured vapour pressure: BRADLEY and CLEASBY (1953) (mm)

t°	p · 10²	t°	p · 10²	t°	p · 10²	t°	p · 10²
15.05	0.312	24.00	0.887	35.05	2.90	23.05	0.77
20.70	0.584	24.10	0.888	35.10	2.91	26.50	1.15
24.70	0.919	27.05	1.20	37.90	3.87	31.25	1.91
—	—	29.15	1.54	40.55	5.02	35.90	3.10
—	—	32.45	2.23	—	—	—	—

Melting point: 68.3 $\quad$ SPAGHT, THOMAS and PARKS (1932)
$\qquad$ 68.84 MARECHAL (1952)

Density at 70°: 0.9939 MARECHAL (1952)

Surface tension at 70°: 35.64 *ibid.*

Specific heat: SPAGHT, THOMAS and PARKS (1932)

t°	cal/gr	t°	cal/gr	
30	0.307	80	0.422	
40	0.320	90	0.430	
50	0.333	100	0.438	
60	0.345	—	—	

TRIPHENYLMETHANE $C_{19}H_{16}$

Melting point: 92.1° SPAGHT, THOMAS and PARKS (1932)

Specific heat: ibid.

t°	cal/gr	t°	cal/gr	
30	0.302	80	0.368	
40	0.314	100	0.442	
50	0.328	110	0.449	
60	0.342	120	0.456	
70	0.355	—	—	

Heat of melting: 21.5 cal/gr *ibid.*

For 2-METHYL, ETHYL, PROPYL and BUTYL-DIPHENYL, see: GOODMAN and WISE (1951)

1,1-DIPHENYLETHANE $C_{14}H_{14}$

Density and Viscosity under high pressure, see LOWITZ, SPENCER *et al.* (1959)

Density: LOWITZ, SPENCER *et al.* (1959)

t°	d	
37.78	0.9860	
60.00	0.9689	
98.89	0.9387	

Viscosity (ibid.)

t°	$\eta \cdot 10^7$	
37.78	2.85	
60.00	1.84	
98.89	1.08	

1,8-DIPHENYLOCTANE $C_{20}H_{26}$

Melting point: 6.30 MARECHAL (1952)

Density at 25°: 0.9359 *ibid.*

Surface tension at 25°: 37.37 *ibid.*

Refractive index: ibid.

$t°$	He_r	H_α	Na_D	He_y	He_{gr}	H_β	Hc_v
15	1.52897	1.52961	1.53387	1.53397	1.54279	1.54511	1.55178
25	1.52534	1.52589	1.53015	1.53025	1.53898	1.54130	1.54799

1,12-DIPHENYLDODECANE $C_{24}H_{34}$

Specific heat: KARASHARLI and STRELKOV (1955)

$t°$	C_p	$t°$	C_p	
−263.16	1.561	−72.16	82.71	Solid I
253.16	8.605	72.16	76.51	Solid II
243.16	15.244	73.16	80.011	
233.16	21.079	73.16	89.69	
223.16	26.549	−23.16	98.318	
198.16	38.510	+ 1.84	107.537	
173.16	49.086	4.24	109.842	Solid
143.16	56.526	4.24	139.308	Liquid
123.16	65.015	+26.84	142.153	
− 98.16	75.854	—	—	

1,1-DIPHENYLTETRADECANE: see LOWITZ, SPENCER *et al.* (1959)

9-(2-PHENYLETHYL)HEPTADECANE $C_{25}H_{44}$

CUTLER, MCMICKLE *et al.* (1958)

Melting point: −26.7

Boiling point: 175.5 (1 mm)

Viscosity at 98.9° : $\eta \cdot 10^7 = 2.03$

Refractive index n_D at 40°: 1.4729

VINYLBENZENE DERIVATIVES see DREISBACH and MARTIN (1949) and DREISBACH and SHRADER (1949).

G. CONDENSED POLYCYCLIC AROMATIC HYDROCARBONS

NAPHTHALENE $C_{10}H_8$

Polyphasic equilibria

Critical temperature: 476.5 ZHURAVLEV (1937)

475.2 AMBROSE, COX and TOWNSEND (1960)

474.85 CHENG, McCOUBREY and PHILLIPS (1962)

Saturated vapour pressure

$t°$	p mm	$t°$	p mm	
218.638	772.00	168.540	214.14	CAMIN and ROSSINI (1955)
217.848	758.40	161.104	171.60	,,
217.237	748.03	155.766	145.78	,,
216.539	736.00	143.930	98.26	,,
200.471	503.08	138.677	82.12	,,
191.702	403.34	134.548	71.53	,,
183.336	323.72	130.836	62.54	,,
175.526	261.16	126.325	52.12	,,
16.15	0.0351	28.6	0.1226	,,
16.15	0.0334	28.6	0.1251	,,
18.15	0.0417	32.5	0.1776	,,
18.15	0.0435	32.5	0.1750	,,
19.8	0.0490	32.5	0.1759	,,
19.8	0.0492	37.4	0.2671	,,
21.1	0.0560	37.4	0.2780	,,
21.1	0.0578	40.25	0.3498	,,
23.2	0.0714	40.25	0.3498	,,
23.2	0.0715	42.6	0.4338	,,
26.15	0.0949	42.6	0.4346	,,
26.15	0.0939	42.6	0.4348	,,
28.6	0.1228	50.3	0.8459	,,
—	—	50.3	0.8401	,,
—	—	50.3	0.8393	,,
8.10	0.0141	18.70	0.0438	BRADLEY and CLEASBY (1953)
12.30	0.0222	20.70	0.0534	,,
13.85	0.0263	—	—	,,
15.65	0.0320	6.70	0.0122	,,
17.35	0.0382	12.70	0.0235	,,
17.55	0.0383	16.85	0.0350	,,

209 mm at 167.7° BARROW and McCLELLAN (1951)

Orthobaric densities: ZHURAVLEV (1937)

Melting point: 80.287 HERINGTON, DENSHAM and MALDEN (1954)
           80.274 STREIFF, HULME *et al.* (1950)
           80.279 MATHIEU (1953)
           80.27   McCULLOUGH, FINKE *et al.* (1957)

N.B. (p. 178): Instead of MAIR and STREIFF (1910) write (1940).

Heat constants

Specific heat of the vapour at 209 mm: BARROW and McCLELLAN (1951)

t°	cal/mol	
177.84	48.34	
249.54	54.27	

Specific heat: SPAGHT *et al.* (1932)

t°	c_p cal/gr	t°	c_p cal/gr	
30	0.315	120	0.447	
40	0.332	130	0.455	
50	0.350	140	0.462	
60	0.367	150	0.470	
70	0.385	160	0.477	
90	0.424	170	0.485	
100	0.432	180	0.493	
110	0.440	190	0.500	

Specific heat: McCULLOUGH, FINKE *et al.* (1957) (cal/mol)

$t°$	c_p	$t°$	c_p	$t°$	c_p	$t°$	c_p
			Crystals				Liquid
−261.35	0.659	−218.80	9.455	−69.12	26.028	83.84	52.260
259.80	0.969	216.48	9.757	62.92	26.840	88.47	52.690
259.74	0.988	213.51	10.149	56.32	27.714	90.68	52.941
258.63	1.227	208.23	10.804	49.38	28.630	92.07	53.129
258.34	1.306	202.96	11.388	42.82	29.567	95.28	53.319
257.41	1.513	197.65	11.947	36.03	30.464	97.63	53.528
256.83	1.669	192.31	12.518	29.14	31.443		
256.02	1.860	187.18	13.069	23.04	32.260		
255.14	2.091	186.92	13.095	16.74	33.212		
254.43	2.287	181.18	13.643	10.04	34.183		
253.36	2.561	175.47	14.175	− 1.36	35.496		
252.72	2.735	170.01	14.702	+ 9.17	37.103		
251.41	3.079	164.33	15.251	19.33	38.719		
250.88	3.220	158.44	15.840	26.68	39.877		
249.32	3.633	152.13	16.480	33.83	41.054		
248.72	3.784	144.35	17.270	35.16	41.443		
246.86	4.251	135.82	18.163	43.20	42.672		
245.89	4.483	127.67	19.042	48.74	43.614		
242.62	5.245	120.90	19.794	52.28	44.272		
239.16	6.015	114.69	20.498	54.80	44.729		
235.54	6.748	108.18	21.253	57.60	45.277		
231.76	7.456	101.87	21.978	63.50	46.461		
227.31	8.194	95.29	22.769	66.19	47.017		
−222.11	8.990	88.48	23.593	68.94	48.257		
		81.85	24.408				
		− 75.40	25.222				

Heat of combustion at 25°: 1232.54 kcal/mol SPEROS and ROSSINI (1960)

Heat of melting: 4536 cal/mol MC CULLOUGH, FINKE *et al.* (1957)

1-METHYLNAPHTHALENE $C_{11}H_{10}$

Saturated vapour pressure: CAMIN and ROSSINI (1955)

$t°$	p mm	$t°$	p mm	$t°$	p mm
245.326	770.74	217.375	403.25	167.212	98.17
244.555	757.79	208.677	323.74	161.689	82.07
243.949	747.48	200.536	261.26	157.539	71.33
243.177	735.67	193.280	214.08	153.600	62.36
236.243	630.25	185.505	171.62	142.140	41.43
226.498	502.97	179.971	145.83		

Boiling point: 244.685 *dt/dp (10 mm):* 0.6047 CAMIN and ROSSINI (1955)

Melting point: −30.496 STREIFF, HULME *et al.* (1955)

−30.46   MCCULLOUGH, FINKE *et al.* (1957)

Transition temperature: −32.37° MCCULLOUGH, FINKE *et al.* (1957)

Density: CAMIN and ROSSINI (1955)

$t°$	d	
20	1.02031	
25	1.01664	
30	1.01304	

Refractive index: CAMIN and ROSSINI (1955)

$t°$	He_r	H_C	Na_D	Hg_{gr}	He_{bl}	H_β	Hg_v
20	1.60828	1.60940	1.61755	1.62488	1.63513	1.63958	—
25	1.60592	1.60703	1.61512	1.62240	1.63259	1.63701	1.65627
30	1.60360	1.60471	1.61278	1.62005	1.63022	1.63463	1.65386

Specific heat: MCCULLOUGH, FINKE *et al.* (1957) (cal/mol)

Crystals II

$t°$	c_p	$t°$	c_p	$t°$	c_p
−261.22	1.015	225.20	9.455	127.21	22.974
259.83	1.364	219.71	10.392	121.39	23.761
259.58	1.426	218.44	10.602	114.79	24.657
258.36	1.741	213.34	11.435	107.71	25.597
258.14	1.814	208.24	12.234	101.60	26.451
256.89	2.134	202.87	12.980	95.56	27.299
256.35	2.282	197.22	13.773	83.14	28.192
255.17	2.603	191.95	14.534	82.89	29.057
254.60	2.767	186.72	15.273	76.79	29.911
253.19	3.172	186.50	15.307	69.95	30.903
252.55	3.352	179.96	16.129	64.87	31.620
251.08	3.757	173.59	16.930	62.39	31.978
250.21	3.997	−167.54	17.712	57.52	32.739
248.62	4.426	−161.74	18.450	55.05	33.105
247.74	4.653	156.18	19.174	51.92	33.584
245.78	5.158	150.29	19.938	50.37	33.869
245.04	5.338	144.10	20.756	48.50	34.106
242.05	6.068	139.12	21.529	45.01	34.547
238.60	6.860	132.83	22.221	42.69	35.190
234.77	7.666	132.34	22.290	− 40.24	35.718
230.32	8.524				

Crystals I		Liquid			
$t°$	c_p	$t°$	c_p	$t°$	c_p
− 31.78	63.6	− 25.19	48.891	26.74	53.816
− 31.45	79.8	19.00	49.427	33.20	54.482
		15.65	49.716	37.08	54.888
		11.13	50.119	47.25	55.958
		− 6.57	50.535	57.64	57.036
		+ 3.20	51.469	68.23	58.132
		13.23	52.440	+ 79.03	59.259
		23.10	53.429		

Heat of melting: 1660 cal/mol McCULLOUGH, FINKE *et al.* (1957)

Heat of transition: 1190 cal/mol McCULLOUGH, FINKE *et al.* (1957)

Heat of combustion at 25°: 1389.59 kcal/mol SPEROS and ROSSINI (1960)

2-METHYLNAPHTHALENE $C_{11}H_{10}$

Saturated vapour pressure: CAMIN and ROSSINI (1955)

$t°$	p mm	$t°$	p mm	
241.760	772.03	182.322	171.63	
240.957	758.42	176.722	145.76	
240.336	748.07	164.155	98.26	
239.613	736.00	158.689	82.07	
223.026	503.21	154.576	71.55	
213.963	403.40	150.665	62.55	
205.329	323.75	145.431	52.14	
197.234	261.17	139.193	41.52	
190.033	214.15	—	—	

Boiling point: 241.052 *dt/dp (10 mm):* 0.5997 CAMIN and ROSSINI (1955)
           241.1   OTHMER, SAVITT *et al.* (1949)

Melting point: +34.527 STREIFF, HULME *et al.* (1955)
           +34.57 McCULLOUGH, FINKE *et al.* (1957)

Specific heat: McCULLOUGH, FINKE *et al.* (1957) (cal/mol)

Crystals II

$t°$	c_p	$t°$	c_p	$t°$	c_p
−262.02	0.872	−203.37	13.716	−54.16	32.629
260.97	1.139	198.01	14.466	53.38	32.715
260.13	1.419	192.53	15.246	50.48	33.147
259.70	1.489	186.95	16.030	46.91	33.644
258.75	1.764	191.26	16.735	43.56	34.11
258.28	1.882	180.21	16.866	40.60	34.52
257.22	2.234	174.65	17.530	40.49	34.39
256.68	2.318	169.32	18.171	36.80	35.01
255.61	2.618	163.68	18.844	34.41	35.39
254.72	2.875	157.76	19.562	33.77	35.36
253.98	3.085	152.05	20.234	30.18	35.85
252.49	3.515	146.53	20.909	28.35	36.21
252.01	3.662	141.17	21.550	27.93	36.23
250.14	4.193	137.77	21.958	27.45	36.43
249.57	4.356	131.98	22.671	27.16	36.40
247.67	4.876	126.25	23.344	22.40	36.98
247.02	5.053	120.33	24.086	20.91	37.28
244.98	5.586	107.73	25.626	20.71	37.35
244.42	5.736	101.19	26.450	20.49	37.47
249.49	6.491	94.34	27.318	20.05	37.40
238.13	7.329	87.66	28.188	14.06	38.36
234.37	8.183	81.16	29.023	13.68	38.44
230.68	8.984	79.97	29.149	8.17	39.61
226.75	9.790	74.44	29.910	7.38	39.49
222.09	10.665	72.30	30.174	0.85	40.68
218.66	11.277	67.51	30.822	− 0.69	40.72
216.99	11.568	64.83	31.172	+ 4.15	42.06
213.69	12.128	60.76	31.743	5.50	42.33
−208.61	12.956	−57.57	32.176	+ 8.75	45.8

Crystals I   Liquid

$t°$	c_p	$t°$	c_p	$t°$	c_p
+ 0.33	43.466	20.91	46.378	+38.92	54.852
5.67	44.245	20.95	46.487	42.75	55.175
8.89	44.646	22.91	46.663	43.75	55.300
11.36	45.105	23.21	46.965	48.06	55.693
14.95	45.518	25.63	47.160	53.31	56.224
20.15	46.103	26.77	47.373	52.94	57.182
				72.80	58.156
				82.86	59.176
				93.47	60.204

Heat of melting: 2898 cal/mol McCULLOUGH, FINKE *et al.* (1957)

Heat of transition: 1341 cal/mol McCULLOUGH, FINKE *et al.* (1957)

Heat of combustion at 25°: 1386.88 kcal/mol SPEROS and ROSSINI (1960)

1-α-NAPHTHYLPENTADECANE $C_{25}H_{38}$

Boiling point: 213 (0.5 mm), ANDERSON, SMITH and RALLINGS (1953)
215 (1 mm) CUTLER, MCMICKLE *et al.* (1958)

Melting point: 41.6 CUTLER, MCMICKLE *et al.* (1958)

Density: CUTLER, MCMICKLE *et al.* (1958)

t°	d	t°	d	
60.0	1.1255	115.0	1.1740	
79.4	1.1418	135.0	1.1927	
98.9	1.1586	—	—	

Viscosity

t°	η		t°	η	
60.00	8.41	LOWITZ, SPENCER *et al.*	98.9	2.891	CUTLER, MCMICKLE *et al.*
79.44	5.05	(1959)		centi-	(1958)
98.89	3.41			poises	
115.00	2.52	*Viscosity under high pressure*			
135.00	1.90	(see authors)			

Refractive index at 40°: 1.5215 CUTLER, MCMICKLE *et al.* (1958)

FLUORENE $C_{10}H_{13}$

Saturated vapour pressure: BRADLEY and CLEASBY (1953)

t°	p · 10³	t°	p · 10³	(mm)
33.30	1.64	34.85	1.95	
37.20	2.50	38.45	2.81	
40.30	3.43	42.45	4.16	(two series)
45.00	5.43	47.75	7.08	
49.25	8.18	49.55	8.33	

Melting point: 113.2 MCLAUGHLIN and UBBELOHDE (1957)
115 FELDMAN, PANTAGES and ORCHIN (1951)

PYRENE $C_{16}H_{10}$

Saturated vapour pressure: BRADLEY and CLEASBY (1953)

t°	p · 10³	t°	p · 10³	(mm)
68.90	0.86	71.75	1.08	
74.15	1.41	75.85	1.67	
78.05	1.97	78.90	2.16	
78.20	2.06	82.70	3.04	(two series)
81.70	2.92	85.25	3.80	
82.65	3.07	—	—	
85.00	3.79	—	—	

Melting point: 150.2 MCLAUGHLIN and UBBELOHDE (1957)

ANTHRACENE $C_{14}H_{10}$

Saturated vapour pressure: BRADLEY and CLEASBY (1953)

$t°$	$p \cdot 10^3$	$t°$	$p \cdot 10^3$	(mm)
65.70	0.86	67.10	1.05	
69.91	1.25	68.75	1.18	
73.55	1.94	71.25	1.56	(two series)
77.25	2.81	72.20	1.67	
79.95	3.67	80.40	3.93	

Melting point: 216.042 FELDMAN, PANTAGES and ORCHIN (1951)

PHENANTHRENE $C_{14}H_{10}$

Saturated vapour pressure: BRADLEY and CLEASBY (1953)

$t°$	$p \cdot 10^3$	$t°$	$p \cdot 10^3$	(mm)
36.70	0.64	39.15	0.81	
39.85	0.89	42.10	1.11	
42.60	1.20	44.62	1.45	(two series)
46.70	1.85	46.70	1.82	
48.80	2.23	49.65	2.41	
48.80	2.25	—	—	

H. POLYMETHYLENES

CYCLOPROPANE C_3H_6

Critical temperature: 124.65° BOOTH and MORRIS (1958)

Critical pressure: 54.23 atm. BOOTH and MORRIS (1958)

Saturated vapour pressure:

BOOTH and MORRIS (1958)   HASELDEN and SNOWDEN

(1962)

$t°$	P atm	$t°$	P atm	$t°$	P atm
115.34	45.26	61.32	16.66	—34.25	0.9681
110.02	40.98	52.42	15.25	38.05	0.8207
105.30	39.20	43.28	12.15	38.15	0.8198
101.31	34.14	36.25	9.60	41.05	0.7240
91.10	30.13	32.42	7.82	47.15	0.5449
88.29	27.18	16.78	5.30	48.35	0.5174
81.19	25.79	11.02	4.01	52.75	0.4116
76.38	23.48	7.56	3.62	58.75	0.3039
71.42	22.32	3.00	2.38	59.45	0.2880
64.92	18.08	—	—	65.05	0.2149
				67.35	0.1880
				74.85	0.1189
				—84.55	0.0608

Viscosity: McCoubrey and Singh (1957)

t°	$\eta \cdot 10^7$	t°	$\eta \cdot 10^7$	
35.04	916	100.04	1094	
44.94	947	123.74	1160	
50.04	966	144.04	1213	
70.14	1011	172.54	1290	

CYCLOBUTANE C_4H_8

Saturated vapour pressure: Rathjens and Gwinn (1953)

t°	mm	t°	mm	
−59.930	18.73	−20.421	190.38	
56.129	24.32	15.817	236.58	
49.001	38.79	10.312	303.59	
45.921	47.27	− 3.057	414.25	
33.859	95.34	+ 5.300	579.31	
−27.261	135.20	+12.198	751.22	

Boiling point: 12.51 Rathjens and Gwinn (1953)

Freezing point: −90.73 Rathjens and Gwinn (1953)
                 −90.59 Pomerantz, Fookson *et al.* (1954)

Transition point: −127.42 Rathjens and Gwinn (1953)

Heat of melting: 260.1 cal/mol Rathjens and Gwinn (1953)

Heat of transition: 1413.24 cal/mol Rathjens and Gwinn (1953)

CYCLOPENTANE C_5H_{10}

Critical temperature: 238.4° Ambrose and Grant (1957); Ambrose *et al.* (1960)
                      238.65 Cheng, McCoubrey and Phillips (1962)

Boiling point: 49.3 Kazanskii, Rozengart *et al.* (1953)
              49.33 Kaarsemaker and Coops (1952)

Freezing point: −93.45 Douslin and Huffman (1946)
                −93.6 Kaarsemaker and Coops (1952)

Density at 20°: 0.7452 Kazanskii, Rozengart *et al.* (1953)

Refractive index

t°	$n_{H\alpha}$	n_D	
20	1.41140	1.40638	Kazanskii, Rozengart *et al.* (1953)
20	—	1.40641	Kaarsemaker and Coops (1952)

Dielectric constant: PHILIPPE and PIETTE (1955)

t°	ε	t°	ε
+ 20.0	1.969	−158.0	2.110
− 12.5	2.015	153.0	2.113
40.0	2.049	150.0	2.121
73.5	2.092	142.0	2.126
110.0	2.139	135.0	2.130
124.0	2.134	125.0	2.136
134.0	2.128	− 27.0	2.034
−145.5	2.123	—	—

Specific heat: McCULLOUGH, PENNINGTON *et al.* (1959)

t°	cal/mol	t°	cal/mol
0	17.84	626.84	56.50
25	19.84	726.84	59.84
26.84	19.99	826.84	62.70
126.84	28.38	926.84	65.17
226.84	36.07	1026.84	67.30
326.84	42.57	1126.84	69.14
426.84	48.01	1226.84	70.74
526.84	52.60	—	—

METHYLCYCLOPENTANE C_6H_{12}

Critical temperature: 259.55° AMBROSE, COX and TOWNSEND (1960)

N.B. (p. 187): Erratum: data of KAY (1947): p cr. 37.364 atm instead of 37364 mm

Saturated vapour pressure: WILLINGHAM, TAYLOR *et al.* (1945)

t°	p mm	t°	p mm
72.634	779.44	46.552	324.95
72.150	768.05	40.791	261.74
71.612	755.29	36.013	217.20
71.128	744.10	30.816	175.91
70.604	732.11	26.935	149.40
65.739	627.96	22.757	124.65
58.847	500.73	18.642	103.66
52.499	402.46	15.035	87.73

Boiling point: 71.9   EVANS (1938)

71.812 FORZIATI, GLASGOW Jr. *et al.* (1946)

Freezing point: −142.45 DOUSLIN and HUFFMAN (1946)
                    −142.468 FORZIATI, GLASGOW JR. *et al.* (1946)

N.B. (p. 188): Suppress: −142.445 from GLASGOW, MURPHY *et al.* (1946) and *triple point of* DOUSLIN and HUFFMAN (1946)

Density: CRANE (1941)

t°	d	
20	0.7480	

N.B. (p. 188): To CHAVANNE and SIMON, add: at 20°: 0.74860; at 25°: 0.74393

Refractive index

t°	nD	
20	1.40969	FORZIATI, GLASGOW Jr. *et al.* (1946)
25	1.40698	,,
20	1.4098	CRANE (1941)

Specific heat

Vapour

t°	cal/mol	t°	cal/mol	
0	23.87	626.85	68.27	SCOTT, BERG *et al.* (1960)
25	26.24	726.85	72.10	
26.85	26.42	826.85	75.39	
126.85	36.16	926.85	78.23	
226.85	44.96	1026.85	80.67	
326.85	52.36	1126.85	82.79	
426.85	58.56	1226.85	84.63	
526.85	63.80	—	—	
60.04	29.70	129.19	36.36	MC CULLOUGH, PENNINGTON *et al.*
89.39	32.55	163.09	39.49	(1959)
		197.89	42.58	

ETHYLCYCLOPENTANE C_7H_{14}

Saturated vapour pressure: FORZIATI, NORRIS and ROSSINI (1949)

t°	p mm	t°	p mm	t°	p mm
28.778	48.11	54.908	149.60	96.910	628.21
32.673	57.72	59.114	176.08	102.173	732.40
36.058	67.42	64.739	217.36	102.739	744.39
39.165	77.46	69.909	261.88	103.264	755.60
42.040	87.93	76.143	325.17	103.855	768.50
45.935	103.80	82.588	402.71	104.382	780.00
50.386	124.81	89.453	500.98		

Boiling point: 103.466 *dt/dp (10 mm):* 0.4623 FORZIATI and ROSSINI (1949)

Freezing point: −138.452 STREIFF, MURPHY, CAHILL *et al.* (1947)
      I −138.44   GROSS, OLIVER and HUFFMAN (1953)
      II −139.14   ,,

Density

t°	d	
20	0.76647	FORZIATI and ROSSINI (1949)
25	0.76217	,,
30	0.75780	,,

Refractive index

t°	He_{red}	H_C	Na_D	Hg_{gr}	He_{blue}	H_F	Hg_g	
20	1.41739	1.41769	1.41981	1.42162	1.42401	1.42501	1.42910	FORZIATI (1950)
25	1.41490	1.41520	1.41730	1.41910	1.42148	1.42247	1.42653	,,
30	1.41241	1.41271	1.41479	1.41658	1.41895	1.41993	1.42396	,,

Heat of melting: I: 1641.8 cal/mol GROSS, OLIVER and HUFFMAN (1953)
          II: 1889.2   ,,

N.B. the data of CRANE (1941) and GREENLEE (1942) do not coincide with those of KAY (1947).

Specific heat: GROSS, OLIVER and HUFFMAN (1953) (cal/mol)

Crystals I

$t°$	c_p	$t°$	c_p	$t°$	c_p
−261.01	1.069	−241.02	7.197	−186.43	17.220
259.45	1.480	237.96	8.051	182.69	17.690
259.22	1.576	233.17	9.289	179.22	18.113
257.52	2.021	222.12	10.456	174.75	18.630
257.28	2.102	223.27	11.452	163.09	19.281
255.08	2.770	218.41	12.392	167,23	19.533
254.65	2.941	218.24	12.400	163.76	19.932
251.92	3.810	212.49	13.434	162.50	20.098
251.91	3.812	206.39	14.430	159.39	20.514
249.18	4.713	205.81	14.519	156.13	20.910
248.40	4.960	200.04	15.336	155.44	21.011
246.05	5.699	198.20	15.600	151.89	21.517
244.75	6.088	193.37	16.263	148.83	21.968
−242.28	6.825	−190.43	16.687	−146.29	22.342

Crystals II

$t°$	c_p	$t°$	c_p	$t°$	c_p
−260.52	0.807	−242.12	5.726	−193.60	15.710
258.71	1.168	237.56	7.004	186.70	16.741
258.59	1.201	232.86	8.220	186.07	16.841
256.49	1.691	228.06	9.380	179.14	17.707
256.33	1.727	222.89	10.544	178.54	17.795
253.58	2.443	217.19	11.712	170.93	18.725
253.54	2.458	212.99	12.541	162.86	19.702
250.14	3.428	207.36	13.562	161.07	19.905
250.13	3.431	207.19	13.594	155.16	20.636
246.39	4.517	200.94	14.594	153.45	20.817
246.38	4.520	200.80	14.619	150.38	21.233
−242.55	5.633	−193.86	15.686	−148.61	21.476

Liquid

$t°$	c_p	$t°$	c_p	$t°$	c_p
−132.92	35.091	−94.36	35.999	− 25.37	39.978
130.40	35.130	84.76	36.368	15.56	40.778
127.20	35.160	74.84	36.817	− 5.93	41.593
123.60	35.238	65.06	37.326	+ 3.53	42.428
119.09	35.304	55.43	37.879	12.81	43.274
112.99	35.444	45.52	38.505	21.18	44.104
−103.62	35.688	−35.55	39.212	+ 28.67	44.843

n-PROPYLCYCLOPENTANE C_8H_{16}

Saturated vapour pressure: FORZIATI, NORRIS and ROSSINI (1949)

t°	p mm	t°	p mm	t°	p mm
51.875	48.01	79.591	149.61	124.015	628.19
56.030	57.70	84.039	176.09	129.579	732.42
59.628	67.45	89.990	217.37	130.176	744.34
62.911	77.49	102.068	325.25	130.731	755.53
65.966	87.92	108.877	402.79	131.379	768.55
70.088	103.83	116.132	501.03	131.917	780.08
74.794	124.78	—	—	—	—

Boiling point: 130.949 *dt/dp (10 mm):* 0.4888 FORZIATI and ROSSINI (1949)

Density (ibid.)

t°	d	
20	0.77633	
25	0.77229	
30	0.76811	

Refractive index

t°	He$_{red}$	H$_C$	Na$_D$	Hg$_{gr}$	He$_{blue}$	H$_F$	Hg$_g$	
20	1.42382	1.42412	1.42626	1.42809	1.43055	1.43156	1.43557	FORZIATI (1950)
25	1.42147	1.42177	1.42389	1.42571	1.42814	1.42915	1.43332	,,
30	1.41912	1.41942	1.42152	1.42333	1.42573	1.42674	1.43087	,,

Iso-PROPYLCYCLOPENTANE C_8H_{16}

Saturated vapour pressure: FORZIATI, NORRIS and ROSSINI (1949)

t°	p mm	t°	p mm	t°	p mm
47.033	48.01	74.827	149.60	119.450	628.19
51.183	57.70	79.275	176.08	125.044	732.42
54.798	67.45	85.265	217.37	125.643	744.34
58.088	77.49	90.769	261.98	126.201	755.53
61.122	87.92	97.396	325.25	126.836	768.55
65.296	103.83	104.235	402.79	127.394	780.08
70.012	124.77	111.532	501.03	—	—

Boiling point: 126.419 *dt/dp (10 mm):* 0.4913 FORZIATI and ROSSINI (1949)

Density: FORZIATI and ROSSINI (1949)

t°	d	
20	0.77653	
25	0.77259	
30	0.76851	

Refractive index

t°	He$_{red}$	H$_C$	Na$_D$	Hg$_{gr}$	He$_{blue}$	H$_F$	Hg$_g$	
20	1.42339	1.42369	1.42582	1.42716	1.43010	1.43112	1.43533	FORZIATI (1950)
25	1.42108	1.42138	1.42350	1.42532	1.42775	1.42876	1.43294	,,
30	1.41877	1.41907	1.42118	1.42298	1.42540	1.42640	1.43055	,,

n-BUTYLCYCLOPENTANE C_9H_{18}

Boiling point: 157.2 FORZIATI and ROSSINI (1949)

Freezing point: −107.992° STREIFF, ZIMMERMAN *et al.* (1948)

Density: FORZIATI and ROSSINI (1949)

t°	d	
15	0.7886	
20	0.7847	

Viscosity: FORZIATI and ROSSINI (1949)

t°	$\eta \cdot 10^5$	t°	$\eta \cdot 10^5$	
15	959.0	60	546.1	
30	779.4	75	467.3	
45	646.3	100	406.1	

Refractive index: n_D 20° = 1.4310 FORZIATI and ROSSINI (1949)

n-DECYLCYCLOPENTANE $C_{15}H_{30}$

Saturated vapour pressure: CAMIN, FORZIATI and ROSSINI (1954)

t°	p mm	t°	p mm	
279.283	758.55	219.377	171.73	
277.907	736.33	213.782	145.93	
260.943	503.23	200.861	98.25	
251.676	403.47	191.085	71.48	
242.859	323.76	181.867	52.01	
227.251	214.10	—	—	

Density: CAMIN, FORZIATI and ROSSINI (1954)

t°	d	
20	0.81097	
25	0.80739	
30	0.80383	

Surface tension: JASPER and KRING (1955)

t°	γ	t°	γ	t°	γ
0	31.11	40	27.57	80	24.02
10	30.22	50	26.68	90	23.14
20	29.34	60	25.80	100	22.25
30	28.45	70	24.91	—	—

Refractive index: CAMIN, FORZIATI and ROSSINI (1954)

t°	He$_r$	H$_C$	Na$_D$	Hg$_e$	He$_{bl}$	H$_\beta$	Hg$_g$
20	1.44605	1.44637	1.44862	1.45056	1.45313	1.45420	1.45861
25	1.44402	1.44434	1.44659	1.44852	1.45109	1.45216	1.45656
30	1.44199	1.44231	1.44456	1.44648	1.44905	1.45012	1.45451

DIMETHYLCYCLOPENTANES   C$_7$H$_{14}$

N.B. (p. 191): Replace this chapter as follows:

1,1- and 1,2-*cis;* 1,2- and 1,3-*trans* STREIFF, MURPHY, CAHILL *et al.* (1947)

1,3-*cis* and -*trans* STREIFF, ZIMMERMAN *et al.* (1948)

1-CYCLOPENTYL-4-(3-CYCLOPENTYLPROPYL)DODECANE,

9-(3-CYCLOPENTYLPROPYL)HEPTADECANE,

1,7-DICYCLOPENTYL-4-(3-CYCLOPENTYLPROPYL)HEPTANE,
see CUTLER, McMICKLE *et al.* (1958) and SCHIESSLER and WHITMORE (1955)

1,1-DIMETHYLCYCLOPENTANE   C$_7$H$_{14}$

Saturated vapour pressure: FORZIATI, NORRIS and ROSSINI (1949)

t°	p mm	t°	p mm	t°	p mm
15.498	48.12	40.744	149.60	81.470	628.20
19.262	57.72	44.815	176.08	86.585	732.40
22.527	67.43	50.257	217.36	87.137	744.40
25.476	77.47	61.312	325.17	87.647	755.59
28.300	87.92	67.558	402.72	88.227	768.49
32.069	103.81	74.228	500.99	88.736	779.99
36.361	124.81	—	—	—	—

Boiling point: 87.846 *dt/dp (10 mm):* 0.4497 FORZIATI and ROSSINI (1949)

Melting point: —69.49 GROSS, OLIVER and HUFFMAN (1953)

Transition point: —126.36 *ibid.*

Density: FORZIATI and ROSSINI (1949)

t°	d	
20	0.75448	
25	0.74991	
30	0.74532	

Refractive index: FORZIATI (1950)

t°	He$_{red}$	H$_C$	Na$_D$	Hg$_{gr}$	He$_{blue}$	H$_F$	Hg$_g$
20	1.41113	1.41144	1.41356	1.41538	1.41778	1.41878	1.42290
25	1.40850	1.40880	1.41091	1.41271	1.41510	1.41609	1.42018
30	1.40587	1.40616	1.40826	1.41004	1.41242	1.41340	1.41746

Specific heat: GROSS, OLIVER and HUFFMAN (1953)

Crystals I

t°	cal/mol	t°	cal/mol	t°	cal/mol
−260.68	0.953	−240.39	6.954	−181.29	17.166
258.89	1.422	235.53	8.153	176.38	17.881
258.89	1.420	229.32	9.485	173.77	18.230
256.78	2.018	223.56	10.586	169.22	18.877
255.48	2.415	218.46	11.481	165.66	19.373
254.17	2.823	216.36	11.842	160.54	20.119
251.54	3.673	211.62	12.626	158.09	20.473
251.15	3.803	209.54	12.966	151.47	21.472
248.18	4.739	203.38	13.926	149.98	21.691
246.97	5.111	197.27	14.826	146.22	22.225
244.61	5.793	190.72	15.816	141.43	23.041
−241.30	6.710	−183.45	16.899	−134.10	24.331

Crystals II   **Liquid**

t°	cal/mol	t°	cal/mol	t°	cal/mol
−114.63	32.055	−67.26	36.652	− 5.56	41.733
104.97	32.322	60.67	37.126	1.55	42.157
94.58	32.840	51.06	37.817	+ 3.04	42.588
83.85	33.379	41.62	38.537	6.83	42.896
− 74.88	33.930	32.36	39.300	11.50	43.375
		23.27	40.087	19.83	44.155
		−14.34	40.886	+26.65	44.783

Heat of melting: 257.8 cal/mol GROSS, OLIVER and HUFFMAN (1953)

Heat of transition: 1551.0 cal/mol *ibid.*

Cis-1,2-DIMETHYLCYCLOPENTANE C_7H_{14}

Saturated vapour pressure: FORZIATI, NORRIS and ROSSINI (1949)

t°	p mm	t°	p mm	t°	p mm
25.347	48.11	51.253	149.60	93.005	628.21
29.195	57.72	55.426	176.08	98.244	732.40
32.555	67.42	61.012	217.36	98.806	744.40
35.616	77.46	66.155	261.88	99.329	755.60
38.482	87.93	72.358	325.17	99.922	768.49
42.346	103.80	78.755	402.71	100.446	780.00
46.770	124.81	85.589	500.99	—	—

Boiling point: 99.532 *dt/dp (10 mm):* 0.4603 FORZIATI and ROSSINI (1949)

Melting point: −53.73 GROSS, OLIVER and HUFFMAN (1953)

Transition point: −131.66 *ibid.*

Density

t°	d	
20	0.77262	FORZIATI and ROSSINI (1949)
25	0.76807	,,
30	0.76364	,,

Refractive index: FORZIATI (1950) and FORZIATI and ROSSINI (1949)

t°	He_red	Hc	Na_D	Hg_gr	He_blue	H_F	Hg_g
20	1.41965	1.41997	1.42217	1.42405	1.42649	1.42751	1.43161
25	1.41714	1.41745	1.41963	1.42148	1.42390	1.42490	1.42895
30	1.41463	1.41493	1.41709	1.41891	1.42131	1.42229	1.42629

Specific heat: GROSS, OLIVER and HUFFMAN (1953)

Crystals I

$t°$	cal/mol	$t°$	cal/mol	$t°$	cal/mol
−260.85	0.771	−241.59	6.369	−178.24	17.349
259.78	1.009	236.87	7.602	173.08	18.013
258.84	1.240	231.66	8.802	168.89	18.493
257.30	1.647	226.23	9.944	166.27	18.767
256.61	1.840	220.30	11.091	159.96	19.543
253.94	2.630	216.31	11.801	157.94	19.776
253.82	2.678	214.63	12.093	152.39	20.421
250.61	3.684	209.79	12.888	149.13	20.790
249.80	3.944	202.99	13.947	145.56	21.209
246.92	4.822	195.05	15.095	144.14	21.359
245.79	5.162	186.93	16.268	140.37	21.776
−243.12	5.943	−178.37	17.346	−138.98	21.961

Crystals II

$t°$	cal/mol	$t°$	cal/mol	$t°$	cal/mol
−126.31	32.186	−99.15	33.200	− 77.65	34.302
123.77	32.327	97.30	33.288	70.51	34.745
118.89	32.472	90.37	33.612	70.19	34.759
115.50	32.588	89.00	33.681	67.82	34.916
109.47	32.793	87.65	33.752	62.46	35.295
106.60	32.903	80.35	34.143	− 60.07	35.466
−100.06	33.083	−79.02	34.231	—	—

Liquid

$t°$	cal/mol	$t°$	cal/mol	$t°$	cal/mol
− 50.08	38.793	− 28.82	40.386	+ 1.28	42.977
45.36	39.110	28.71	40.393	10.91	43.820
43.10	39.300	23.54	40.807	20.38	44.682
37.47	39.708	18.52	41.228	+ 29.68	45.567
33.76	40.008	− 8.53	42.083	—	—

Heat of transition: 1593.9 cal/mol GROSS, OLIVER and HUFFMAN (1953)

Trans-1,2-DIMETHYLCYCLOPENTANE $\qquad$ C_7H_{14}

Saturated vapour pressure: FORZIATI, NORRIS and ROSSINI (1949)

$t°$	C_p	$t°$	C_p	$t°$	C_p
26.113	67.42	48.564	176.08	85.463	628.22
29.113	77.46	54.047	217.36	90.608	732.40
31.934	87.93	59.094	261.88	91.160	744.40
35.719	103.80	65.178	325.17	91.673	755.61
40.055	124.81	71.466	402.71	92.255	768.90
44.460	149.60	78.181	500.99	92.769	780.01

Boiling point: 91.869 *dt/dp (10 mm):* 0.4521 FORZIATI and ROSSINI (1949)

Density

t°	d	
20	0.75144	FORZIATI and ROSSINI (1949)
25	0.74686	,,
30	0.74241	,,

Refractive index

t°	He$_{red}$	H$_C$	Na$_D$	Hg$_{gr}$	He$_{blue}$	H$_F$	Hg$_g$	
20	1.40963	1.40992	1.41200	1.41377	1.41612	1.41717	1.42118	FORZIATI (1950)
25	1.40706	1.40735	1.40941	1.41117	1.41351	1.41455	1.41853	and FORZIATI
30	1.40449	1.40478	1.40682	1.40857	1.41090	1.41193	1.41588	and ROSSINI (1949)

Cis-1,3-DIMETHYLCYCLOPENTANE C_7H_{14}

Saturated vapour pressure: FORZIATI, NORRIS and ROSSINI (1949)

t°	p mm	t°	p mm	t°	p mm
25.977	67.60	48.422	176.26	85.315	628.32
28.970	77.64	53.902	217.54	90.465	732.53
31.784	88.06	58.949	262.13	91.018	744.49
35.582	104.00	65.039	325.41	91.533	755.74
39.912	124.95	71.323	402.93	92.115	768.63
44.323	149.76	78.030	501.15	92.628	780.20

Boiling point: 91.725 *dt/dp (10 mm):* 0.4525 FORZIATI and ROSSINI (1949)

Density

t°	d	
20	0.74880	FORZIATI and ROSSINI (1949)
25	0.74435	,,
30	0.73985	,,

Refractive index

t°	He$_{red}$	H$_C$	Na$_D$	Hg$_{gr}$	He$_{blue}$	H$_F$	Hg$_g$	
20	1.40836	1.40865	1.41074	1.41250	1.41487	1.41586	1.41989	FORZIATI (1950)
25	1.40577	1.40606	1.40813	1.40988	1.41223	1.41321	1.41721	and FORZIATI
30	1.40318	1.40347	1.40552	1.40726	1.40959	1.41056	1.41453	and ROSSINI (1949)

Specific heat: SCOTT, BERG and McCULLOUGH (1960)

t°	cal/mol	t°	cal/mol	t°	cal/mol	t°	cal/mol
0	29.79	226.85	54.01	626.85	80.83	1026.85	95.14
25.00	32.52	326.85	62.51	726.85	85.24	1126.85	97.58
26.85	32.72	426.85	69.65	826.85	89.04	1226.85	99.71
126.85	43.91	526.85	75.68	926.85	92.31	—	—

McCULLOUGH, PENNINGTON *et al.* (1959)

t°	cal/mol	t°	cal/mol	
79.04	38.64	182.04	49.65	
102.04	41.16	227.04	54.04	
142.04	45.54	—	—	

Trans-1,3-DIMETHYLCYCLOPENTANE   C$_7$H$_{14}$

Saturated vapour pressure: FORZIATI, NORRIS and ROSSINI (1949)

t°	p mm	t°	p mm	t°	p mm
18.005	48.11	43.417	149.60	77.092	500.99
21.782	57.72	47.510	176.08	84.368	628.22
25.081	67.42	52.985	217.36	90.062	744.40
28.099	77.46	58.029	261.88	90.575	755.61
30.906	87.93	64.105	325.18	91.156	768.50
34.685	103.80	70.388	402.71	91.670	780.01
39.010	124.81	—	—	—	—

Boiling point: 90.773 *dt/dp (10 mm):* 0.4518 FORZIATI and ROSSINI (1949)

Freezing point: −133.69 GROSS, OLIVER and HUFFMAN (1953)

Density

t°	d	
20	0.74479	FORZIATI and ROSSINI (1949)
25	0.74025	,,
30	0.73573	,,

$t°$	He_{red}	H_C	Na_D	Hg_{gr}	He_{blue}	H_F	Hg_g	
20	1.40657	1.40686	1.40894	1.41071	1.41307	1.41411	1.41812	Forziati (1950)
25	1.40398	1.40427	1.40633	1.40809	1.41044	1.41147	1.41545	and Forziati
30	1.40139	1.40168	1.40372	1.40547	1.40781	1.40883	1.41278	and Rossini (1949)

Specific heat: GROSS, OLIVER and HUFFMAN (1953)

$t°$	cal/mol	$t°$	cal/mol	$t°$	cal/mol	$t°$	cal/mol
C							
−260.67	0.858	−234.32	8.136	−158.07	19.674	−82.36	36.645
260.18	0.965	228.24	9.420	153.22	20.339	72.58	37.212
258.70	1.268	222.15	10.588	149.89	20.782	62.49	37.813
258.39	1.347	215.19	11.648	146.01	21.383	52.03	38.494
256.42	1.860	214.37	11.910	139.97	22.425	41.88	39.225
255.93	1.991	207.65	12.933	L		31.86	39.990
253.69	2.650	201.07	13.849	129.46	34.552	22.01	40.773
252.65	2.974	194.09	14.856	126.26	34.659	18.43	41.081
250.27	3.720	186.80	15.905	122.10	34.815	12.35	41.593
248.83	4.161	179.21	16.894	118.90	34.939	− 8.89	41.895
246.49	4.874	171.68	17.870	113.27	35.170	+ 1.35	42.806
244.68	5.420	168.79	18.253	110.59	35.274	11.38	43.729
242.60	6.012	164.05	18.882	101.88	35.657	21.22	44.676
−239.93	6.749	−160.79	19.325	− 92.30	36.118	+30.87	45.617

Heat of melting: 1768.2 cal/mol *(ibid.)*

1,1,2-TRIMETHYLCYCLOPENTANE C_8H_{16}

Saturated vapour pressure: FORZIATI, NORRIS and ROSSINI (1949)

$t°$	p mm	$t°$	p mm	$t°$	p mm
36.207	48.10	63.251	149.61	106.900	628.24
40.224	57.72	67.615	176.09	112.381	732.42
43.728	67.41	73.455	217.37	112.971	744.42
46.937	77.46	85.302	325.18	113.517	755.64
49.920	87.94	91.992	402.71	114.138	768.52
53.962	103.81	99.144	501.00	114.686	780.04
58.562	124.82	—	—	—	—

Boiling point: 113.729 *dt/dp (10 mm):* 0.4818 FORZIATI and ROSSINI (1949)
Density: FORZIATI and ROSSINI (1949)

$t°$	d	
20	0.77252	
25	0.76817	
30	0.76399	

Refractive index: FORZIATI (1950) and FORZIATI and ROSSINI (1949)

t°	He$_{red}$	H$_C$	Na$_D$	Hg$_{gr}$	He$_{blue}$	H$_F$	Hg$_g$
20	1.42051	1.42081	1.42298	1.42482	1.42728	1.42830	1.43251
25	1.41806	1.41836	1.42051	1.42234	1.42478	1.42580	1.42998
30	1.41561	1.41591	1.41804	1.41986	1.42228	1.42330	1.42745

1,1,3-TRIMETHYLCYCLOPENTANE C_8H_{16}

Saturated vapour pressure: FORZIATI, NORRIS and ROSSINI (1949)

t°	p mm	t°	p mm	t°	p mm
28.944	48.11	55.423	149.61	98.197	628.23
32.881	57.72	65.411	217.37	103.572	732.42
36.299	67.41	70.674	261.88	104.148	744.42
39.432	77.46	77.023	325.18	104.688	755.63
42.361	87.94	83.585	402.71	105.292	768.52
46.308	103.81	90.594	501.00	105.830	780.03
50.828	124.82	—	—	—	—

Boiling point: 104.893 *dt/dp (10 mm):* 0.4724 FORZIATI and ROSSINI (1949)

Density: FORZIATI and ROSSINI (1949)

t°	d	
20	0.74825	
25	0.74392	
30	0.73958	

Refractive index: FORZIATI (1950) and FORZIATI and ROSSINI (1949)

t°	He$_{red}$	H$_C$	Na$_D$	Hg$_{gr}$	He$_{blue}$	H$_F$	Hg$_g$
20	1.40872	1.40904	1.41119	1.41302	1.41543	1.41644	1.42053
25	1.40626	1.40657	1.40870	1.41051	1.41290	1.41389	1.41794
30	1.40380	1.40410	1.40621	1.40799	1.41037	1.41134	1.41435

Cis, cis, trans-1,2,4-TRIMETHYLCYCLOPENTANE C_8H_{16}

Saturated vapour pressure: FORZIATI, NORRIS and ROSSINI (1949)

t°	p mm	t°	p mm	t°	p mm
38.907	48.12	66.100	149.60	109.887	628.21
42.972	57.72	70.477	176.08	115.378	732.41
46.426	67.43	76.327	217.36	115.969	744.40
49.701	77.47	81.725	261.89	116.518	755.60
52.704	87.93	88.224	325.17	117.140	768.49
56.756	103.81	94.942	402.72	117.690	780.00
61.380	124.82	102.109	500.99	—	—

Boiling point: 116.731 *dt/dp (10 mm):* 0.4827 FORZIATI and ROSSINI (1949)

Density

t°	d	
20	0.76345	FORZIATI and ROSSINI (1949)
25	0.75920	,,
30	0.75504	,,

Refractive index: FORZIATI (1950) and FORZIATI and ROSSINI (1949)

t°	He$_{red}$	H$_C$	Na$_D$	Hg$_{gr}$	He$_{blue}$	H$_F$	Hg$_g$
20	1.41615	1.41644	1.41855	1.42035	1.42276	1.42376	1.42787
25	1.41374	1.41403	1.41612	1.41791	1.42030	1.42129	1.42537
30	1.41133	1.41162	1.41369	1.41547	1.41784	1.41882	1.42287

Cis, trans, cis-1,2,4-TRIMETHYLCYCLOPENTANE C_8H_{16}

Saturated vapour pressure: FORZIATI, NORRIS and ROSSINI (1949)

t°	p mm	t°	p mm	t°	p mm
32.948	48.11	59.599	149.60	102.571	628.22
36.878	57.72	63.892	176.08	107.962	732.41
40.338	67.43	69.641	217.36	108.541	744.41
43.487	77.47	74.929	261.89	109.082	755.60
46.454	87.93	81.310	325.18	109.690	768.50
50.433	103.81	87.906	402.72	110.229	780.01
54.976	124.82	94.940	500.99	—	—

Boiling point: 109.290 *dt/dp (10 mm):* 0.4738 FORZIATI and ROSSINI (1949)

Density: FORZIATI and ROSSINI (1949)

t°	d	
20	0.74727	
25	0.74302	
30	0.73873	

Refractive index: FORZIATI (1950) and FORZIATI and ROSSINI (1949)

t°	He$_{red}$	H$_C$	Na$_D$	Hg$_{gr}$	He$_{blue}$	H$_F$	Hg$_g$
20	1.40821	1.40851	1.41060	1.41239	1.41475	1.41574	1.41980
25	1.40575	1.40605	1.40812	1.40990	1.41225	1.41324	1.41727
30	1.40329	1.40359	1.40564	1.40741	1.40975	1.41074	1.41474

1-METHYL-1-ETHYLCYCLOPENTANE C_8H_{16}

Saturated vapour pressure: FORZIATI, NORRIS and ROSSINI (1949)

t°	p mm	t°	p mm	t°	p mm
43.056	48.10	70.476	149.61	114.622	628.24
47.137	57.71	74.888	176.09	120.159	732.41
50.691	67.41	80.796	217.37	120.752	744.41
53.937	77.46	86.232	261.87	121.307	755.64
56.967	87.94	92.783	325.18	121.933	768.52
61.049	103.80	99.559	402.71	122.484	780.04
65.724	124.81	106.833	501.00	—	—

Boiling point: 121.522 *dt/dp (10 mm):* 0.4863 FORZIATI and ROSSINI (1949)

Density: FORZIATI and ROSSINI (1949)

t°	d	
20	0.78093	
25	0.77670	
30	0.77260	

Refractive index: FORZIATI (1950) and FORZIATI and ROSSINI (1949)

t°	He$_{red}$	H$_C$	Na$_D$	Hg$_{gr}$	He$_{blue}$	H$_F$	Hg$_g$
20	1.42473	1.42501	1.42718	1.42903	1.43148	1.43251	1.43671
25	1.42233	1.42261	1.42476	1.42660	1.42903	1.43005	1.43421
30	1.41993	1.42021	1.42234	1.42417	1.42657	1.42759	1.43171

1-METHYL-*cis*-2-ETHYLCYCLOPENTANE C_8H_{16}

Saturated vapour pressure: FORZIATI, NORRIS and ROSSINI (1949)

t°	p mm	t°	p mm	t°	p mm
48.846	48.02	76.582	149.61	121.105	628.19
52.975	57.71	81.050	176.09	126.684	732.43
56.539	67.45	87.011	217.38	127.281	744.34
59.862	77.50	92.490	261.98	127.832	755.54
62.935	87.93	99.105	325.25	128.463	768.55
67.070	103.84	105.929	402.79	129.021	780.09
71.792	124.78	113.205	501.03	—	—

Boiling point: 128.050 *dt/dp (10 mm):* 0.4897 FORZIATI and ROSSINI (1949)

Density: FORZIATI and ROSSINI (1949)

t°	d
20	0.78522
25	0.78113
30	0.77698

Refractive index: FORZIATI (1950) and FORZIATI and ROSSINI (1949)

t°	He$_{red}$	H$_C$	Na$_D$	Hg$_{gr}$	He$_{blue}$	H$_F$	Hg$_g$
20	1.42689	1.42719	1.42933	1.43116	1.43360	1.43461	1.43877
25	1.42451	1.42481	1.42695	1.42878	1.43121	1.43222	1.43637
30	1.42213	1.42243	1.42457	1.42640	1.42882	1.42983	1.43397

CYCLOPENTENE C_5H_8

Critical temperature: 232.9° AMBROSE, COX and TOWNSEND (1960); AMBROSE and GRANT (1957)

Freezing point: −135.036 HUFFMAN, EATON and OLIVER (1948)

Transition point: −186.09 HUFFMAN, EATON and OLIVER (1948)

Density: FORZIATI, CAMIN and ROSSINI (1950)

t°	d
20	0.77199
25	0.76653
30	0.76124

Refractive index: FORZIATI, CAMIN and ROSSINI (1950)

t°	He$_r$	H$_C$	Na$_D$	Hg$_{gr}$	He$_{b1}$	H$_\beta$	Hg$_g$
20	1.41947	1.41984	1.42246	1.42472	1.42773	1.42900	1.43423
25	1.41643	1.41680	1.41940	1.42165	1.42464	1.42590	1.43110
30	1.41339	1.41376	1.41634	1.41858	1.42155	1.42280	1.42797

Dielectric constant: PHILIPPE and PIETTE (1955)

t°	ε	t°	ε
+20.00	2.095	−138.5	2.420
−12.5	2.156	134.0	2.405
42.0	2.209	125.0	2.386
72.0	2.268	113.0	2.358
105.5	2.341	100.0	2.327
−147.0	2.441	− 28.0	2.185

Heat of combustion at 25°: 744.55 kcal/mol LABBAUF and ROSSINI (1961)

CYCLOHEXANE C_6H_{12}

Critical temperature: 280.3° AMBROSE, COX and TOWNSEND (1960); AMBROSE and
GRANT (1957)
280.35 CHENG, McCOUBREY and PHILLIPS (1962)

Saturated vapour pressure

t°	p mm	t°	p mm	
80.72	760.00	50.00	272.02	BROWN and EWALD (1950) and
70.00	544.23	40.00	184.75	BROWN (1952)
60.00	389.60	30.00	121.91	„
40.0	184.3	—	—	ROCK and SIEG (1955)

Boiling point: 80.72 BROWN and EWALD (1950)
80.74 GRUNBERG (1954)
80.75 DE BROUCKERE and GILLET (1935)

Critical solution point with CH_3OH: 46.20 DE BROUCKERE and GILLET (1935)

Melting point: 6.54 BROWN and EWALD (1950)
6.55 ROCK and SIEG (1955)
6.554 MECKE, JOECKLE and KLINGENBERG (1962)
6.59 THOMPSON and UBBELOHDE (1950)

Density

t°	d	
20	0.7785	DE BROUCKERE and GILLET (1935)
20	0.7783	KAZANSKII, ROZENGART et al. (1953)
25	0.7737	HAMMOND and STOKES (1955)
25	0.77375	ADCOCK and McGLASHAN (1954)
25	0.77399	BROWN and EWALD (1950)
30	0.7693	KURMANADHARAO, KRISHNAMURTY and VENKATARAO (1957)

Viscosity

t°	$\eta \cdot 10^5$	
25	885.6	GRUNBERG (1954)
25	900	HAMMOND and STOKES (1955)

Refractive index

t°	n_D	
20	1.4263	ROCK and SIEG (1955)
20	1.4262	GRUNBERG (1954)
20	1.42637	KORTÜM and FREIHER (1954)
25	1.4233	BROWN (1952)

t°	$n_{H\alpha}$	n_D	
20	1.43147	1.42615	KAZANSKII, ROZENGART et al. (1953)
30	—	1.4210	KURMANADHARAO, KRISHNAMURTY and VENKATARAO (1957)

Dielectric constant

t°	ε	t°	ε	
+ 26.40	2.013	−122.5	1.812	PHILIPPE and PIETTE (1955)
20.00	2.021	158.5	1.808	,,
8.0	2.041	144.0	1.808	,,
− 18.0	2.026	122.0	1.808	,,
37.2	1.994	90.5	1.809	,,
43.0	1.990	60.8	1.982	,,
60.5	1.970	− 34.8	1.997	,,
−120.5	1.811	—	—	

20° : 2.0230 MECKE and JOECKLE (1962)

METHYLCYCLOHEXANE C_7H_{14}

Critical temperature: 298.97° AMBROSE, COX and TOWNSEND (1960)

Saturated vapour pressure

t°	p mm	t°	p mm	
0	12.4	40	91.9	NICOLINI (1951)
5	16.4	45	113.1	,,
10	21.6	50	137.9	,,
15	28.1	55	167.3	,,
20	36.5	60	200.7	,,
25	46.5	65	241.6	,,
30	58.8	70	286.6	,,
35	73.7	—	—	,,
51.5	146.5	—	—	ROCK and SIEG (1955)

Boiling point: 100.6 NICOLINI (1951); 100.9 KYLE and REED (1958)

Freezing point: −126.587 DOUSLIN and HUFFMAN (1946)

Density

t°	d	
19.7	0.7694	ROCK and SIEG (1955)
25	0.76511	KYLE and REED (1958)

Refractive index

t°	n_D	
−25	1.4453	BENOLIEL (1941)
+20	1.4231	,,
+20	1.4230	ROCK and SIEG (1955)
+25	1.4206	KYLE and REED (1958)

Dielectric constant at 24.8°: 2.071 PYLE (1931)

ETHYLCYCLOHEXANE C_8H_{16}

Freezing point: −111.325 GLASGOW JR., MURPHY *et al.* (1946)
−111.335 STREIFF, MURPHY, CAHILL *et al.* (1947)

Boiling point: 131.6 EVANS (1938)

Density: EVANS (1938)

t°	d	
15	0.7914	
20	0.7875	

Refractive index $n_D^{20°}$: 1.4320 EVANS (1938)

Viscosity: EVANS (1938)

t°	$\eta \cdot 10^5$	
5	1061.0	
15	905.7	
30	731.8	
45	589.3	
60	511.1	
75	440.0	
100	380.3	

n-PROPYLCYCLOHEXANE C_9H_{18}

Saturated vapour pressure: FORZIATI, NORRIS and ROSSINI (1949)

t°	p mm	t°	p mm	t°	p mm
72.691	48.01	102.111	149.60	149.347	628.19
77.085	57.70	106.842	176.08	155.269	732.42
80.871	67.44	113.165	217.37	155.904	744.34
84.375	77.49	118.982	261.97	156.494	755.53
87.641	87.92	126.004	325.24	157.166	768.55
92.026	103.83	133.245	402.79	157.756	780.09
97.017	124.77	140.965	501.03	—	—

Boiling point: 156.724 *dt/dp (10 mm):* 0.5200 FORZIATI and ROSSINI (1949)

Density: FORZIATI and ROSSINI (1949)

t°	d	
20	0.79360	
25	0.78977	
30	0.78581	

Refractive index: FORZIATI (1950)

t°	He$_{red}$	H$_C$	Na$_D$	Hg$_{gr}$	He$_{blue}$	H$_F$	Hg$_g$
20	1.43450	1.43481	1.43705	1.43895	1.44149	1.44254	1.44686
25	1.43224	1.43255	1.43478	1.43667	1.43919	1.44024	1.44454
30	1.42998	1.43029	1.43251	1.43439	1.43689	1.43794	1.44222

Iso-PROPYLCYCLOHEXANE C_9H_{18}

Saturated vapour pressure: FORZIATI, NORRIS and ROSSINI (1949)

t°	p mm	t°	p mm	t°	p mm
70.515	48.09	99.887	149.67	147.177	628.25
74.868	57.78	104.612	176.16	153.109	732.47
78.690	67.51	110.953	217.44	153.747	744.41
82.165	77.56	116.782	262.04	154.334	755.63
85.400	87.98	123.806	325.32	155.009	768.59
89.788	103.90	131.051	402.85	155.602	780.14
94.793	124.85	138.782	501.08	—	—

Boiling point: 154.563 *dt/dp (10 mm):* 0.5210 FORZIATI and ROSSINI (1949)

Density: FORZIATI and ROSSINI (1949)

t°	d	
20	0.80221	
25	0.79833	
30	0.79444	

Refractive index: FORZIATI (1950) and FORZIATI and ROSSINI (1949)

t°	He$_{red}$	H$_C$	Na$_D$	Hg$_{gr}$	He$_{blue}$	H$_F$	Hg$_g$
20	1.43831	1.43862	1.44087	1.44277	1.44524	1.44637	1.45070
25	1.43607	1.43638	1.43861	1.44050	1.44296	1.44408	1.44839
30	1.43383	1.43414	1.43635	1.43823	1.44068	1.44179	1.44608

n-BUTYLCYCLOHEXANE $C_{10}H_{20}$

Saturated vapour pressure: FORZIATI, NORRIS and ROSSINI (1949)

t°	p mm	t°	p mm	t°	p mm
93.369	48.00	124.056	149.60	173.272	628.19
97.950	57.69	128.988	176.08	179.433	732.43
101.946	67.44	135.579	217.36	180.093	744.34
105.579	77.48	141.651	261.97	180.706	755.53
108.963	87.91	145.963	325.24	181.406	768.56
113.535	103.82	156.504	402.79	182.024	780.09
118.743	124.77	164.544	501.03	—	—

Boiling point: 180.947 *dt/dp (10 mm):* 0.5412 FORZIATI and ROSSINI (1949)

Density: FORZIATI and ROSSINI (1949)

t°	d	
20	0.79918	
25	0.79551	
30	0.79176	

Refractive index: FORZIATI (1950) and FORZIATI and ROSSINI (1949)

t°	He_{red}	H_C	Na_D	Hg_{gr}	He_{blue}	H_F	Hg_g
20	1.43819	1.43852	1.44075	1.44266	1.44520	1.44627	1.45061
25	1.43600	1.43632	1.43855	1.44045	1.44298	1.44404	1.44837
30	1.43381	1.43412	1.43635	1.43824	1.44076	1.44181	1.44613

Iso-BUTYLCYCLOHEXANE $C_{10}H_{20}$

Saturated vapour pressure: FORZIATI, NORRIS and ROSSINI (1949)

t°	p mm	t°	p mm	t°	p mm
84.752	48.09	115.008	149.68	163.711	628.26
89.248	57.78	119.887	176.17	169.822	732.49
93.184	67.51	126.405	217.45	170.480	744.43
96.767	77.56	132.404	262.05	171.089	755.65
100.094	87.98	139.640	325.33	171.780	768.60
104.610	103.91	147.103	402.86	172.394	780.16
109.766	124.86	155.065	501.09	—	—

Boiling point: 171.321 *dt/dp (10 mm):* 0.5367 FORZIATI and ROSSINI (1949)

Density

t°	d	
20	0.79521	FORZIATI and ROSSINI (1949)
25	0.79141	,,
30	0.78750	,,

Refractive index: FORZIATI (1950) and FORZIATI and ROSSINI (1949)

t°	He$_{red}$	H$_C$	Na$_D$	Hg$_{gr}$	He$_{blue}$	H$_F$	Hg$_g$
20	1.43606	1.43637	1.43861	1.44052	1.44307	1.44412	1.44849
25	1.43382	1.43413	1.43636	1.43826	1.44080	1.44185	1.44620
30	1.43158	1.43189	1.43411	1.43600	1.43853	1.43958	1.44391

Sec.-BUTYLCYCLOHEXANE   C$_{10}$H$_{20}$

Saturated vapour pressure: FORZIATI, NORRIS and ROSSINI (1949)

t°	p mm	t°	p mm	t°	p mm
91.458	48.09	122.224	149.67	171.626	628.26
96.042	57.78	127.163	176.16	177.817	732.48
100.048	67.51	133.786	217.45	178.481	744.42
103.688	77.56	139.861	262.05	179.098	755.64
107.082	87.98	147.212	325.32	179.799	768.60
111.660	103.90	154.776	402.86	180.421	780.15
116.900	124.85	162.856	501.09	—	—

Boiling point: 179.335 *dt/dp (10 mm):* 0.5440 FORZIATI and ROSSINI (1949)

Density

t°	d	
20	0.81314	FORZIATI and ROSSINI (1949)
25	0.80935	,,
30	0.80565	,,

Refractive index: FORZIATI (1950) and FORZIATI and ROSSINI (1949)

$t°$	He$_{red}$	H$_C$	Na$_D$	Hg$_{gr}$	He$_{blue}$	H$_F$	Hg$_g$
20	1.44416	1.44446	1.44673	1.44864	1.45120	1.45219	1.45664
25	1.44198	1.44228	1.44454	1.44644	1.44899	1.44998	1.45441
30	1.43980	1.44010	1.44235	1.44424	1.44678	1.44777	1.45218

Tert.-BUTYLCYCLOHEXANE $C_{10}H_{20}$

Saturated vapour pressure: FORZIATI, NORRIS and ROSSINI (1949)

$t°$	p mm	$t°$	p mm	$t°$	p mm
84.033	48.00	114.649	149.60	163.894	628.20
88.600	57.70	119.573	176.08	170.071	732.43
92.550	67.44	126.159	217.37	170.735	744.35
96.200	77.49	132.228	261.98	171.351	755.54
99.582	87.92	139.542	325.25	172.054	768.56
104.146	103.83	147.093	402.79	172.670	780.10
109.341	124.77	155.147	501.03	—	—

Boiling point: 171.591 *dt/dp (10 mm):* 0.5429 FORZIATI and ROSSINI (1949)

Density

$t°$	d	
20	0.81267	FORZIATI and ROSSINI (1949)
25	0.80890	,,
30	0.80513	,,

Refractive index: FORZIATI (1950) and FORZIATI and ROSSINI (1949)

$t°$	He$_{red}$	H$_C$	Na$_D$	Hg$_{gr}$	He$_{blue}$	H$_F$	Hg$_g$
20	1.44435	1.44467	1.44694	1.44887	1.45145	1.45252	1.45693
25	1.44215	1.44247	1.44473	1.44666	1.44923	1.45030	1.45470
30	1.43995	1.44027	1.44252	1.44445	1.44701	1.44808	1.45247

n-DECYLCYCLOHEXANE $C_{16}H_{32}$

Saturated vapour pressure: CAMIN, FORZIATI and ROSSINI (1954)

t°	p mm	t°	p mm	
297.507	758.50	235.626	171.71	
296.058	736.32	229.848	145.88	
268.976	403.47	216.465	98.22	
259.864	323.79	206.361	71.50	
243.758	214.15	196.812	52.08	

Density: CAMIN, FORZIATI and ROSSINI (1954)

t°	d	
20	0.81858	
25	0.81517	
30	0.81183	

Surface tension: JASPER and KRING (1955)

t°	γ	t°	γ	
0	31.49	60	26.34	
10	30.63	70	25.49	
20	29.77	80	24.63	
30	28.92	90	23.77	
40	28.06	100	22.91	
50	27.20	—	—	

Refractive index: CAMIN, FORZIATI and ROSSINI (1954)

t°	He$_r$	H$_C$	D	Hg$_{gr}$	He$_{bl}$	H$_\beta$	Hg$_g$
20	1.45074	1.45108	1.45338	1.45536	1.45798	1.45908	1.46357
25	1.44878	1.44911	1.45141	1.45338	1.45599	1.45708	1.46156
30	1.44682	1.44714	1.44944	1.45140	1.45400	1.45508	1.45955

1,1-DIMETHYLCYCLOHEXANE C_8H_{16}

Saturated vapour pressure: FORZIATI, NORRIS and ROSSINI (1949)

t°	p mm	t°	p mm	t°	p mm
40.497	48.10	68.047	149.61	112.575	628.24
44.531	57.71	72.496	176.09	118.168	732.42
48.153	67.40	78.447	217.37	118.768	744.42
51.399	77.46	83.925	261.87	119.327	755.65
54.450	87.94	90.497	325.18	119.959	768.52
58.564	103.80	97.361	402.70	120.520	780.05
63.260	124.81	104.658	501.00	—	—

Boiling point: 119.543 FORZIATI and ROSSINI (1949)

Refractive index: FORZIATI (1950)

t°	H$_{red}$	H$_C$	Na$_D$	Hg$_{gr}$	He$_{blue}$	H$_F$	Hg$_g$
20	1.42644	1.42676	1.42900	1.43090	1.43341	1.43446	1.43872
25	1.42408	1.42440	1.42662	1.42851	1.43100	1.43204	1.43627
30	1.42172	1.42204	1.42424	1.42612	1.42859	1.42962	1.43382

cis-1,2-DIMETHYLCYCLOHEXANE C_8H_{16}

N.B. (p. 202): For the *freezing point:* —50.00, the authors are: STREIFF, MURPHY, CAHILL, FLANAGAN, SEDLAK, WILLINGHAM and ROSSINI (1947).

trans-1,3-DIMETHYLCYCLOHEXANE C_8H_{16}

Freezing point: —90.134 STREIFF, MURPHY, ZIMMERMAN *et al.* (1947)

1,3,5-TRIMETHYLCYCLOHEXANE C_9H_{18}

CHIURDOGLU (1951)

Melting point: cis: —50   trans: —107.5

Boiling point: cis: 138.55   trans: 140.5

Density

	cis	trans		cis	trans
t°	d	d	t°	d	d
0	0.78600	0.79440	20	0.77050	0.77887
15	0.77438	0.78275	30	0.76275	0.77110

Refractive index

	t°	H$_\alpha$	He$_y$	H$_\beta$	H$_\gamma$
cis	20	1.42446	1.42680	1.43229	1.43678
trans	20	1.42859	1.43100	1.43635	1.44088

Viscosity

cis		*trans*		
t°	$\eta \cdot 10^3$	t°	$\eta \cdot 10^3$	
20	632	20	714	
30	558	30	624	

N.B. (p. 204): Invert the data of 1,3-DIMETHYLCYCLOHEXENE *trans* and *cis*.

CYCLO HEXYL DERIVATIVES of HEPTADECANE and HENDECANE, see CUTLER, McMICKLE *et al.* (1958)

DECALYL DERIVATIVES of HENDECANE and of PENTADECANE, DODECAHYDROCHRYSENE and PERHYDROCHRYSENE, see LOWITZ, SPENCER *et al.* (1959)

1,1,3-TRIMETHYLCYCLOHEXANE C_9H_{18}

Saturated vapour pressure: FORZIATI, NORRIS and ROSSINI (1949)

t°	p mm	t°	p mm	t°	p mm
54.669	47.99	82.305	149.59	129.411	628.18
58.950	57.68	87.915	176.07	135.203	732.42
62.624	67.43	94.080	217.35	135.824	744.34
66.058	77.48	99.762	261.96	136.401	755.52
69.180	87.91	106.606	325.23	137.058	768.55
73.481	103.82	113.678	402.78	137.636	780.06
78.336	124.76	121.220	501.02	—	—

Boiling point: 136.626 FORZIATI and ROSSINI (1949)

Refractive index: FORZIATI (1950)

t°	He$_{red}$	H$_C$	Na$_D$	Hg$_{gr}$	He$_{blue}$	H$_F$	Hg$_g$
20	1.42702	1.42734	1.42955	1.43146	1.43399	1.43504	1.43940
25	1.42473	1.42505	1.42725	1.42915	1.43167	1.43272	1.43706
30	1.42244	1.42276	1.42495	1.42684	1.42935	1.43040	1.43472

CYCLOHEXENE C_6H_{10}

Critical temperature: 287.27° AMBROSE, COX and TOWNSEND (1960)
287.25° CHENG, McCOUBREY and PHILLIPS (1962)

Boiling point: 83.0 THOMPSON and UBBELOHDE (1950)

Freezing point: −103.497 HUFFMAN, EATON and OLIVER (1948)

Density: 20°: 0.81096; 25°: 0.80609; 30°: 0.80141 FORZIATI, CAMIN and ROSSINI (1950)

Refractive index: FORZIATI, CAMIN and ROSSINI (1950)

$t°$	He_r	H_C	D	Hg_{gr}	He_{bl}	H_β	Hg_g
20	1.44344	1.44383	1.44654	1.44888	1.45201	1.45333	1.45877
25	1.44069	1.44108	1.44377	1.44610	1.44921	1.45052	1.45593
30	1.43794	1.43833	1.44100	1.44332	1.44641	1.44771	1.45309

Dielectric constant: PHILIPPE and PIETTE (1955)

$t°$	ε	$t°$	ε	
+ 20.00	2.214	−132.0	2.575	
− 12.5	2.280	150.0	2.475	
42.0	2.339	155.5	2.475	
74.5	2.413	142.5	2.474	
110.5	2.509	−134.0	2.474	
−122.5	2.543			

Heat of combustion at 25°: 896.62 kcal/mol LABBAUF and ROSSINI (1961)

CYCLOOCTATETRAENE C_8H_8

ECCLESTON, COLEMAN and ADAMS (1950)

Density

$t°$	d
20	0.92094
25	0.91963
30	0.91172

Viscosity

$t°$	$\eta \cdot 10^5$
20	1422.0
25	1297.1
30	1182.6

Refractive index

t°	He$_r$	H$_C$	Na$_D$	Hg$_{gr}$	He$_{bl}$	H$_\beta$	Hg$_g$
20	1.53181	1.53260	1.53790	1.54253	1.54885	1.55153	1.56240
25	1.52893	1.52972	1.53501	1.53964	1.54594	1.54866	1.55945
30	1.52632	1.52710	1.53229	1.53693	1.54318	1.54576	1.55663

TETRALIN or 1,2,3,4-TETRAHYDRONAPHTHALENE $C_{10}H_{12}$

Boiling point: 207.0 HAMMOND and STOKES (1955)

Freezing point: −35.814 STREIFF, HULME *et al.* (1955)
             −35.80 Mc CULLOUGH, FINKE *et al.* (1957)

Density at 25°: 0.96324 HAMMOND and STOKES (1955)

Refractive index at 25°: 1.5394 HAMMOND and STOKES (1955)

Viscosity: HAMMOND and STOKES (1955)

t°	$\eta \cdot 10^5$	
25	2030	

Heat of melting: 2975 cal/mol McCULLOUGH, FINKE *et al.* (1957)

Specific heat: McCULLOUGH, FINKE *et al.* (1957)

Crystals   **Liquid**

t°	cal/mol	t°	cal/mol	t°	cal/mol	t°	cal/mol
−261.03	1.009	−235.05	7.672	−150.71	18.886	−24.74	46.604
259.85	1.312	231.15	8.447	144.60	19.607	23.05	46.780
258.54	1.646	227.02	9.206	138.24	20.374	19.90	47.089
257.71	1.863	222.53	9.960	131.09	21.113	13.59	47.748
257.08	2.028	218.30	10.623	126.14	21.829	− 4.31	48.729
255.89	2.352	217.58	10.730	121.84	22.324	+ 1.74	49.379
255.55	2.449	213.34	11.357	120.36	22.551	11.33	50.442
253.85	2.930	207.77	12.139	115.69	23.106	15.27	50.872
253.84	2.935	201.90	12.873	109.17	23.937	25.52	52.032
251.93	3.478	195.93	13.609	102.85	24.750	35.55	53.184
251.71	3.539	190.35	14.313	96.70	25.547	+45.38	54.307
249.70	4.100	187.32	14.692	90.23	26.439		
249.54	4.146	185.08	14.954	83.46	27.394		
247.25	4.762	182.12	15.281	76.90	28.378		
247.11	4.795	175.69	15.992	70.52	29.372		
244.75	5.407	169.02	16.756	64.32	30.386		
241.95	6.120	162.66	17.480	58.55	31.438		
−238.69	6.895	−156.57	18.206	52.17	32.531		
				− 45.72	33.798		

cis-DECALIN or *cis*-DECAHYDRONAPHTHALENE $C_{10}H_{18}$

N.B. (p. 209): Invert the data of *cis* and *trans* from SEYER and DAVENPORT (1941)

Critical temperature: 429.05 CHENG, McCOUBREY and PHILLIPS (1962)

Boiling point: 195.774 *dt/dp (10 mm):* 0.5710 CAMIN and ROSSINI (1955)

Freezing point: —42.98 McCULLOUGH, FINKE *et al.* (1957)
          —43.048 STREIFF, SOULE *et al.* (1950)
          —43.15 STAUDHAMMER and SEYER (1958)

Transition point: —57.05 McCULLOUGH, FINKE *et al.* (1957)

Saturated vapour pressure: CAMIN and ROSSINI (1955)

t°	p mm	t°	p mm	t°	p mm	t°	p mm
196.376	770.52	178.629	503.05	140.176	171.62	114.152	71.43
195.635	757.57	170.056	403.33	135.021	145.76	110.490	62.49
195.055	747.50	161.885	323.76	128.731	118.71	105.685	52.06
194.370	735.66	154.245	261.15	123.132	98.17	99.883	41.47
187.823	630.29	147.456	214.11	118.004	82.08	—	—

Density: CAMIN and ROSSINI (1955)

t°	d
20	0.89671
25	0.89291
30	0.88911

Refractive index

t°	n_D	
20	1.48098	MIZUHARA and SEYER (1953)
80	1.45841	,,
20	1.48097	STAUDHAMMER and SEYER (1958)

Specific heat: McCullough, Finke *et al.* (1957)

Crystals I-A		Crystals I-B		Crystals I-C	
t°	cal/mol	t°	cal/mol	t°	cal/mol
−56.08	38.10	−57.24	37.82	−54.75	39.08
54.83	38.51	54.03	39.04	53.74	39.53
53.01	39.13	53.50	39.30	53.42	39.67
52.87	39.21	53.42	39.23	53.28	39.65
49.79	40.76	53.37	39.36	51.69	40.68
−49.73	40.70	50.99	40.59	50.56	41.54
		50.91	40.58	50.51	41.63
		50.52	41.08	−50.27	41.80
		−50.29	41.11		

Liquid

t°	cal/mol	t°	cal/mol	t°	cal/mol
−38.97	47.716	+38.42	57.333	+48.58	58.85
31.81	48.390	39.86	57.496	48.81	58.84
28.61	48.716	42.43	57.88	49.60	58.92
23.92	49.255	42.95	57.95	50.45	59.09
21.48	49.525	43.46	58.05	50.60	59.10
14.95	50.272	44.49	58.18	50.75	59.08
− 5.34	51.440	44.92	58.29	51.63	59.23
+ 4.07	52.637	45.52	58.37	52.67	59.35
11.16	53.561	46.26	58.45	54.61	59.648
13.28	53.833	46.54	58.51	55.70	59.794
20.55	54.845	46.86	58.46	61.48	60.664
29.80	56.114	+47.56	58.74	+71.29	62.038
30.49	56.221	—	—	—	—

Specific heat: McCULLOUGH, FINKE *et al.* (1957) (continued)

t°	cal/mol	t°	cal/mol	t°	cal/mol	t°	cal/mol
	Crystals II				Crystals I		
−260.66	0.958	−176.89	17.072	−261.44	1.070	−180.37	16.923
260.45	1.000	172.37	17.695	260.90	1.225	175.19	17.639
259.18	1.337	170.35	17.965	260.13	1.438	174.33	17.749
259.05	1.345	163.56	18.895	259.62	1.559	169.40	18.316
257.92	1.677	157.10	19.794	258.72	1.829	163.86	19.232
257.58	1.745	150.42	20.715	258.22	1.986	158.18	20.052
256.58	2.034	143.51	21.647	257.30	2.233	152.36	21.100
256.13	2.165	138.38	22.330	256.65	2.458	146.58	22.049
255.06	2.480	136.87	22.557	255.78	2.685	140.37	23.347
254.44	2.674	132.81	23.119	254.97	2.952	133.55	24.751
253.29	3.036	131.16	23.316	253.98	3.241	129.60	25.591
252.51	3.267	130.03	23.501	252.97	3.573	122.82	26.87
251.24	3.654	127.40	23.864	251.90	3.890	116.34	27.66
250.46	3.896	125.54	24.077	250.70	4.264	109.90	29.09
248.72	4.413	124.95	24.178	249.47	4.618	106.58	29.63
248.39	4.505	122.98	24.473	248.31	4.952	103.33	30.21
246.16	5.126	118.80	25.021	246.67	5.404	97.32	31.04
245.18	5.177	118.07	25.139	245.69	5.660	96.43	31.31
243.26	5.879	117.29	25.240	242.76	6.415	91.88	31.49
239.93	6.752	112.28	25.922	239.38	7.241	86.99	32.36
235.93	7.660	111.41	26.057	235.60	8.067	84.19	32.88
231.72	8.536	110.25	26.223	231.21	8.954	76.57	34.06
227.32	9.381	102.40	27.279	226.12	9.898	− 61.91	37.06
222.57	10.232	94.06	28.464	221.11	10.761	—	—
217.38	11.098	89.19	29.110	218.05	11.266	—	—
216.91	11.173	87.98	29.259	216.16	11.567	—	—
211.86	11.996	86.00	29.613	212.15	12.221	—	—
211.85	11.999	84.90	29.793	206.20	13.140	—	—
206.06	12.887	83.17	30.023	200.22	13.999	—	—
199.93	13.766	81.98	30.167	194.17	14.903	—	—
193.34	14.738	79.93	30.543	199.53	15.771	—	—
186.32	15.797	76.14	31.096	187.09	15.976	—	—
183.18	16.235	74.60	31.383	182.79	16.597	—	—
−179.34	16.740	− 68.90	32.276	−180.82	16.861	—	—

Heat of combustion at 25°: 1502.92 kcal/mol SPEROS and ROSSINI (1960)

Heat of melting: 2268 cal/mol McCULLOUGH, FINKE *et al.* (1957)

Heat of transition: 510.6 cal/mol *ibid.*

trans-DECALIN or *trans*-DECAHYDRONAPHTHALENE $C_{10}H_{18}$

Critical temperature: 413.85° CHENG, McCOUBREY and PHILLIPS (1962)

Saturated vapour pressure: CAMIN and ROSSINI (1955)

t°	p mm	t°	p mm	t°	p mm	t°	p mm
187.867	770.55	170.297	503.06	132.255	171.62	106.500	71.42
187.140	757.60	161.801	403.33	127.140	145.77	102.891	62.49
186.563	747.55	153.719	323.75	120.918	118.72	98.129	52.07
185.885	735.67	146.156	261.15	115.358	98.15	92.360	41.48
179.395	630.29	139.441	214.13	110.316	82.10	—	—

N.B. (p. 209): Suppress the data of SEYER (1941, '42 and '45)

Boiling point: 187.273 *dt/dp (10 mm):* 0.5656 CAMIN and ROSSINI (1955)

Freezing point: —30.56 STAUDHAMMER and SEYER (1958)
          —30.41 STREIFF, SOULE *et al.* (1950)
          —30.36 McCULLOUGH, FINKE *et al.* (1957)

Density: CAMIN and ROSSINI (1955)

t°	d	
20	0.86971	
25	0.86592	
30	0.86222	

Refractive index

t°	He$_r$	H$_C$	Na$_D$	Hg$_{gr}$	He$_{bl}$	H$_\beta$	Hg$_g$	
20	1.46654	1.46688	1.46932	1.47141	1.47420	1.47535	1.48011	CAMIN and ROSSINI
25	1.46438	1.46472	1.46715	1.46923	1.47200	1.47315	1.47789	,, (1955)
30	1.46222	1.46256	1.46498	1.46705	1.46980	1.47095	1.47567	,,
20	—	—	1.46934	—	—	—	—	MIZUHARA and SEYER
80	—	—	1.44577	—	—	—	—	,, (1953)
20	—	—	1.46932	—	—	—	—	STAUDHAMMER and SEYER (1958)

Specific heat: McCullough, Finke *et al.* (1957)

Crystals   **Liquid**

t°	cal/mol	t°	cal/mol	t°	cal/mol	t°	cal/mol
−261.62	0.633	−240.54	5.929	−150.46	20.540	−24.41	48.156
260.22	0.901	237.53	6.653	144.42	21.416	19.05	48.786
259.72	1.011	237.31	7.377	138.61	22.242	16.64	49.088
258.82	1.190	230.29	8.221	133.00	23.075	− 7.40	50.248
258.59	1.234	225.66	9.107	128.40	23.727	+ 2.50	51.548
257.45	1.493	220.72	9.999	127.56	23.844	12.60	52.905
257.06	1.584	219.10	10.276	122.20	24.625	21.81	54.162
256.02	1.835	215.34	10.903	114.49	25.743	22.47	54.262
255.40	2.003	213.89	11.148	106.41	26.908	32.10	55.616
254.48	2.224	208.33	12.052	98.82	28.014	42.18	57.098
253.67	2.455	202.48	12.935	90.96	29.189	52.03	58.529
252.69	2.713	196.79	13.776	82.86	30.443	61.67	59.960
251.68	2.996	191.06	14.669	75.02	31.637	+71.11	61.348
250.73	3.252	185.21	15.552	67.44	32.840	—	—
249.23	3.663	179.26	16.393	60.15	34.040	—	—
248.46	3.874	178.05	16.578	53.91	35.081	—	—
246.47	4.410	173.30	17.231	47.05	36.292	—	—
245.83	4.572	167.92	18.006	43.19	37.028	—	—
243.55	5.165	161.98	18.864	− 40.38	37.578	—	—
−243.00	5.299	−156.22	19.702	—	—	—	—

Heat of combustion at 25°: 1500.23 kcal/mol Speros and Rossini (1960)

Heat of melting: 3445 cal/mol McCullough, Finke *et al.* (1957)

cis-HEXAHYDROINDANE C_9H_{16}

Saturated vapour pressure: Camin and Rossini (1955)

t°	p mm	t°	p mm	t°	p mm	t°	p mm
168.407	770.57	151.698	503.06	115.466	171.62	90.961	71.43
167.718	757.63	143.611	403.32	110.605	145.76	87.511	62.48
167.170	747.63	135.917	323.76	99.401	98.16	82.973	52.03
166.527	735.68	128.708	261.15	94.583	82.08	77.497	41.49
160.350	630.29	122.308	214.15	—	—	—	—

Boiling point: 167.846 *dt/dp (10 mm):* 0.5381 Camin and Rossini (1955)

Density: Camin and Rossini (1955)

t°	d
20	0.88445
25	0.88031
30	0.87623

Refractive index: CAMIN and ROSSINI (1955)

t°	He$_r$	H$_\alpha$	Na$_D$	Hg$_{gr}$	He$_{bl}$	H$_\beta$	Hg$_v$
20	1.46932	1.46968	1.47210	1.47417	1.47690	1.47803	1.48265
25	1.46700	1.46735	1.46976	1.47182	1.47453	1.47566	1.48025
30	1.46468	1.46502	1.46742	1.46947	1.47216	1.47329	1.47785

Heat of combustion: 1351.60 kcal/mol BROWNE and ROSSINI (1960)

trans-HEXAHYDROINDANE C_9H_{16}

Saturated vapour pressure: CAMIN and ROSSINI (1955)

t°	p mm	t°	p mm	t°	p mm	t°	p mm
161.642	770.58	145.118	503.07	109.299	171.61	81.651	62.48
160.955	757.63	137.115	403.33	104.486	145.76	77.171	51.99
160.413	747.64	129.500	323.76	93.415	98.19	71.756	41.49
159.779	735.68	122.378	261.15	88.648	82.06	—	—
153.673	630.29	116.059	214.13	85.066	71.45	—	—

Refractive index: CAMIN and ROSSINI (1955)

t°	He$_r$	H$_\alpha$	Na$_D$	Hg$_{gr}$	He$_{bl}$	H$_\beta$	Hg$_v$
20	1.46092	1.46126	1.46363	1.46567	1.46839	1.46953	1.47419
25	1.45860	1.45893	1.46130	1.46333	1.46604	1.46717	1.47182
30	1.45628	1.45660	1.45897	1.46099	1.46369	1.46481	1.46945

Heat of combustion: 1350.86 kcal/mol BROWNE and ROSSINI (1960)

ADAMANTANE or TRICYCLO [3,3,1,1³,⁷] DECANE $_3{}_{10}H_{16}$

SHU-SING CHANG and WESTRUM Jr. (1960)

Transition point: −64.56

Specific heat (Series I)

t°	cal/mol	t°	cal/mol	t°	cal/mol
−268.06	0.040	−224.75	9.185	−86.22	26.41
267.46	0.055	219.95	9.730	78.83	28.29
266.33	0.088	214.92	10.24	70.80	31.12
265.09	0.170	213.55	10.39	65.51	285.27
264.04	0.278	208.37	10.91	60.78	52.33
263.09	0.405	202.71	11.39	51.86	32.52
262.08	0.562	196.47	11.95	41.67	34.04
260.91	0.783	189.86	12.60	32.23	35.55
259.61	1.083	181.51	13.32	23.21	36.97
258.10	1.482	174.42	14.14	14.44	38.45
256.34	1.996	166.59	14.96	16.60	38.05
254.35	2.617	158.66	15.81	− 7.85	39.48
252.18	3.311	150.24	16.75	+ 0.9	41.00
249.75	4.039	142.07	17.77	9.61	42.57
247.34	4.803	133.54	18.83	18.31	44.13
244.59	5.584	124.71	20.08	27.00	45.85
241.34	6.369	115.83	21.38	35.68	47.41
237.83	7.138	107.08	22.54	44.39	48.72
233.77	7.887	98.43	23.83	53.10	50.15
−229.35	8.577	− 89.83	25.57	62.05	51.76
—	—	—	—	+71.10	53.39

Series II				Series III		Series IV	
−86.22	26.41	−64.58	2470.76	−124.06	20.07	−71.26	31.03
79.92	27.98	64.54	3513.07	121.40	20.43	68.25	32.46
78.83	28.23	66.51	3864.16	118.87	20.78	66.10	34.50
74.66	29.69	64.49	4389.12	116.39	21.13	−65.06	65.20
71.54	30.87	64.41	1583.61	114.27	21.47		
69.07	32.07	63.15	44.73	112.18	21.75		
66.67	34.04	61.05	31.41	109.39	22.21		
−65.05	125.48	−59.23	31.47	105.90	22.72		
				−101.26	23.43		

Series V		Series VI				Series VII	
−64.53	2688.94	− 4.01	40.21	31.95	46.81	+64.51	3150.43
64.40	535.22	+ 4.46	41.72	40.78	48.18	64.45	2402.83
63.60	48.41	5.29	41.75	48.64	49.41		
−61.38	31.74	14.32	43.48	58.04	51.10		
		23.30	45.05	+67.88	52.91		

α-PINENE $C_{10}H_{16}$

Hawkins and Armstrong (1954)

Saturated vapour pressure

t°	p mm	t°	p mm	t°	p mm
19.44	3.06	66.53	38.41	105.89	175.74
21.29	3.43	68.26	41.66	106.75	181.64
27.24	4.91	70.44	45.55	110.52	205.80
29.71	5.93	75.09	55.73	113.49	226.03
37.06	9.01	76.03	57.74	115.06	238.48
46.91	15.11	77.11	60.25	122.10	296.11
53.68	21.24	79.74	66.79	125.01	322.25
54.17	21.58	84.70	81.45	129.86	371.35
56.56	24.26	86.22	86.53	135.71	440.12
57.08	24.82	88.41	93.85	147.47	605.53
57.52	25.45	92.00	107.25	155.76	754.57
62.27	31.66	95.26	121.24	155.75	756.01
65.52	36.44	102.24	155.39	—	—

Density at 25°: 0.8539; n_D at 25°: 1.4631; $(\alpha)_D$ at 25°: +29.12

β-PINENE $C_{10}H_{16}$

Hawkins and Armstrong (1954)

Saturated vapour pressure

t°	p mm	t°	p mm	t°	p mm
18.71	1.89	56.56	17.01	94.11	85.10
20.04	2.13	56.93	17.56	97.32	96.22
23.08	2.59	58.85	19.13	103.40	119.62
26.81	3.35	59.47	19.65	108.75	144.67
29.44	3.88	62.61	22.92	115.49	180.89
31.67	4.44	62.97	23.13	120.05	209.81
32.02	4.44	65.91	26.51	125.32	248.11
36.77	5.95	68.74	30.11	131.38	298.24
37.08	6.03	72.22	35.08	136.01	338.32
39.40	6.97	75.42	40.38	149.54	488.06
41.33	7.78	78.58	46.06	161.21	672.31
45.51	9.67	80.87	51.08	165.79	755.97
49.40	11.85	81.22	52.12	165.91	759.02
50.10	12.33	85.85	62.00	—	—
52.31	13.59	90.79	74.88	—	—

Density at 25°: 0.8667; n_D at 25°: 1.4768; $(\alpha)_D$ at 25°: −18.54

2. HALOGENATED DERIVATIVES

A. DERIVATIVES OF METHANE

METHYL FLUORIDE CH_3F

P.V.-values MICHELS, VISSER *et al.* (1952)

Vapour

d	0°	25°	50°	75°	100°	125°	150°
8.8734	0.91114	1.01574	1.11823	1.21868	1.31790	1.41650	1.51464
10.9715	0.88854	0.99589	1.10041	1.20258	1.30333	1.40326	1.50268
13.6284	0.86094	0.97147	1.07848	1.18291	1.28551	1.38705	1.48790
16.9559	0.82711	0.94157	1.05164	1.15865	1.26357	1.36707	1.46971
20.9108	0.78827	0.90721	1.02073	1.13071	1.23824	1.34415	1.44878
25.4575	0.74529	0.86915	0.98654	1.09976	1.21018	1.31856	1.42546
30.0481	—	0.83226	0.95332	1.06958	1.18276	1.29353	1.40269
31.8992	—	0.81778	0.94027	1.05789	1.17205	1.28372	1.39378
34.5325	—	0.79755	0.92207	1.04128	1.15687	1.26994	1.38118
38.5317	—	0.76794	0.89533	1.01706	1.13468	1.24979	1.36294
46.9276	—	0.70871	0.84181	0.96830	1.09028	1.20929	1.32608
57.3762	—	0.64058	0.78045	0.91222	1.03888	1.16238	1.28342
69.7725	—	—	0.71428	0.85158	0.98332	1.11187	1.23753
85.7481	—	—	0.63892	0.78227	0.91979	1.05382	1.18538
105.4737	—	—	0.55922	0.70862	0.85217	0.99261	1.13062
130.4944	—	—	0.47663	0.63188	0.78219	0.93004	1.07595
159.3765	—	—	0.40268	0.56270	0.72008	0.87629	1.03154

METHYL CHLORIDE CH_3Cl

Critical temperature: 143.00° KREGLEWSKI (1955)

METHYL IODIDE CH_3I

Adiabatic compressibility: HARRISON and MOELWYN-HUGHES (1957)

Refractive index: n_D at 20°: 1.5310 HARRISON and MOELWYN-HUGHES (1957)

Specific heat: HARRISON and MOELWYN-HUGHES (1957)

$t°$	c_p
−29.7	19.52
−27.9	19.55
−18.9	19.50
−12.7	19.45
+ 1.4	19.25
11.2	19.40
21.2	19.64
30.1	19.95

METHYLENE DICHLORIDE CH_2Cl_2

Saturated vapour pressure: MUELLER and IGNATOWSKI (1960)

t°	p mm	
29.993	529.02	
34.993	638.87	
38.993	739.34	
39.933	765.94	

Second virial coefficient: PEREZ MASIA and DIAZ PENA (1958)

t°	−B (cc/mol)	
50.0	676.5	
75.0	544.8	
100.0	467.2	
125.0	389.2	
150.0	348.9	

Boiling point: 39.8 MUMFORD and PHILLIPS (1950)

Density: (ibid.)

t°	d	
20	1.3283	
25	1.3191	

Viscosity at 20°: 437 cp; at 25°: 416 cp *ibid.*

Surface tension: (ibid.)

t°	γ	
20	28.0	
25	27.15	

METHYLENE DIBROMIDE CH_2Br_2

Adiabatic compressibility, see HARRISON and MOELWYN-HUGHES (1957)

Refractive index: n_D at 20°: 1.5415 HARRISON and MOELWYN-HUGHES (1957)

Heat capacity: HARRISON and MOELWYN-HUGHES (1957)

$t°$	c_p	
−28.2	25.05	
−19.2	25.09	
− 8.1	25.00	
+ 1.2	24.87	
11.0	24.69	
21.1	25.01	
30.1	25.21	

METHYLENE DIIODIDE CH_2I_2

Compressibility (vapour), see PEREZ MASIA and DIAZ PENA (1958)

CHLOROFORM $CHCl_3$

Adiabatic compressibility, see HARRISON and MOELWYN-HUGHES (1957)

Density

$t°$	d	
25.0	1.4799	KOEFOED and VILLADSEN (1958)
20.0	1.4892	MUMFORD and PHILLIPS (1950)
25.0	1.4798	,,

Surface tension

$t°$	γ	
25	26.56	KOEFOED and VILLADSEN (1958)
20	27.2	MUMFORD and PHILLIPS (1950)
25	26.55	,,

Dielectric constant: PHILIPPE and PIETTE (1955)

t°	ε	t°	ε	
+ 20.00	4.777	− 77.0	2.517	(two series)
− 5.5	5.258	70.0	2.609	
47.5	6.127	68.0	2.728	
61.5	6.477	65.5	3.417	
82.5	2.511	65.5	3.650	
96.5	2.482	65.0	4.296	
118.5	2.473	64.5	5.589	
−149.0	2.466	63.5	6.586	
		63.0	6.625	
		63.0	6.581	
		− 29.5	5.703	

Specific magnetic susceptibility at 20°: −0.493.10^{-6} VON RAUTENFELD and STEURER (1942)

CHLORODIFLUOROMETHANE CHF_2Cl

NEILSON and WHITE (1957)

Boiling point: −40.66

Melting point: −157.43

Transition point: −214

Heat of melting: 985.47 cal/mol

Heat of vaporization: 4832.5 cal/mol

Specific heat

Crystals (Series I)

t°	c_p	t°	c_p	t°	c_p
C. I −256.39	3.162	−237.45	8.165	−190.84	12.228
255.73	3.586	234.40	8.787	184.11	12.690
252.67	3.971	230.46	9.464	179.59	13.123
248.24	5.663	C. II −214.17	12.121	172.48	14.025
245.64	6.395	208.54	11.539	166.82	15.049
242.97	7.032	203.37	11.635	162.22	15.992
−240.27	7.620	−197.76	11.822	−161.34	17.664

Crystals (Series II)		(Series III)		**Liquid** (Series I)	
t°	C_p	t°	C_p	t°	C_p
−256.41	3.184	−252.03	3.942	−151.32	22.081
254.67	3.695	250.91	4.619	145.34	22.037
247.59	5.720	248.60	5.472	139.00	21.951
245.50	6.369	244.54	6.456	132.31	21.943
241.98	7.253	232.34	9.212	124.29	21.847
230.01	9.507	228.60	9.691	110.15	21.868
226.29	9.949	224.12	10.282	97.52	21.961
222.19	10.312	−219.62	11.252	84.66	22.050
217.78	11.627			78.83	22.113
−213.58	12.224			72.98	22.068
				53.12	22.191
				− 47.07	22.152

FLUOROFORM   CHF$_3$

See Addenda, p. 435

CARBON TETRAFLUORIDE   CF$_4$

See also Addenda, p. 436

Transition point under high pressure: STEWART and LaROCK (1958)

Viscosity: (vapour) McCOUBREY and SINGH (1957)

t°	$\eta \cdot 10^7$	
41.5	1827	
65.5	1943	
75.0	1992	
101.3	2124	
124.5	2212	
240.0	2285	
248.8	2345	
268.8	2367	
275.1	2398	
282.6	2436	

Compressibility of the gas from 0° to 400°: McCORMACK and SCHNEIDER (1951)

Compressibility of the gas: DOUSLIN, HARRISON, MOORE and McCULLOUGH (1961)

P atm: mole/litre

t°	0.75	1.0	1.5	2.0	2.5	3.0	3.5	4.0	4.5
0.00	15.480	20.086	28.559	36.149	42.974	49.150	54.804	60.039	64.967
25	17.194	22.453	32.339	41.486	50.000	58.012	65.628	72.967	80.130
30	17.538	22.923	33.087	42.538	51.387	59.764	67.756	75.520	83.129
50	18.898	24.792	36.057	46.720	56.893	66.701	76.251	85.656	95.045
75	20.591	27.116	39.749	51.903	63.709	75.279	86.735	98.206	109.825
100	22.275	29.426	43.412	57.049	70.468	83.789	97.142	110.662	124.512
125	23.952	31.725	47.047	62.155	77.175	92.224	107.462	123.034	139.086
150	25.625	34.021	50.671	67.233	83.830	100.617	117.715	135.322	153.553
175	27.296	36.304	54.274	72.282	90.460	108.963	127.937	147.553	168.020
200	28.964	38.585	57.868	77.316	97.066	117.270	138.103	159.733	182.364
225	30.627	40.860	61.455	82.331	103.639	125.550	148.221	171.872	196.686
250	32.289	43.132	65.034	87.334	110.200	133.807	158.325	183.973	210.974
275	33.949	45.398	68.596	92.326	116.738	142.032	168.391	196.014	225.145
300	35.609	47.661	72.165	97.306	123.266	150.212	178.382	207.995	239.280
325	37.266	49.924	75.723	102.278	129.773	158.415	188.385	219.957	253.412
350	38.921	52.187	79.273	107.240	136.267	166.576	198.378	231.925	267.505

t°	5.0	5.5	6.0	6.5	7.0	7.5	8.0	8.5	9.0
0.00	69.704	74.369	79.050	83.903	89.061	94.676	100.960	108.149	116.575
25	87.251	94.473	101.908	109.726	118.131	127.244	137.455	148.916	162.056
30	90.736	98.470	106.456	114.879	123.929	133.791	144.774	157.077	171.140
50	104.587	114.393	124.621	135.468	147.186	159.922	174.093	189.908	207.791
75	121.755	134.178	147.212	161.150	176.143	192.482	210.584	230.884	253.472
100	138.840	153.853	169.728	186.712	205.075	225.134	247.200	271.743	299.330
125	155.832	173.413	192.127	212.147	233.889	257.529	283.630	312.493	344.771
150	172.699	192.863	214.330	237.418	262.452	289.777	319.795	353.276	390.238
175	189.528	212.277	236.618	262.764	291.064	322.043	356.107	393.701	—
200	206.259	231.582	258.762	287.988	319.607	354.291	392.333	—	—
225	222.912	250.816	280.728	312.999	348.121	386.496	—	—	—
250	239.569	270.100	302.842	338.173	376.424	—	—	—	—
275	256.087	289.161	324.652	362.875	—	—	—	—	—
300	272.536	308.116	346.323	387.599	—	—	—	—	—
325	288.853	327.091	368.163	—	—	—	—	—	—
350	305.438	346.066	389.660	—	—	—	—	—	—

t°	9.5	10.0	10.5	11.0	11.5	12.0	12.5
0.00	126.561	138.458	152.884	170.481	192.000	218.629	251.029
25	177.339	195.101	216.126	241.054	270.777	306.072	342.263
30	187.469	206.428	228.708	254.939	286.356	323.269	367.430
50	228.320	251.970	279.425	311.330	348.658	392.619	—
75	279.421	308.736	342.440	381.498	—	—	—
100	330.350	365.751	—	—	—	—	—
125	381.244	—	—	—	—	—	—

CARBON TETRACHLORIDE   CCl$_4$

(See also Addenda, p. 434)

Saturated vapour pressure

t°	p mm	
76.75	760	DREISBACH and SHRADER (1949)
64.02	507.50	,,
50.41	315.52	,,
26.03	123.76	,,

t°	p mm	
25	114	NEFF and HICKMAN (1955)
35	176	,,
50	317	,,
60	451	,,
76.66	760.00	SMITH and BONNER (1949)
70.00	617.43	,,
60.00	444.45	,,
65	525.48	BARKER, BROWN and SMITH (1953)
50.00	312.23	,,
45	258.84	,,
40.00	213.42	,,

Boiling point: 76.75 DREISBACH and MARTIN (1949)
76.65 BARKER, BROWN and SMITH (1953)

Freezing point: −22.782 DUNLOP (1955)
−22.820 MATHIEU (1953)

Density

t°	d	
20	1.59397	DREISBACH and MARTIN (1949)
25	1.58429	,,
25	1.5841	HAMMOND and STOKES (1955)
25	1.58429	BARKER, BROWN and SMITH (1953)
25	1.58435	BROWN and FOCH (1955)
20	1.59404	NYVLT and ERDOS (1961)
25	1.58437	,,
30	1.57456	,,
35	1.56478	,,
40	1.55498	,,

Compressibility: SACKMANN and BOCZEK (1961)

Viscosity

t°	η · 10⁵	
25	904	HAMMOND and STOKES (1955)
25	901.9	GRUNBERG (1954)

Surface tension at 20° : 26.75 MUMFORD and PHILLIPS (1950)
　　　　　　　　25°: 26.15　　　　　　,,
　　　　　　　　25°: 26.14 KOEFOED and VILLADSEN (1958)

Refractive index

t°	n$_D$	
15	1.4631	HAMMOND and STOKES (1955) and BROWN and FOCH (1955)
20	1.46005	DREISBACH and MARTIN (1949)
25	1.45704	,,

Dielectric constant: PHILIPPE and PIETTE (1955)

t°	ε	t°	ε	
C. −68.7	2.373	L.−22.4	2.333	
58.1	2.378	19.2	2.327	
48.0	2.384	15.0	2.318	
46.4	2.386	10.1	2.308	
45.8	2.418	0.0	2.288	
44.3	2.418	+ 4.75	2.279	
40.2	2.419	9.80	2.268	
35.1	2.421	15.40	2.258	
25.2	2.425	19.95	2.249	
24.0	2.337			
23.3	2.425			
25.0	2.227	THOMAS and HAWKINS (1954)		

Specific heat: HARRISON and MOELWYN-HUGHES (1957)

t°	c$_p$	
−18.7	30.81	
−10.5	31.09	
+ 1.2	31.10	
11.1	31.15	
21.2	31.20	
30.2	31.31	

DIFLUORODICHLOROMETHANE   CF$_2$Cl$_2$

Specific heat: MASI (1952)

t°	cal/mol	t°	cal/mol	
− 73.16	14.043	+526.84	24.003	
0	16.654	626.84	24.448	
+ 25	17.407	726.84	24.791	
26.84	17.456	826.84	25.060	
126.84	19.831	926.84	25.277	
226.84	21.469	1026.84	25.454	
326.84	22.605	1126.84	25.602	
+426.84	23.411	1226.84	25.728	

Viscosity of the vapour: BUDDENBERG and WILKE (1951)

CHLOROBROMODIFLUOROMETHANE   CF$_2$ClBr

Saturated vapour pressure: GLEW (1960)

t°	p mm	t°	p mm	
−95.335	2.45	−4.078	758.14	
−78.798	11.19	−3.957	761.71	
−45.305	110.29	−3.860	764.59	
−21.531	366.06	−2.080	818.57	
−20.002	392.03	−0.093	882.05	
−17.398	439.49	+1.914	949.98	
−15.034	486.39	3.909	1020.9	
−12.447	542.26	5.925	1097.6	
−10.049	598.46	7.907	1177.0	
− 7.455	664.05	9.890	1260.8	
− 5.074	701.64	153.8	30770	
− 4.161	755.85	—	—	

TRIFLUOROCHLOROMETHANE   CF$_3$Cl

ALBRIGHT and MARTIN (1952)

Critical temperature: 28.85°

Critical pressure: 10.854 mm

Critical density: 578.2

Saturated vapour pressure

t°	p mm	t°	p mm	t°	p mm	t°	p mm
26.87	10.40	−26.23	2.6577	− 81.54	0.28277	−127.89	0.009276
0.00	5.528	−57.88	0.8986	−100.47	0.009276	—	—

Density

t°	d	t°	d	t°	d	t°	d
25.60	0.8153	4.522	1.0834	−32.30	1.3104	−105.57	1.6100
21.50	0.9058	−3.789	1.1461	−61.58	1.4434	−142.25	1.7377
16.77	1.0243	−14.0	1.2113	−87.367	1.5395	—	—

B. DERIVATIVES OF ETHANE

ETHYL CHLORIDE C_2H_5Cl

Dielectric constant: NICKERSON and MC INTOSH (1957)

t°	ε	t°	ε	
20.0	9.45	−11.0	11.07	
19.0	9.52	13.6	11.26	
10.0	9.92	19.0	11.58	
5.8	10.14	19.8	11.67	
0.2	10.41	24.1	12.04	
0.0	10.43	35.0	12.95	
− 4.5	10.64	−36.0	13.02	

ETHYL BROMIDE C_2H_5Br

MUMFORD and PHILLIPS (1950)

Density

t°	d	
20	1.4612	
25	1.4515	

Refractive index: $n_D^{20°} = 1.4242$

Surface tension

t°	γ	
20	24.1	
25	23.45	

Viscosity

t°	$\eta \cdot 10^5$	
20	397	
25	379	

ETHYL IODIDE $\qquad$ C_2H_5I

MUMFORD and PHILLIPS (1950)

Density

t°	d	
20	1.9364	
25	1.9253	

Surface tension

t°	γ	
20	28.85	
25	28.2	

ETHYLIDENE DIFLUORIDE (1,1-DIFLUOROETHANE) $\qquad$ $C_2H_4F_2$

MEARS, STAHL, ORFEO, SHAIR, KELLS, THOMPSON and MC CANN (1955)

Critical constants

Temperature: 113.5°

Pressure: 44.37 atm

Density: 0.365

Saturated vapour pressure: see authors

Viscosity

t°	$\eta \cdot 10^5$	t°	$\eta \cdot 10^5$	
− 30.6	369	+ 30.0	227	
− 24.7	350	+ 40.0	207	
− 0.1	289	+ 50.0	193	
+ 20.0	251	+ 60.0	180	

ETHYLENE DICHLORIDE (1,2-DICHLOROETHANE) $C_2H_4Cl_2$

Boiling point: 83.5 RUITER (1955)
83.6 MUMFORD and PHILLIPS (1950)

Density

t°	d	
20	1.25294	RUITER (1955)
20	1.2527	MUMFORD and PHILLIPS (1950)
25	1.2454	

Viscosity: DENISON and RAMSEY (1955)

t°	$\eta \cdot 10^5$	
20	830	
25	778	
30	730	
35	685	

Surface tension: MUMFORD and PHILLIPS (1950)

t°	γ	
20	32.45	
25	31.75	

Refractive index

t°	n_D	
25	1.4422	RUITER (1955)
25	1.4423	JONES, SCHOENBORN and COLBURN (1943)

Dielectric constant: DENISON and RAMSEY (1955)

t°	ε	
20	10.52	
25	10.23	
30	9.96	
35	9.67	

Specific heat: RUITER (1955)

t°	C_p	
7.68	127.8	
20.45	128.8	
35.65	131.1	
50.58	132.2	

ETHYLIDENE DICHLORIDE (1,1-DICHLOROETHANE) $C_2H_4Cl_2$

Boiling point: 57.3 MUMFORD and PHILLIPS (1950)

N.B. (p. 238): *Freezing point:* —96.5° instead of —97.8 TIMMERMANS

Density: MUMFORD and PHILLIPS (1950)

t°	d	
20	1.1757	
25	1.1680	

Viscosity

t°	$\eta \cdot 10^5$	
20	490	MUMFORD and PHILLIPS (1950)
25	465	,,
20	480	DENISON and RAMSEY (1955)
25	455	,,
30	430	,,
35	408	,,

Surface tension: MUMFORD and PHILLIPS (1950)

t°	γ	
20	24.75	
25	24.1	

Dielectric constant: DENISON and RAMSEY (1955)

t°	ε	
20	10.15	
25	9.90	
30	9.67	
35	9.44	

ETHYLENE DIBROMIDE (1,2-DIBROMOETHANE) $C_2H_4Br_2$

Density

t°	d	
20	2.1802	MUMFORD and PHILLIPS (1950)
25	2.1700	,,
17.15	2.1826	KETELAAR and VAN MEURS (1957)
26.20	2.1638	,,
38.40	2.1384	,,

Surface tension: MUMFORD and PHILLIPS (1950)

t°	γ	
20	38.85	
25	38.2	

Refractive index: KETELAAR and VAN MEURS (1957)

t°	n_D	
17.15	1.53997	
26.20	1.53526	
38.40	1.52808	

Dielectric constant at 20°: 4.791 *ibid.*

METHYLCHLOROFORM (1,1,1-TRICHLOROETHANE) $C_2H_3Cl_3$

Boiling point: +74.0 CROWE and SMYTH (1950)

Melting point: −33.0 CROWE and SMYTH (1950)

Transition points: I. −68.1 CROWE and SMYTH (1950)

               II. −49.5   ,,

Dielectric constant: CROWE and SMYTH (1950)

t°	ε	t°	ε	t°	ε
C. −141.0	2.20	−53.0	2.65	−44.5	8.72
106.0	2.25	50.5	2.75	39.0	8.66
81.5	2.30	49.0	2.86	35.7	8.75
73.0	2.36	48.8	4.07	L. 33.5	8.75
70.0	2.40	48.5	5.62	28.5	8.57
67.0	2.48	48.2	6.85	26.0	8.45
65.7	2.48	47.8	7.55	20.0	8.26
58.5	2.54	47.0	8.05	−14.5	8.19
−55.5	2.60	−45.8	8.40	—	—

t°	ε	t°	ε	
+24.15	5.454	−51.5	3.013	PHILIPPE and PIETTE (1955)
−30.0	8.283	48.8	3.088	(two series)
33.2	8.479	37.0	8.533	
46.2	8.940	33.9	8.359	
48.8	9.032	32.4	8.267	
63.0	2.810	20.1	7.682	
−75.3	2.707	− 9.0	7.073	
—	—	+ 1.65	6.513	
—	—	13.05	5.957	
—	—	34.90	5.007	

Specific heat: CROWE and SMYTH (1950)

t°	cal/mol	t°	cal/mol	t°	cal/mol
−156.0	18.1	−104.0	22.9	−60.0	32.5
151.0	18.2	100.5	22.9	57.0	35.6
147.5	19.0	97.0	23.1	54.0	41.5
143.0	19.1	93.5	23.4	42.0	40.3
139.0	19.8	90.0	24.0	39.0	44.8
135.0	19.7	86.5	24.3	30.0	32.9
131.0	20.2	83.0	24.6	27.5	33.1
126.5	20.6	80.0	25.2	24.5	33.0
122.5	20.6	76.5	25.3	21.5	33.1
118.5	21.4	73.0	27.0	18.5	33.1
115.5	21.7	70.0	32.1	− 16.0	33.2
111.5	22.1	66.5	32.8	—	—
−108.0	22.5	− 63.5	30.0	—	—

Heat of melting: 450 cal/mol CROWE and SMYTH (1950)

Heat of transition: I. 50 cal/mol ,,
              II. 1780 cal/mol ,,

1,1,2-TRICHLOROETHANE $C_2H_3Cl_3$

Saturated vapour pressure

t°	p mm	t°	p mm	
113.67	760	61.29	123.76	DREISBACH and SHRADER (1949)
100.34	507.50	49.97	75.86	
85.99	315.52	—	—	

Boiling point: 113.6 CROWE and SMYTH (1950)
              113.67 DREISBACH and MARTIN (1949)
              114.1 MUMFORD and PHILLIPS (1950)

Freezing point: −36.57 DREISBACH and MARTIN (1949)
  −36.0 CROWE and SMYTH (1950)

Density

t°	d	
20	1.43952	DREISBACH and MARTIN (1949)
25	1.43188	,,
20	1.4424	MUMFORD and PHILLIPS
25	1.4355	,,

Viscosity

t°	$\eta \cdot 10^5$	t°	$\eta \cdot 10^5$	
20	119	25	110	MUMFORD and PHILLIPS (1950)

Surface tension

t°	γ	
20	33.75	MUMFORD and PHILLIPS (1950)
25	33.0	,,

Dielectric constant: CROWE and SMYTH (1950)

t°	ε	t°	ε	t°	ε
−132.8	2.47	−55.5	2.63	−35.7	8.45
113.5	2.49	49.3	2.65	35.4	8.77
91.5	2.51	43.4	2.72	35.3	9.22
84.7	2.53	40.5	2.77	28.6	9.00
78.0	2.55	37.3	3.05	23.0	8.78
− 61.8	2.61	−36.6	3.60	−20.2	8.65

Specific heat: CROWE and SMYTH (1950)

t°	cal/mol	t°	cal/mol	t°	cal/mol
C.−156.0	16.9	−104.0	24.6	−60.0	29.9
151.0	17.3	100.5	25.2	57.0	30.3
147.5	18.1	97.0	25.7	54.0	30.6
143.0	18.1	93.5	26.3	51.0	30.8
139.0	18.8	90.0	26.8	48.0	31.5
135.0	19.1	86.5	27.4	45.0	34.7
131.0	19.8	83.0	27.8	42.0	42.0
126.5	20.2	80.0	28.2	L. 33.0	33.6
122.5	20.9	76.5	28.6	30.0	34.1
118.5	22.0	73.0	28.9	27.5	34.4
115.5	22.6	70.0	29.1	24.5	34.0
111.5	23.3	66.5	29.4	−21.5	34.2
−108.0	24.0	− 63.5	30.0	—	—

Heat of melting: 2720 cal/mol *(ibid.)*

METHYLFLUOROFORM or 1,1,1-TRIFLUOROETHANE $C_2H_3F_3$

MEARS, STAHL, ORFEO, SHAIR, KELLS, THOMPSON and McCANN (1955)

Critical constants

Temperature: 73.1°

Pressure: 37.09 atm

Density: 0.434

Saturated vapour pressure: see authors.

1,1-DIFLUORO-1-CHLOROETHANE $C_2H_3F_2Cl$

MEARS, STAHL, ORFEO, SHAIR, KELLS, THOMPSON and McCANN (1955)

Critical constants:

Temperature: 137.1°

Pressure: 40.69 atm

Density: 0.435

Saturated vapour pressure: see authors.

Viscosity

t°	$\eta \cdot 10^5$	
−30.9	503	
−20.9	453	
− 0.8	381	
+20.0	334	
+40.0	281	
+60.0	238	

ACETYLENE TETRACHLORIDE or 1,1,2,2-TETRACHLOROETHANE

$$C_2H_2Cl_4$$

MUMFORD and PHILLIPS (1950)

Boiling point: 146.1

Density

t°	d	
20	1.5953	
25	1.5876	

Surface tension

t°	γ	
20	35.6	
25	34.9	

Refractive index: $n_D^{20°} = 1.4940$

1,1-DIFLUORO-1,2-DICHLOROETHANE $C_2H_2F_2Cl_2$

DEVINEY and FELSING (1957)

Saturated vapour pressure:

t°	P atm	t°	P atm	
110	5.973	170	19.493	
120	7.460	180	23.000	
130	9.205	190	27.010	
140	11.261	200	31.514	
150	13.639	210	36.643	
160	16.386	220	43.576	

Boiling point: 46.64

Isotherms (specific volume/total pressure)

cc/gr	P atm	cc/gr	P atm	cc/gr	P atm
80°		100°		125°	
0.7759	5.602	0.8063	5.598	0.8494	13.500
0.7736	13.504	0.8033	13.500	0.8460	21.397
0.7718	21.399	0.8013	21.397	0.8414	31.901
0.7695	31.903	0.7984	31.901	0.8350	49.008
0.7662	49.010	0.7942	49.008	0.8165	101.513
0.7553	101.514	0.7813	101.513	0.7982	154.058
0.7473	154.061	0.7710	154.058	0.7909	206.689
0.7401	206.692	0.7621	206.689	0.7805	259.357
0.7331	259.359	0.7533	259.377	0.7710	311.799
0.7272	311.801	0.7457	311.799	—	—

cc/gr	P atm	cc/gr	P atm	cc/gr	P atm
150°		175°		200°	
0.9078	21.395	0.9862	31.894	1.1293	37.145
0.8996	31.899	0.9627	49.001	1.0811	48.988
0.8882	49.006	0.9167	101.503	1.0209	75.229
0.8606	101.509	0.8865	154.048	0.9853	101.489
0.8405	154.056	0.8642	206.678	0.9387	154.035
0.8246	206.687	0.8466	259.344	0.9072	206.663
0.8107	259.353	0.8314	311.786	0.8834	259.330
0.7993	311.795	—	—	0.8643	311.771

cc/gr	P atm	cc/gr	P atm	cc/gr	P atm
225°					
2.0149	45.578	1.5956	47.296	1.2301	62.906
1.9626	45.667	1.5433	47.903	1.1612	75.209
1.9101	45.800	1.4909	48.687	1.0828	101.466
1.8567	46.008	1.4386	49.783	1.0046	154.009
1.8053	46.181	1.3863	51.367	0.9580	206.637
1.7528	46.380	1.3340	53.826	0.9279	259.302
1.7005	46.618	1.2819	57.425	0.9037	311.744
1.6480	46.926	—	—	—	—

1,1,1,2-TETRAFLUORO-2,2-DICHLOROETHANE $C_2F_4Cl_2$

MEARS, STAHL, ORFEO, SHAIR, KELLS, THOMPSON and McCANN (1955)
Critical constants:

Temperature: 145.5°

Pressure: 32.60 atm

Density: 0.582

Saturated vapour pressure: see authors.

Viscosity

t°	$\eta \cdot 10^5$
18.5	480
24.9	465
31.5	436
40.7	406
50.9	371
61.3	333
70.1	301

PENTACHLOROETHANE C_2HCl_5

MUMFORD and PHILLIPS (1950)

Density

t°	d
20	1.6813
25	1.6740

Surface tension

t°	γ
20	34.55
25	33.85

Refractive index: $n_D^{20°} = 1.5030$

PENTAFLUOROCHLOROETHANE C_2F_5Cl

ASTON, WILLS and ZOLKI (1955)

Saturated vapour pressure

t°	p mm	t°	p mm
−95.322	23.45	−56.029	332.74
90.330	35.415	47.818	506.08
82.432	64.47	39.857	735.32
−65.094	200.26	−39.235	756.20

Specific heat

t°	c_p	t°	c_p	
−258.16	4.22	−158.16	24.67	ASTON, WILLS and ZOLKI (1955)
257.16	4.70	153.16	25.00	,,
256.16	5.22	148.16	25.35	,,
255.16	5.76	143.16	25.72	,,
254.16	6.26	138.16	26.11	,,
253.16	6.675	133.16	26.53	,,
252.16	7.02	128.16	26.99	,,
251.16	7.34	123.16	27.48	,,
250.16	7.65	118.16	28.00	,,
249.16	7.945	113.16	28.55	,,
248.16	8.23	108.16	29.15	,,
243.16	9.58	103.16	29.80	,,
238.16	10.68	99.44	30.33	,,
233.16	11.57	99.44	31.13	,,
228.16	12.31	98.16	31.18	,,
223.16	12.96	93.16	31.36	,,
218.16	13.56	88.16	31.57	,,
213.16	14.15	83.16	31.80	,,
208.16	14.75	78.16	32.07	,,
203.16	15.40	73.16	32.38	,,
198.16	16.16	68.16	32.71	,,
192.92	17.13	63.16	33.04	,,
192.16	23.00	58.16	33.38	,,
188.16	23.18	53.16	33.73	,,
183.16	23.37	48.16	34.08	,,
178.16	23.58	43.16	34.44	,,
173.16	23.81	− 39.12	34.72	,,
168.16	24.07	—	—	
−163.16	24.36	—	—	

Heat of melting at −99.44: 448.9 cal/mol

C. DERIVATIVES OF PROPANE

PROPYL and *Iso*-PROPYL CHLORIDE C_3H_7Cl

Second virial coefficient: PEREZ MASIA and DIAZ PENA (1958)

1-BROMOPROPANE or *n*-PROPYL BROMIDE C_3H_7Br

Density

t°	d	
20	1.3550	BJELLERUP (1961)
25	1.3465	,,

Refractive index

t°	H$_\alpha$	Na$_D$	H$_\beta$	
20	1.4318	1.4346	1.4412	BJELLERUP (1961)
25	1.4292	1.4320	1.4385	,,

Heat of combustion at 25°: 491.54 kcal/mol *(ibid)*.

2-BROMOPROPANE or *Iso*-PROPYL BROMIDE   C$_3$H$_7$Br

Boiling point: 59.4 MUMFORD and PHILLIPS (1950)
            59.5 KUSHNER, CROWE and SMYTH (1950)

Melting point: −89.0 KUSHNER, CROWE and SMYTH (1950)

Density

t°	d	
20	1.3096	MUMFORD and PHILLIPS (1950)
25	1.3017	,,

Viscosity

t°	$\eta \cdot 10^5$	
20	487	MUMFORD and PHILLIPS (1950)
25	463	,,

Surface tension

t°	γ	
20	23.1	MUMFORD and PHILLIPS (1950)
25	22.5	,,

Refractive index: $n_D^{20°}$: 1.4251 MUMFORD and PHILLIPS (1950)

1.4250 KUSHNER, CROWE and SMYTH (1950)

Dielectric constant: KUSHNER, CROWE and SMYTH (1950)

t°	ε	t°	ε	
−147.5	2.21	−97.0	2.56	
143.0	2.21	93.5	2.59	
135.0	2.22	91.0	2.65	
131.0	2.22	89.5	3.17	
126.5	2.22	88.5	11.75	
122.5	2.23	87.5	13.43	
118.5	2.25	87.3	14.56	
115.5	2.28	86.9	14.60	
111.5	2.32	84.2	14.41	
108.0	2.38	77.5	14.05	
104.0	2.46	71.0	13.65	
−100.5	2.52	−57.5	12.87	

Specific heat: KUSHNER, CROWE and SMYTH (1950)

t°	cal/mol	t°	cal/mol	
−156.0	17.7	−108.0	22.6	
151.0	18.0	104.0	23.3	
147.5	18.3	100.5	23.9	
143.0	18.7	97.0	24.6	
139.0	19.1	93.5	25.4	
135.0	19.4	83.0	30.0	
131.0	19.7	80.0	29.9	
126.5	20.1	76.5	29.9	
122.5	20.4	73.0	30.1	
118.5	20.9	70.0	30.2	
115.5	21.5	66.5	30.3	
−111.5	22.2	− 63.5	30.3	

n-PROPYL IODIDE C_3H_7I

MUMFORD and PHILLIPS (1950)

Boiling point: 102.5

Density

t°	d	
20	1.7478	
25	1.7385	

Surface tension

t°	γ	
20	29.2	
25	28.6	

1,2-DICHLOROPROPANE $C_3H_6Cl_2$

Saturated vapour pressure

t°	p mm	
96.20	760	DREISBACH and SHRADER (1949)
83.18	507.50	,,
69.00	315.52	,,
44.78	123.76	,,

DREISBACH and MARTIN (1949)

Boiling point: 96.20

Freezing point: −100.42

Density

t°	d	
20	1.15577	
25	1.14925	

Refractive index

t°	n_D	
20	1.43901	
25	1.43638	

1,3-DICHLOROPROPANE $C_3H_6Cl_2$

MUMFORD and PHILLIPS (1950)

Boiling point: 120.8

Density   *Surface tension*

$t°$	d		$t°$	γ	
20	1.1859		20	33.8	
25	1.1800		25	33.05	

2,2-DICHLOROPROPANE $C_3H_6Cl_2$

Dielectric constant: PHILIPPE and PIETTE (1955)

$t°$	ε	$t°$	ε	
+ 20.00	11.37	−103.0	2.221	
13.0	11.62	97.0	2.237	
− 21.0	14.26	94.0	2.564	
28.5	14.74	93.0	2.771	
40.0	13.45	92.0	5.23	
61.0	12.19	89.5	8.68	
74.5	11.50	88.0	13.09	
121.0	2.201	87.0	13.43	
155.0	2.172	70.0	11.71	
140.0	2.170	65.5	11.91	
124.0	2.189	− 61.0	12.18	
−114.0	2.201	+ 18.0	14.00	

1,3-DIBROMOPROPANE or TRIMETHYLENE DIBROMIDE $C_3H_6Br_2$

Boiling point: 166.2 MUMFORD and PHILLIPS (1950)

Freezing point: −34.5 CROWE and SMYTH (1950)

Density

$t°$	d	
20	1.9812	MUMFORD and PHILLIPS (1950)
25	1.9727	,,
16.90	1.9868	KETELAAR and VAN MEURS (1957)
25.95	1.9707	,,
38.25	1.9488	,,

Surface tension

t°	γ	
20	40.1	MUMFORD and PHILLIPS (1950)
25	39.4	,,

Refractive index

t°	n_D	
20	1.5230	MUMFORD and PHILLIPS (1950)
16.90	1.52469	KETELAAR and VAN MEURS (1957)
25.95	1.52034	,,
38.25	1.51444	,,

Dielectric constant

t°	ε	
20	9.482	KETELAAR and VAN MEURS (1957)
45	8.524	,,
70	7.720	,,
95	6.994	,,

CROWE and SMYTH (1950)

t°	ε	t°	ε	t°	ε
C. −151.0	2.45	−54.0	2.60	−36.5	3.95
126.5	2.47	45.0	2.65	36.2	4.65
100.5	2.49	41.3	2.75	35.9	5.27
90.0	2.51	38.9	2.86	35.5	6.32
76.5	2.53	37.8	3.06	L. 33.7	11.05
− 60.0	2.55	−36.7	3.50	− 27.5	10.96

Heat of melting: 3500 cal/mol CROWE and SMYTH (1950)

Specific heat: CROWE and SMYTH (1950)

t°	cal/mol	t°	cal/mol	t°	cal/mol
−156.0	18.8	−108.0	21.8	−66.5	27.2
151.0	18.7	104.0	22.5	63.5	27.5
147.5	18.9	100.5	22.8	60.0	28.5
143.0	19.1	97.0	23.0	57.0	29.2
139.0	19.2	93.5	23.4	54.0	30.2
135.0	19.8	90.0	23.6	51.0	31.3
131.0	19.8	86.5	24.3	48.0	32.5
126.5	20.2	83.0	24.4	45.0	33.9
122.5	20.6	80.0	24.6	42.0	35.8
118.5	21.2	76.5	25.1	30.0	37.0
115.5	21.2	73.0	25.9	−27.5	37.3
−111.5	21.6	−70.0	26.2	—	—

1,2,3-TRICHLOROPROPANE $C_3H_5Cl_3$

MUMFORD and PHILLIPS (1950)

Boiling point: 156.0

Density

t°	d	
20	1.3880	
25	1.3818	

Surface tension

t°	γ	
20	37.8	
25	37.05	

Refractive index: $n_D^{20°}$ 1.4834

PERFLUOROPROPANE C_3F_8

Vapour

Specific heat: MASI, FLIEGER and WICKLUND (1954)

P atm	t°	−30.00	+10.00	+50.00	+90.00
1.50		—	34.93	37.42	39.84
1.00		32.02	34.68	37.29	39.71
0.67		31.73	—	—	—
0.50		—	34.45	37.15	39.61
0.33		31.40	—	—	—

D. DERIVATIVES OF BUTANE
BUTYL CHLORIDE C_4H_9Cl

Boiling point: 78.4 MUMFORD and PHILLIPS (1950)

Second virial coefficient: PEREZ MASIA and DIAZ PENA (1958)

$t°$	$-B$ (cc/mol)	
85	1025.9	
100	924.4	
150	672.9	

Density: MUMFORD and PHILLIPS (1950)

$t°$	d	
20	0.8866	
25	0.8811	

Surface tension (ibid.)

$t°$	γ	
20	23.75	
25	23.1	

Viscosity (ibid.)

$t°$	$\eta \cdot 10^5$	
20	450	
25	427	

Refractive index: $n_D^{20°} = 1.4021$ *(ibid.)*

Iso-BUTYL CHLORIDE C_4H_9Cl

Second virial coefficient: PEREZ MASIA and DIAZ PENA (1958)

t°	−B (cc/mol)	
75	1021.3	
100	953.7	

Boiling point: 68.4 MUMFORD and PHILLIPS (1950)

Density   *Surface tension*

t°	d		t°	γ	
20	0.8780		20	21.95	*ibid.*
25	0.8725		25	21.4	,,

Refractive index: $n_D^{20°} = 1.3978$ *(ibid.)*

Viscosity: DENNEY (1953)

t°	$\eta \cdot 10^5$		t°	$\eta \cdot 10^5$		t°	$\eta \cdot 10^5$
−154.4	0.0011		−164.2	0.11		−170.2	10
155.3	0.0021		166.4	0.42		170.9	18
158.2	0.0043		167.3	0.87		171.7	36
161.2	0.020		168.3	2.1		172.6	88
−162.5	0.040		−169.3	4.4		−173.9	340
20	457		MUMFORD and PHILLIPS (1950)				
25	431		,,				

Dielectric constant: DENNEY (1957)

t°	ε		t°	ε		t°	ε
L.+ 23.2	6.99		C.−139.0	16.88		−162.4	20.25
− 42.9	9.45		−147.8	18.04		−165.3	20.70
− 95.6	12.62		−153.5	18.86		−168.0	21.07
−128.8	15.64		−159.6	19.45			

Tert.-BUTYL CHLORIDE C_4H_9Cl

N.B. (p. 264): **Constants:** replace data of B. E., by those of Kushner, Crowe and Smyth (1950):

Boiling point: 50.5   *Melting point:* −25.0   *Refractive index:* $n_D^{20°} = 1.3859$

Dielectric constant: Kushner, Crowe and Smyth (1950)

t°	ε	t°	ε	t°	ε
−151.0	2.05	−58.5	2.33	−40.5	13.47
108.0	2.07	54.2	2.40	37.5	13.42
97.0	2.07	53.8	3.58	31.6	13.25
90.2	2.14	53.7	5.17	28.6	13.11
90.0	2.21	53.3	9.46	25.8	13.00
83.0	2.23	53.0	10.68	25.0	12.24
80.0	2.23	52.5	11.60	23.7	12.00
73.0	2.25	50.5	12.95	20.2	11.76
66.5	2.27	49.3	13.40	14.7	11.45
− 61.7	2.30	−43.3	13.47	−12.0	11.27

Philippe and Piette (1955)

t°	ε	t°	ε	t°	ε
L.+20.00	9.90	−65.5	2.361	−53.5	12.49
− 2.0	11.00	63.5	2.370	52.5	12.91
8.5	11.33	61.0	2.387	51.5	13.03
25.0	12.12	59.0	2.395	50.5	13.13
		57.0	2.754	44.0	13.28
C. 69.0	2.348	56.0	4.304	40.0	13.60
−93.0	2.261	−55.0	8.97	−33.5	13.69

Specific heat: Kushner, Crowe and Smyth (1950) (cal/mol)

t°	c_p	t°	c_p	t°	c_p	t°	c_p
−151.0	19.1	−115.5	23.8	−76.5	26.4	−39.0	29.2
147.5	19.5	111.5	24.9	73.0	26.5	36.0	29.6
143.0	19.9	108.0	25.7	70.0	26.5	33.0	30.2
139.0	20.3	104.0	26.8	66.5	26.8	30.0	31.1
135.0	20.6	100.5	27.6	63.5	27.2	21.5	36.4
131.0	21.1	97.0	28.2	60.0	27.7	18.5	36.2
126.5	21.2	93.5	29.5	57.0	28.2	16.0	36.4
122.5	22.0	83.0	26.4	45.0	28.5	−13.5	36.5
−118.5	23.2	− 80.0	26.4	−42.0	28.7	—	—

1-BROMOBUTANE or *n*-BUTYL BROMIDE C_4H_9Br

Boiling point: 101.5 MUMFORD and PHILLIPS (1950)

Density

t°	d	
20	1.2758	MUMFORD and PHILLIPS (1950)
25	1.2687	,,
20	1.2758	BJELLERUP (1961)
25	1.2686	,,

Viscosity

t°	$\eta \cdot 10^5$	
20	633	MUMFORD and PHILLIPS (1950)
25	597	,,

Surface tension

t°	γ	
20	26.6	MUMFORD and PHILLIPS (1950)
25	26.0	,,

Refractive index

t°	Na_D	H_α	H_β	
20	1.4397	—	—	MUMFORD and PHILLIPS (1950)
20	1.4398	1.4371	1.4463	BJELLERUP (1961)
25	1.4374	1.4347	1.4438	,,

Heat of combustion at 25° : 649.17 kcal/mol BJELLERUP (1961)

Iso-BUTYL BROMIDE $\qquad$ C₄H₉Br

Boiling point: 91.1 MUMFORD and PHILLIPS (1950)

Density $\qquad$ *Surface tension Viscosity*

t°	d	γ	$\eta \cdot 10^5$	
20	1.2641	24.75	637	MUMFORD and PHILLIPS (1950)
25	1.2568	24.1	601	,,

t°	$\eta \cdot 10^5$	t°	$\eta \cdot 10^5$	t°	$\eta \cdot 10^5$	
−148.9	0.0024	−159.5	0.81	−164.5	44	DENNEY (1953)
154.2	0.031	160.2	1.4	165.5	110	,,
155.6	0.073	161.9	4.5	166.4	420	,,
−158.0	0.25	−163.4	19	−167.1	880	,,

Refractive index

t°	nD	
20	1.4362	MUMFORD and PHILLIPS (1950)

Dielectric constant: DENNEY (1957)

t°	ε	t°	ε	t°	ε
0.1	7.70	−135.1	15.75	−158.7	18.88
− 46.2	9.48	−145.7	16.96	−161.2	19.1
− 95.8	12.24	−150.0	17.66	—	—
−128.6	15.03	−154.0	18.09	—	—

Tert.-BUTYL BROMIDE C_4H_9Br

Saturated vapour pressure: BRYCE-SMITH and HOWLETT (1951)

t°	p mm	t°	p mm
0.0	42.8	31.3	174.5
6.8	59.0	35.7	209.3
10.6	70.7	40.0	243.4
15.7	90.0	49.3	344.5
20.8	112.9	56.6	450.4
22.7	121.9	63.5	567.6
25.0	135.3	72.8	758.0
28.4	155.4	—	—

Specific heat: KUSHNER, CROWE and SMYTH (1950)

t°	cal/mol	t°	cal/mol	t°	cal/mol
− 156.0	20.0	− 118.5	24.6	− 83.0	33.0
151.0	20.1	115.5	25.4	80.0	33.5
147.5	20.5	111.5	26.2	76.5	34.0
143.0	20.9	108.0	27.2	73.0	35.1
139.0	21.2	104.0	28.1	70.0	35.9
135.0	21.7	97.0	29.8	66.5	36.7
131.0	22.1	93.5	30.4	57.0	31.7
126.5	23.0	90.0	31.2	− 54.0	31.8
− 122.5	23.4	− 86.5	32.1		

Heat of fusion (ibid.)

t°	kcal/mol
−17.0	0.47

Heat of transition (ibid.)

t°	kcal/mol
−64.5	1.35
−41.6	0.25

n-BUTYL IODIDE C_4H_9I

MUMFORD and PHILLIPS (1950)

Boiling point: 130.2

Density

t°	d	
20	1.6150	
25	1.6070	

Surface tension

t°	γ	
20	29.25	
25	28.7	

Viscosity

t°	$\eta \cdot 10^5$	
20	877	
25	826	

1,4-DICHLOROBUTANE $C_4H_8Cl_2$

MUMFORD and PHILLIPS (1950)

Boiling point: 155.0

Density

t°	d	
20	1.1408	
25	1.1353	

Surface tension

t°	γ	
20	34.8	
25	34.05	

Viscosity

t°	$\eta \cdot 10^5$	
20	143	
25	131.5	

Refractive index: $n_D^{20°} = 1.4549$

1,2-DIBROMOBUTANE $C_4H_8Br_2$

Density: BJELLERUP (1961)

t°	d	
20	1.7954	
25	1.7870	

1,4-DIBROMOBUTANE $C_4H_8Br_2$

KETELAAR and VAN MEURS (1957)

Density and refractive index

t°	d	n_D	
16.90	1.8318	1.52047	
26.00	1.8176	1.51628	
38.40	1.7983	1.51058	

Dielectric constant

t°	ε	
20	8.829	
45	8.162	
70	7.561	

PERFLUORO-*n*-BUTANE C_4F_{10}

Critical temperature: 113.2° BROWN and MEARS (1958)

Critical density: 0.600 *ibid.*

Critical pressure: 22.93 atm *ibid.*

Saturated vapour pressure

t°	p mm	t°	p mm	
−13.21	477	−34.73	163	SIMONS and MAUSTELLER (1952)
−19.54	356	−39.93	121	,,
−26.81	249	—	—	,,

t°	P atm	t°	P atm	
−39.88	0.164	+ 50.41	5.55	BROWN and MEARS (1958)
31.91	0.254	60.47	7.23	,,
24.32	0.372	70.02	9.08	,,
15.27	0.569	85.17	12.86	,,
− 3.91	0.926	100.26	17.69	,,
+31.73	3.26	109.89	21.50	,,
39.70	4.09	—	—	,,

Densities of the liquid and the saturated vapour: BROWN and MEARS (1958)

t°	d		t°	d	
	V	L		V	L
−40.0	0.00202	1.723	49.1	0.0589	1.395
−20.0	0.00547	1.659	60.0	0.0797	1.340
0	0.0121	1.592	74.3	0.118	1.260
+20.0	0.0246	1.517	80.0	0.137	1.222
28.8	0.0326	1.482	100.0	0.296	1.002
40.0	0.0454	1.436	113.2	0.600	0.600
40.5	0.0461	1.433	—	—	—

Isochors (vapour): BROWN and MEARS (1958)

Vol. l/g mol	t°	P atm	Vol. l/g mol	t°	P atm
0.38144	115.08	23.90	0.44006	121.64	26.37
	119.08	25.83		135.09	31.70
	125.87	29.04		152.55	38.53
	133.46	32.59		173.08	46.58
	145.40	38.36	0.53647	115.17	23.39
	176.26	53.31		120.87	25.24
0.39960	113.07	22.86	3.25586	65.18	6.89
	121.07	26.52		90.27	7.72
	136.77	33.49		125.09	8.83
	150.92	39.88		147.02	9.50
	174.66	50.58		162.37	9.97
				175.87	10.36

Boiling point: −2.00 BROWN and MEARS (1958)
　　　　　　　−2.2 SIMONS and MAUSTELLER (1952)

Freezing point: −128.20 *ibid.*

Heat of vaporization: BROWN and MEARS (1958)

t°	cal/mol	t°	cal/mol	
−40.0	6100	40.0	4650	
−20.0	5750	60.0	4080	
− 2.0	5480	80.0	3410	
0.0	5460	100.0	1920	
+20.0	5030	113.2	0	

E. DERIVATIVES OF PENTANE
and HIGHER PARAFFINS

n-AMYL CHLORIDE $C_5H_{11}Cl$

Boiling point:　107.9 MUMFORD and PHILLIPS (1950)
　　　　　　　　108.35 SIMON (1929)

Freezing point:　−99.0 *ibid.*

Density:

t°	d		t°	d	
20	0.8840	MUMFORD and PHILLIPS (1950)	0	0.90137	SIMON (1929)
25	0.8795		15	0.88657	
			30	0.87163	

MUMFORD and PHILLIPS (1950)

Viscosity   *Surface tension*

t°	$\eta \cdot 10^5$	t°	γ	
20	580	20	25.15	
25	547	25	24.55	

Refractive index: $n_D^{20°} = 1.4125$ MUMFORD and PHILLIPS (1950)

SIMON (1929)

t°	He_r	H_α	Na_D	He_y	He_{gr}	H_β	He_v	H_y
15	1.41238	1.41266	1.41481	1.41492	1.41910	1.42017	1.42351	1.42457
25	1.40780	1.40816	1.41026	1.41027	1.41446	1.41552	1.41863	1.42007

Tert.-AMYL CHLORIDE $\qquad$ $C_5H_{11}Cl$

MUMFORD and PHILLIPS (1950)

Boiling point: 85.6

Density

t°	d	
20	0.8659	
25	0.8612	

Viscosity

t°	$\eta \cdot 10^5$	
20	599	
25	560	

Surface tension

t°	γ	
20	22.3	
25	21.8	

Refractive index: $n_D^{20°} = 1.4050$

n-AMYL BROMIDE $C_5H_{11}Br$

Boiling point: 129.4 MUMFORD and PHILLIPS (1950)
129.70 *dt/dp (10 mm):* 0.47 SIMON (1929)

Freezing point: −95.25 SIMON (1929)

Density

t°	d	
0	1.24264	SIMON (1929)
15	1.22367	,,
30	1.20456	,,
20	1.2186	BJELLERUP (1961)
25	1.2123	,,
20	1.2190	MUMFORD and PHILLIPS (1950)
25	1.2132	,,

MUMFORD and PHILLIPS (1950)

Viscosity   *Surface tension*

t°	$\eta \cdot 10^5$	t°	γ	
20	803	20	27.35	
25	753	25	26.8	

Refractive index

t°	Na_D	H_α	H_β	
20	1.4444	1.4418	1.4509	BJELLERUP (1961)
25	1.4420	1.4394	1.4485	,,
20	1.4443	—	—	MUMFORD and PHILLIPS (1950)

SIMON (1929)

t°	He_r	H_α	Na_D	He_y	He_{gr}	H_β	He_v	H_γ
15	1.44393	1.44421	1.44684	1.44701	1.45210	1.45329	1.45744	1.45880
20	1.43925	1.43967	1.44231	1.44235	1.44749	1.44871	1.45262	1.45410

Heat of combustion at 25° : 805.30 kcal/mol BJELLERUP (1961)

Iso-AMYL BROMIDE $\qquad$ $C_5H_{11}Br$

DENNEY (1953)

Viscosity

$t°$	$\eta \cdot 10^5$	$t°$	$\eta \cdot 10^5$	$t°$	$\eta \cdot 10^5$
−136.2	0.0049	−146.9	0.72	−153.9	42.0
140.5	0.0330	148.8	2.1	155.6	136.0
143.4	0.099	150.5	5.7	156.2	232.0
−144.5	0.21	−151.9	13.0	−159.9	6000.0

Dielectric constant

$t°$	ε	$t°$	ε	$t°$	ε
+ 18.4	6.33	−116.5	11.34	−142.9	13.50
− 58.7	8.47	−127.1	12.18	−146.6	13.79
− 93.3	10.02	−134.0	12.69	−150.6	14.16
−105.4	10.67	−139.3	13.16	—	—

n-AMYL IODIDE $\qquad$ $C_5H_{11}I$

Boiling point: 157.00 SIMON (1929)

Freezing point: −85.6 ibid.

Density: (ibid.)

$t°$	d
0	1.54572
15	1.52384
30	1.50181

1,5-DIBROMOPENTANE $\qquad$ $C_5H_{10}Br_2$

KETELAAR and VAN MEURS (1957)

$t°$	d	n_D	α_D	(= *polarisability for* Na_D *line*)
16.90	1.7035	1.51325	15.473	
25.90	1.6909	1.50934	15.475	
38.45	1.6734	1.50369	15.473	

Dielectric constant

$t°$	ε
20	9.183
45	8.287
70	7.453

PERFLUORO-*n*-PENTANE C_5F_{12}

Boiling point: 29.19 SIMONS and DUNLAP (1950)

Freezing point: −125.36 BURGER and CADY (1951)
          −125.65 SIMONS and DUNLAP (1950)

Transition point: −128.56 BURGER and CADY (1951)
          −128.65 SIMONS and DUNLAP (1950)

Saturated vapour pressure:

$\lg_{10} p = -2108.0/T - 4.9814 \lg T + 22.2092$ SIMONS and DUNLAP (1950)

Critical solution temperature; with *n*-pentane: −7.66° SIMONS and DUNLAP (1950)

Density: BURGER and CADY (1951)

$t°$	d	$t°$	d	$t°$	d
29.98	1.5869	14.67	1.6372	−17.13	1.7359
28.14	1.5932	12.67	1.6437	−31.30	1.7772
26.30	1.5995	10.65	1.6502	−65.19	1.8727
19.20	1.6223	1.30	1.6800	−74.06	1.8971
17.73	1.6276	0.30	1.6830	−88.19	1.9356
15.25	1.6351	− 9.35	1.7128	—	—

Viscosity: BURGER and CADY (1951)

$t°$	$\eta \cdot 10^6$	$t°$	$\eta \cdot 10^6$	$t°$	$\eta \cdot 10^6$
24.90	4619	− 4.74	7087	−63.37	22660
23.53	4708	18.32	8856	67.62	25650
15.28	5273	35.95	12310	76.10	32610
14.11	5349	36.61	12450	79.17	35980
6.28	5996	51.45	16910	84.61	43150
2.45	6342	−58.18	19850	−88.41	49610

Refractive index: $n_D^{20°} = 1.245$ SIMONS and DUNLAP (1950)

PERFLUORO-*iso*-PENTANE $\qquad$ C_5F_{12}

BURGER and CADY (1951)

Melting point: —96.66

Density

t°	d	t°	d	t°	d
30.80	1.6286	14.39	1.6833	−39.14	1.8455
29.86	1.6317	13.40	1.6859	52.19	1.8832
23.99	1.6514	10.22	1.6967	67.65	1.9267
20.03	1.6645	9.21	1.7000	78.98	1.9579
17.55	1.6726	2.17	1.7221	−88.91	1.9851
17.33	1.6739	−13.14	1.7691	—	—
15.45	1.6793	−17.06	1.7808	—	—

Viscosity

t°	$\eta \cdot 10^6$	t°	$\eta \cdot 10^6$	t°	$\eta \cdot 10^6$
21.60	6107	− 9.16	10470	−59.09	36420
20.93	6178	−19.45	12930	−62.90	41570
13.66	6954	−34.96	18440	−71.28	55800
3.78	8238	−46.71	25110	−74.93	64390
—	—	−54.21	31380	−79.40	77490

n-HEXYL FLUORIDE $\qquad$ $C_6H_{13}F$

MACEY (1960)

Boiling point: 92.1

Refractive index

t°	C	D	F	
20	1.37308	1.37499	1.37920	

Sec.-HEXYL FLUORIDE $\qquad$ $C_6H_{13}F$

N.B. (p. 272): *Surface tension:* 20°: 20.39 instead of 20°.

n-HEXYL CHLORIDE $C_6H_{13}Cl$

MUMFORD and PHILLIPS (1950)

Boiling point: 134.3

Density		Viscosity		Surface tension	
$t°$	d	$t°$	$\eta \cdot 10^5$	$t°$	γ
20	0.8790	20	743	20	26.15
25	0.8745	25	696	25	25.55

n-HEXYL BROMIDE $C_6H_{13}Br$

Boiling point: 154.6 MUMFORD and PHILLIPS (1950)

Density

$t°$	d	
20	1.1746	MUMFORD and PHILLIPS (1950)
25	1.1691	,,
20	1.1745	BJELLERUP (1961)
25	1.1688	,,

Viscosity: MUMFORD and PHILLIPS (1950)

$t°$	$\eta \cdot 10^5$	
20	1013	
25	941	

Surface tension: (ibid.)

$t°$	γ	
20	28.2	
25	27.65	

Refractive index

t°	Na$_D$	H$_\alpha$	H$_\beta$	
20	1.4475	1.4449	1.4539	BJELLERUP (1961)
25	1.4452	1.4426	1.4516	,,

$n_D^{20°} = 1.4475$ MUMFORD and PHILLIPS (1950)

Heat of combustion at 25° : 962.82 kcal/mol BJELLERUP (1961)

n-HEXYL IODIDE $\qquad$ C$_6$H$_{13}$I

MUMFORD and PHILLIPS (1950)

Boiling point: 76.5 (23 mm)

Density

t°	d	
20	1.4391	
25	1.4326	

Viscosity

t°	$\eta \cdot 10^5$	
20	1390	
25	1285	

Surface tension

t°	γ	
20	30.25	
25	29.75	

Refractive index: $n_D^{20°} = 1.4926$

1,6-DIBROMOHEXANE $C_6H_{12}Br_2$

KETELAAR and VAN MEURS (1957)

Density and refractive index

t°	d	n_D	
13.50	1.6129	1.51018	
19.62	1.6049	1.50743	
29.23	1.5924	1.50339	

Dielectric constant

t°	ε	
20	8.436	
45	7.756	
70	7.155	
95	6.587	

n-HEPTYL FLUORIDE $C_7H_{15}F$

MACEY (1960)

Boiling point: 119.3

Density: 0.8060 at 20°

Refractive index

t°	C	D	F	
20	1.38442	1.38611	1.39080	

n-HEPTYL CHLORIDE $C_7H_{15}Cl$

MUMFORD and PHILLIPS (1950)

Boiling point: 160.0

Density

t°	d	
20	0.8759	
25	0.8715	

Viscosity

t°	$\eta \cdot 10^5$	
20	956	
25	890	

Surface tension at 20°: 26.9; at 25°: 26.35
Refractive index: $n_D^{20°} = 1.4255$

n-HEPTYL BROMIDE $\qquad$ C$_7$H$_{15}$Br

Boiling point: 69.5 (17 mm) MUMFORD and PHILLIPS (1950)

Density

t°	d	
20	1.1406	MUMFORD and PHILLIPS (1950)
25	1.1352	,,
20	1.1402	BJELLERUP (1961)
25	1.1348	,,

Viscosity

t°	$\eta \cdot 10^5$	
20	1290	MUMFORD and PHILLIPS (1950)
25	1190	,,

Surface tension

t°	γ	
20	28.6	MUMFORD and PHILLIPS (1950)
25	28.1	,,

Refractive index

t°	Na$_D$	H$_\alpha$	H$_\beta$	
20	1.4503	1.4477	1.4566	BJELLERUP (1961)
25	1.4481	1.4456	1.4544	,,
20	1.4498			MUMFORD and PHILLIPS (1950)

Dielectric constant: CROWE and SMYTH (1950)

Metastable form		Stable form			
t°	ε	t°	ε	t°	ε
−160.5	2.38	−160.5	2.35	−57.6	2.87
118.5	2.39	143.0	2.36	57.3	3.69
108.0	2.40	135.0	2.37	57.0	4.70
104.0	2.42	111.5	2.38	56.7	5.52
100.5	2.43	93.5	2.39	56.4	5.80
97.0	2.44	83.0	2.40	54.9	7.00
80.0	2.44	76.5	2.41	51.0	6.92
72.8	2.43	70.0	2.42	48.0	6.84
− 70.0	2.40	66.5	2.43	−42.0	6.71
—	—	− 63.5	2.44	—	—

Specific heat: CROWE and SMYTH (1950)

Metastable form				Stable form			
t°	cal/mol	t°	cal/mol	t°	cal/mol	t°	cal/mol
−160.5	26.4	−115.5	35.1	−160.5	24.7	−97.0	33.4
156.0	27.0	111.5	38.2	156.0	25.3	93.5	33.8
151.0	27.3	108.0	41.7	151.0	25.9	90.0	34.4
147.5	27.7	104.0	52.9	147.5	26.3	86.5	34.8
143.0	28.3	100.5	52.7	143.0	26.9	83.0	35.3
139.0	29.1	97.0	40.4	139.0	27.4	80.0	35.7
135.0	29.6	93.5	37.8	135.0	28.0	76.5	36.0
131.0	30.3	90.0	38.1	131.0	28.6	73.0	36.6
126.5	31.0	86.5	38.9	126.5	29.3	70.0	37.5
122.5	31.6	83.0	39.6	122.5	29.7	66.5	38.6
−118.5	32.5	80.0	35.9	118.5	30.1	63.5	40.7
		− 76.5	14.7	115.5	30.6	51.0	46.7
				111.5	31.3	48.0	47.0
				108.0	31.7	45.0	47.1
				104.0	32.4	−42.0	47.1
				−100.5	33.0		

Heat of combustion at 25° : 118.52 kcal/mol BJELLERUP (1961)

PERFLUORO-*n*-HEPTANE C_7F_{16}

Critical constants: OLIVER and GRISARD (1951)

Temperature: 201.7°

Pressure: 16.0 atm

Density: 0.584

Saturated vapour pressure: OLIVER and GRISARD (1951)

t°	p mm	t°	p mm	t°	p mm
− 1.89	16.88	41.80	166.62	85.27	830.09
+ 1.57	20.94	46.86	206.57	90.08	963.72
6.93	29.09	52.56	260.63	95.03	1118.0
13.54	41.72	58.99	334.70	99.93	1288.7
19.19	56.64	64.03	403.91	104.54	1467.0
23.95	72.52	68.96	482.15	106.03	1528.8
30.49	99.68	74.27	579.51	—	—
35.91	128.39	79.71	694.49	—	—

t°	p mm	t°	p mm	
94.89	1113.4	156.03	5048.9	MILTON and OLIVER (1952)
100.92	1324.4	164.08	5952.4	,,
104.84	1479.5	171.87	6966.0	,,
110.04	1704.5	180.01	8129.6	,,
117.87	2092.9	187.98	9432.8	,,
125.96	2561.4	196.05	10932.5	,,
129.98	2826.7	198.24	11377.3	,,
136.04	3254.9	200.79	11930.6	,,
144.05	3901.9	201.5	12101.3	,,

Boiling point: 81.5 NEFF and HICKMAN (1955)

82.51 OLIVER, BLUMKIN and CUNNINGHAM (1951)

Vapour pressure at high temperature: MILTON and OLIVER (1952)

Freezing point: −51.29 OLIVER, BLUMKIN and CUNNINGHAM (1951)

Transition point: −92.70 OLIVER and GRISARD (1951)

OLIVER, BLUMKIN and CUNNINGHAM (1951)	20°	25°	30°
Density:	1.73184	1.71802	1.70419
Surface tension:	13.19	12.78	12.37
Refractive index:			
n_C	1.25947	1.25736	1.25532
n_D	1.26020	1.25818	1.25610
n_E	1.26080	1.25879	1.25669
n_F	1.26188	1.25976	1.25761
n_G	1.26314	1.26109	1.25904

Heat of melting: 1660.5 cal/mol at −51.29° OLIVER and GRISARD (1951)

Heat of transition: 1594 cal/mol at −92.70° OLIVER and GRISARD (1951)

n-FLUORIDES in C_8, C_9, C_{10}, C_{11}, C_{12}, C_{14}, C_{16}

Boiling point, Density at 20° and *Refractive index* at 20°: see MACEY (1960)

n-OCTYL CHLORIDE $C_8H_{17}Cl$

MUMFORD and PHILLIPS (1950)

Boiling point: 183.8

Density

t°	d	
20	0.8735	
25	0.8695	

Viscosity

t°	$\eta \cdot 10^5$	
20	1230	
25	1135	

Surface tension

t°	γ	
20	27.65	
25	27.15	

Refractive index: $n_D^{20°} = 1.4298$

Sec.-OCTYL CHLORIDE $C_8H_{17}Cl$

MUMFORD and PHILLIPS (1950)

Boiling point: 171.9

Density

t°	d	
20	0.8660	
25	0.8616	

Viscosity

t°	$\eta \cdot 10^5$	
20	1055	
25	973	

Surface tension

t°	γ	
20	26.4	
25	25.9	

Refractive index: $n_D^{20°} = 1.4283$

1-BROMO-OCTANE or *n*-OCTYL BROMIDE $C_8H_{17}Br$

Boiling point: 202.2 MUMFORD and PHILLIPS (1950)

Freezing point: −55.0 CROWE and SMYTH (1950)

Density

t°	d	
20	1.1126	MUMFORD and PHILLIPS (1950)
25	1.1077	,,
20	1.1129	BJELLERUP (1961)
25	1.1077	,,

Viscosity

t°	$\eta \cdot 10^5$	
20	1640	MUMFORD and PHILLIPS (1950)
25	1500	,,

Surface tension

t°	γ	
20	29.1	Mumford and Phillips (1950)
25	28.6	,,

Refractive index

t°	D	H$_\alpha$	H$_\beta$	
20	1.45267	—	—	Crowe and Smyth (1950)
20	1.4526	1.4499	1.4588	Bjellerup (1961)
25	1.4505	1.4478	1.4567	,,

Dielectric constant: Crowe and Smyth (1950)

t°	ε	t°	ε	t°	ε
−160.5	2.38	−60.0	2.43	−53.0	6.41
118.5	2.39	56.7	2.50	51.0	6.37
80.0	2.40	55.7	4.35	42.0	6.29
− 70.0	2.41	−55.2	5.65	−39.0	6.15

Specific heat: Crowe and Smyth (1950)

t°	cal/mol	t°	cal/mol	t°	cal/mol
−160.5	27.9	− 115.5	34.5	−80.0	39.3
156.0	28.7	111.5	35.3	76.5	40.1
151.0	29.0	108.0	35.7	73.0	40.7
147.5	29.8	104.0	35.8	70.0	41.2
143.0	30.1	100.5	36.6	66.5	42.0
139.0	30.7	97.0	37.0	63.5	42.7
135.0	31.1	93.5	37.5	60.0	47.4
131.0	31.8	90.0	38.0	51.0	62.4
126.5	32.6	86.6	38.5	42.0	62.3
122.5	33.2	− 83.0	38.8	−39.0	62.3
−118.5	33.9	—	—	—	—

Heat of melting: 5900 cal/mol Crowe and Smyth (1950)

Heat of combustion at 25° : 1274.52 kcal/mol Bjellerup (1961)

n-NONYL BROMIDE $C_9H_{19}Br$

CROWE and SMYTH (1950)

Freezing point: −29.0

Transition point: −30.8

Refractive index: $n_D^{20°} = 1.45467$

Dielectric constant

Metastable form		Stable form			
$t°$	ε	$t°$	ε	$t°$	ε
I. −160.5	2.36	−160.5	2.35	−42.0	2.46
126.5	2.37	143.0	2.36	39.0	2.48
118.5	2.38	126.5	2.37	36.0	2.49
111.5	2.39	111.5	2.38	31.6	2.67
100.5	2.40	104.0	2.39	II. 30.2	4.26
97.0	2.42	93.5	2.40	29.5	4.97
93.5	2.43	80.0	2.41	28.3	5.53
76.5	2.44	70.0	2.42	24.5	5.48
70.0	2.45	63.5	2.43	21.5	5.44
63.5	2.46	60.0	2.43	18.5	5.40
57.0	2.47	57.0	2.44	−16.0	5.37
51.0	2.48	− 48.0	2.45	—	—
45.0	2.49				
42.8	2.50				
− 39.8	2.49				

Heat of melting: 7200 cal/mol

Heat of transition: 190 cal/mol

Specific heat (cal/mol)

Metastable form				Stable form			
$t°$	c_p	$t°$	c_p	$t°$	c_p	$t°$	c_p
−160.5	32.6	−97.0	53.3	−160.5	31.9	− 83.0	41.0
156.0	32.8	93.5	47.6	156.0	32.2	80.0	41.5
151.0	33.2	90.0	44.0	151.0	33.2	76.5	42.0
147.5	33.7	86.5	44.2	147.5	33.0	73.0	42.7
143.0	34.0	83.0	44.4	143.0	33.4	70.0	43.0
139.0	34.1	80.0	44.7	139.0	33.4	66.5	43.2
135.0	35.1	76.5	45.2	135.0	33.8	63.5	44.0
131.0	35.9	73.0	45.9	131.0	34.9	60.0	44.6
126.5	36.8	70.0	46.5	126.5	35.4	57.0	45.1
122.5	37.8	66.5	46.7	122.5	35.9	54.0	46.1
118.5	39.2	63.5	47.6	118.5	36.6	51.0	46.6
115.5	41.0	60.0	47.8	115.5	37.3	48.0	47.9
111.5	43.7	57.0	48.0	111.5	38.1	45.0	49.8
108.0	47.3	54.0	48.5	108.0	38.5	42.0	51.7
104.0	53.2	51.0	49.4	104.0	39.3	39.0	57.1
−100.5	60.7	48.0	50.5	100.5	39.5	36.0	74.4
—	—	−45.0	23.5	97.0	40.0	24.5	68.8
				93.5	39.8	21.5	68.9
				90.0	40.5	−18.5	68.5
				−86.5	40.9	—	—

1,9-DIBROMONONONANE $C_9H_{18}Br_2$

and

1,10-DIBROMODECANE $C_{10}H_{20}Br_2$

Density and *Dielectric constant:* KETELAAR and VAN MEURS (1957)

n-DECYL BROMIDE $C_{10}H_{21}Br$

CROWE and SMYTH (1950)

Freezing point: −29.2   *Refractive index:* $n_D^{20°} = 1.45607$

Dielectric constant

$t°$	ε	$t°$	ε	$t°$	ε
−151.0	2.32	−51.0	2.39	−16.0	2.46
126.5	2.33	45.0	2.40	11.9	2.57
93.5	2.34	39.0	2.41	10.5	3.42
86.5	2.36	33.0	2.42	10.0	3.87
83.0	2.37	27.5	2.43	9.3	4.74
73.0	2.37	21.5	2.44	3.3	4.63
− 57.0	2.38	− 18.5	2.45	− 0.6	4.61

Specific heat (cal/mol)

t°	c_p	t°	c_p	t°	c_p
C. −151.0	37.6	−97.0	55.7	−51.0	54.4
147.5	38.0	93.5	62.8	48.0	54.9
143.0	38.9	90.0	76.3	45.0	55.5
139.0	39.4	86.5	71.4	42.0	55.7
135.0	39.7	83.0	57.1	39.0	56.9
131.0	40.7	80.0	51.3	36.0	58.1
126.5	41.7	76.5	49.8	33.0	59.4
122.5	42.3	73.0	50.2	30.0	60.3
118.5	43.2	70.0	50.9	L. 27.5	61.1
115.5	43.7	66.5	51.2	24.5	61.7
111.5	44.6	63.5	52.1	21.5	68.6
108.0	45.4	60.0	52.8	18.5	72.2
104.0	48.0	57.0	53.0	−16.0	78.7
−100.5	51.2	−54.0	53.6	—	—

n-UNDECYL BROMIDE $\qquad$ C$_{11}$H$_{23}$Br

CROWE and SMYTH (1950)

Freezing point: −9.9

Refractive index: $n_D^{20°} = 1.45777$

n-DODECYL BROMIDE $\qquad$ C$_{12}$H$_{25}$Br

Dielectric constant: HOFFMAN and SMYTH (1950)

t°	ε	t°	ε	t°	ε
31.5	4.15	−10.6	3.80	−32.0	2.27
6.6	4.38	10.7	2.95	45	2.25
− 1.0	4.46	10.8	2.53	56	2.24
4.9	4.50	11.0	2.40	92	2.22
9.9	4.55	11.2	2.35	−134	2.20
11.9	4.57	12.3	2.33	—	—
−10.0	4.48	−25.0	2.28	—	—

n-HEXADECYL CHLORIDE $\qquad$ $C_{16}H_{33}Cl$

MUMFORD and PHILLIPS (1950)

Boiling point: 195 (22.5 mm)

Density

t°	d	
20	0.8649	
25	0.8616	

Refractive index: $n_D^{20°} = 1.4495$

Viscosity

t°	$\eta \cdot 10^4$	
20	634	
25	551	

Surface tension

t°	γ	
20	31.1	
25	30.6	

n-HEXADECYL BROMIDE $\qquad$ $C_{16}H_{33}Br$

Boiling point: 190 (11 mm) MUMFORD and PHILLIPS (1950)

Melting point: 17.33 HOFFMAN and SMYTH (1950)

Density

t°	d	
20	0.9992	MUMFORD and PHILLIPS (1950)
25	0.9952	„

Refractive index: $n_D^{20°} = 1.4614$ MUMFORD and PHILLIPS (1950)
$\qquad\qquad\qquad$ $n_D^{25°} = 1.46075$ HOFFMAN and SMYTH (1950)

Viscosity

t°	$\eta \cdot 10^4$	
20	781	MUMFORD and PHILLIPS (1950)
25	675	,,

Surface tension

t°	γ	
20	31.8	MUMFORD and PHILLIPS (1950)
25	31.4	,,

Dielectric constant: HOFFMAN and SMYTH (1950)

t°	ε	t°	ε	t°	ε
+37.4	3.66	+ 12.2	2.40	+ 12.0	2.41
23.5	3.74	8.6	2.38	13.0	2.43
18.7	3.78	0.0	2.36	14.5	2.48
15.7	3.80	− 8.0	2.35	15.0	2.50
12.0	3.85	63	2.24	15.4	2.53
16.0	3.47	80	2.22	16.3	2.71
16.2	3.38	102	2.21	16.5	2.90
16.2	3.25	−140	2.20	16.9	3.48
16.1	2.85	—	—	17.0	3.73
16.0	2.71	−160	2.20	17.2	3.78
14.9	2.45	− 60	2.24	17.3	3.83
13.9	2.43	− 9.9	2.39	+19.9	3.80

n-OCTADECYL CHLORIDE $\qquad$ $C_{18}H_{37}Cl$

WATERMAN, LEENDERTSE and VAN KREVELEN (1939)

Freezing point: 19.5

Density: 0.8490

Refractive index

t°	n_D	
39	1.4450	
40	1.4445	
41	1.4440	

n-OCTADECYL BROMIDE $C_{18}H_{37}Br$

Dielectric constant: HOFFMAN and SMYTH (1950)

t°	ε	t°	ε	t°	ε
+58.4	3.40	+24.8	2.40	−53	2.25
32.4	3.52	21.5	2.35	39	2.30
24.0	3.59	9.4	2.34	−18.0	2.34
22.5	3.60	− 16.0	2.31	+ 3.0	2.37
25.9	3.32	28.0	2.29	25.0	2.42
26.1	3.24	79.0	2.24	25.5	2.53
26.0	3.08	120	2.21	26.6	2.90
25.8	2.60	160	2.20	27.3	3.54
25.7	2.50	−178	2.20	+30.2	3.53
+25.4	2.45	—	—	—	—

n-DOCOSYL BROMIDE $C_{20}H_{41}Br$

Dielectric constant: HOFFMAN and SMYTH (1950)

t°	ε	t°	ε	t°	ε
+55.2	3.12	+30.3	2.85	+14.0	2.25
39.8	3.20	30.3	2.70	25.3	2.27
39.5	3.10	30.0	2.40	29.1	2.30
39.3	3.02	29.9	2.38	40.6	2.30
38.5	2.92	27.4	2.27	41.4	2.35
36.5	2.91	23.0	2.26	42.1	2.50
34.4	2.90	20.7	2.26	42.7	2.85
32.9	2.90	+14.0	2.25	42.7	3.20
+30.9	2.88	—	—	+60.2	3.10

F. HALOGENATED DERIVATIVES
OF UNSATURATED ALIPHATIC HYDROCARBONS

VINYL CHLORIDE C_2H_3Cl

Saturated vapour pressure: DREISBACH and SHRADER (1949)

t°	p mm	
−13.70	760	
−23.35	507.50	
−33.51	315.52	

1,2-DICHLOROETHYLENE $C_2H_2Cl_2$

Melting temp. cis: $-81.510°$ JOHNSEN and FITZPATRICK (1951)

trans: $-49.585°$ *ibid.*

VINYLIDENE FLUORIDE or

1,1-DIFLUOROETHYLENE $C_2H_2F_2$

MEARS, STAHL, ORFEO, SHAIR, KELLS, THOMPSON and McCANN (1955)

Cr. temperature: 30.1°

Cr. pressure: 43.76 atm

Cr. density: 0.417

Saturated vapour pressure: see authors.

VINYLIDENE CHLORIDE or

1,1-DICHLOROETHYLENE $C_2H_2Cl_2$

Saturated vapour pressure: HILDENBRAND, McDONALD *et al.* (1959)

$t°$	p mm	$t°$	p mm	$t°$	p mm
-28.36	50.95	$+13.75$	389.38	$+31.73$	764.95
-17.72	91.54	30.39	729.37	32.50	784.76
-2.96	189.61	31.56	760.00	—	—

Specific heat: McDONALD, HILDENBRAND *et al.* (1953)

$t°$	c_p	$t°$	c_p	$t°$	c_p
0	0	327	22.44	827	26.91
25.00	16.02	427	23.69	927	27.44
27.00	16.08	527	24.71	1027	27.90
127	18.80	627	25.57	1127	28.29
227	20.86	727	26.29	1227	28.64

For *Specific heat* (continued) see p. 236

Specific heat: HILDENBRAND, McDONALD, KRAMER and STULL (1959)

$t°$	c_p	$t°$	c_p	$t°$	c_p	$t°$	c_p
		Series I				Series II	
−260.49	1.043	−115.68	24.18	−260.35	1.105	−115.79	24.17
258.33	1.601	109.42	24.07	258.26	1.687	109.90	24.19
256.39	2.196	103.68	24.08	256.38	2.172	104.04	24.05
254.46	2.768	97.95	24.08	252.26	3.432	98.19	24.12
252.31	3.420	92.26	24.12	249.47	4.186	92.37	24.17
249.62	4.206	86.60	24.15	246.56	4.948	86.59	24.20
246.68	4.923	80.96	24.21	243.48	5.744	80.83	24.16
243.56	5.708	75.35	24.23	239.94	6.522	75.09	24.29
239.98	6.560	69.76	24.24	235.91	7.400	69.38	24.30
235.77	7.387	64.21	24.42	231.66	8.082	63.71	24.50
231.35	8.097	58.69	24.45	227.12	8.746	58.08	24.52
226.80	8.812	53.20	24.53	222.52	9.275	52.27	24.59
222.18	9.285	− 47.73	24.65	217.77	9.790	46.88	24.65
217.39	9.734			212.84	10.259	41.23	24.74
211.97	10.315			208.23	10.700	35.81	25.04
206.46	10.805			203.85	10.959	24.91	25.07
201.26	11.164			198.94	11.341	19.47	25.15
196.01	11.492			193.52	11.726	14.06	25.24
190.71	11.953			188.34	12.120	8.63	25.44
185.62	12.309			183.36	12.467	− 3.30	25.58
180.72	12.645			178.53	12.779	+ 2.00	25.74
175.96	12.907			173.83	13.014	7.28	25.86
171.33	13.186			169.25	13.262	12.52	26.09
166.82	13.485			164.75	13.352	17.71	26.33
162.43	14.032			160.36	13.869		
158.19	14.563			156.11	14.602		
154.04	14.780			151.99	14.926		
149.98	15.216			146.90	15.463		
146.00	15.457			140.92	16.072		
141.47	15.984			134.09	16.589		
136.42	16.524			−129.44	17.373		
131.49	17.072						
−126.73	18.153						

1,2-DIIODOETHYLENE *(cis)* $C_2H_2I_2$

Freezing point: -13 R. M. NOYES, W. A. NOYES and STEINMETZ (1950)

Saturated vapour pressure: R. M. NOYES, W. A. NOYES and STEINMETZ (1950)

t°	p mm	t°	p mm	t°	p mm
+48.24	4.2	+85.44	24.4	+119.74	99.9
41.04	4.7	88.54	25.5	132.34	147
44.04	6.6	94.04	33.0	132.84	148.5
61.34	6.9	98.64	44.4	136.84	175.6
69.54	11.0	105.44	52.3	144.84	214
74.24	16.1	111.84	70.3	151.84	286

1,2-DIIODOETHYLENE *(trans)* $C_2H_2I_2$

Melting point: $+73$ R. M. NOYES, W. A. NOYES and STEINMETZ (1950)

Saturated vapour pressure: R. M. NOYES, W. A. NOYES and STEINMETZ (1950)

t°	p mm	t°	p mm	t°	p mm
+77.24	20.8	+105.94	62.9	+118.54	94.6
99.64	32.9	112.44	76.9	130.04	136.5
102.04	52.7	—	—	—	—

TRICHLOROETHYLENE C_2HCl_3

MUMFORD and PHILLIPS (1950)

Boiling point: 86.9

Density: $d^{20°} = 1.4642$

Refractive index: $n_D^{20°} = 1.4775$

Viscosity and Surface tension

t°	$\eta \cdot 10^5$	γ	
20	566	29.5	
25	532	28.5	

1,1-DIFLUORO-2-CHLOROETHYLENE C_2HF_2Cl

MEARS, STAHL, ORFEO, SHAIR, KELLS, THOMPSON and McCANN (1955)

Critical constants

Temperature: 127.4°

Pressure: 44.03 atm

Density: 0.499

Saturated vapour pressure: see authors.

TRIFLUOROCHLOROETHYLENE C_2F_3Cl

OLIVER, GRISARD and CUNNINGHAM (1951)

Critical constants

Temperature: 105.8°

Density: 0.55

Pressure: 40.1 atm

Saturated vapour pressure

t°	p mm	t°	p mm	t°	p mm
−66.82	97.24	−33.12	614.50	−23.05	953.71
−52.46	231.17	−30.29	698.40	−19.00	1126.4
−44.57	352.35	−28.36	760.62	−15.61	1287.3
−40.74	427.87	−26.47	825.21	−10.87	1540.7
−36.97	513.42	—	—	—	—

Melting point: −158.16

Specific heat

$t°$	c_p	$t°$	c_p	$t°$	c_p	$t°$	c_p
Crystals				Liquid			
−257.16	3.09	−208.16	12.38	−158.16	27.15	−93.16	27.39
255.16	3.76	203.16	12.89	153.16	27.11	83.16	27.61
253.16	4.38	198.16	13.41	143.16	27.03	73.16	27.87
248.16	5.84	193.16	13.92	133.16	26.97	53.16	28.47
243.16	7.11	188.16	14.43	123.16	26.98	33.16	29.11
238.16	8.18	183.16	14.94	113.16	27.09	−28.36	29.26
233.16	9.10	178.16	15.45	−103.16	27.23		
228.16	9.88	173.16	15.95				
223.16	10.57	163.16	16.97				
218.16	11.23	−158.16	17.48				
−213.16	11.83						

Heat of melting: 1327.1 cal/mol

Heat of vaporization: 4965 cal/mol

PERFLUOROPROPENE C_3F_6

Saturated vapour pressure: WHIPPLE (1952)

$t°$	p mm	$t°$	p mm	$t°$	p mm
− 40.70	463	− 24.83	963	+ 1.95	2771
37.20	552	15.87	1403	7.00	3293
35.56	597	8.30	1889	12.10	3867
− 30.11	769	− 3.30	2273	+ 19.75	4896

G. HALOGENATED DERIVATIVES OF THE AROMATIC SERIES

FLUOROBENZENE C_6H_5F

Critical constants

Temperature: 286.55° YOUNG (1910)

286.95° AMBROSE, COX and TOWNSEND (1960)

286.92° DOUSLIN, MOORE et al. (1958)

Pressure: 44.910 atm DOUSLIN, MOORE et al. (1958)

Volume (l/mol) 0.2714 YOUNG (1910)

0.2688 DOUSLIN, MOORE et al. (1958)

Saturated vapour pressure: DOUSLIN, MOORE *et al.* (1954)

t°	P atm	t°	P atm	t°	P atm
84.734	1.000	200.000	13.122	286.500	44.659
96.497	1.414	225.000	19.412	286.600	44.723
108.431	1.959	250.000	27.728	286.700	44.786
120.538	2.666	275.000	38.563	286.800	44.839
135.000	3.753	275.000	38.573	286.900	44.894
150.000	5.197	285.000	43.804	286.920	44.910
175.000	8.489	286.000	44.375	—	—

Orthobaric densities

t°	d_L	d_V	d_L	d_V
	DOUSLIN *et al.* (1958)		YOUNG (1910)	
150	0.8544	—	0.8519	—
175	0.8150	—	0.8122	—
200	0.7698	—	0.7671	—
225	0.7159	—	0.7160	—
250	0.6541	0.1013	0.6504	0.1008
275	0.5539	0.1725	0.5470	0.1750

N.B. (p. 281): Instead of MORRE and HOBBS (1949), write MOORE and HOBBS (1949).

Second virial coefficient: see SCOTT, McCULLOUGH *et al.* (1956)

Boiling point: 84.734 SCOTT, McCULLOUGH (1956)
                 DOUSLIN, MOORE *et al.* (1958)

Dielectric constant: PHILIPPE and PIETTE (1955)

t°	ε	t°	ε	
+16.50	6.420	−65.1	2.766	
+ 6.15	6.563	46.5	3.116	
−14.9	6.939	42.2	3.387	
29.6	7.244	25.3	7.148	
36.0	7.384	17.7	6.996	
40.1	7.477	5.1	6.757	
43.1	7.544	+ 6.45	6.559	
55.2	2.919	16.35	6.420	
65.0	2.767	24.75	6.311	
−74.9	2.663	—	—	

ε 20° : 5.4667 MECKE and KLINGENBERG (1962)

CHLOROBENZENE C_6H_5Cl

Saturated vapour pressure: BROWN (1952)

t°	p mm	t°	p mm	t°	p mm
62.04	72.43	98.79	284.73	123.39	606.63
62.06	72.48	103.18	328.29	126.18	652.69
66.38	86.69	106.25	361.75	128.45	695.11
74.13	117.91	110.35	410.99	130.37	732.69
81.60	156.48	114.48	465.85	131.40	753.43
89.06	204.36	115.89	485.69	131.70	749.55
94.04	242.84	117.94	515.85	131.73	760.28
94.47	246.45	121.10	565.34	—	—

Boiling point: 131.72 BROWN (1952)

Density: 20°: 1.1065 MUMFORD and PHILLIPS (1950)
25°: 1.1013 MUMFORD and PHILLIPS (1950)
25°: 1.10112 BROWN (1952)

NYVLT and ERDOS (1961)

t°	d
20	1.10654
25	1.10118
30	1.09574
35	1.09038
40	1.08484

Viscosity: MUMFORD and PHILLIPS (1950)

t°	$\eta \cdot 10^5$
20	801
25	756

Surface tension: MUMFORD and PHILLIPS (1950)

t°	γ
20	33.25
25	32.65

Refractive index

t°	n_D	
20	1.5246	MUMFORD and PHILLIPS (1950)
25	1.5219	BROWN (1952)

Dielectric constant: PHILIPPE and PIETTE (1955)

t°	ε	t°	ε	
+ 30.00	5.447	−124.0	2.638	
+ 20.00	5.641	161.0	2.630	
− 4.5	6.081	54.5	2.705	
23.5	6.456	52.5	2.728	
42.0	6.856	50.0	2.793	
55.5	7.173	47.0	3.312	
58.5	2.685	46.0	4.330	
72.0	2.672	45.5	6.789	
97.0	2.643	− 12.5	6.239	

Heat of combustion: 742.45 kcal/mol HUBBARD, KNOWLTON and HUFFMAN (1954)

BROMOBENZENE C_6H_5Br

Saturated vapour pressure: DREISBACH and SHRADER (1949)

t°	p mm	t°	p mm	
156.06	760	83.99	75.86	
140.69	507.50	80.08	66.39	
124.47	315.52	76.39	57.04	
96.32	123.76	71.76	47.16	

DREYER, MARTIN and VON WEBER (1954–55)

t°	p mm	t°	p mm	t°	p mm
154.24	725.2	115.59	239.1	88.53	92.5
151.95	682.9	109.50	195.9	85.55	82.4
149.51	640.8	105.00	168.2	81.90	71.6
144.73	566.5	101.26	147.8	78.25	61.6
139.94	496.0	99.41	138.5	74.88	53.4
135.48	437.1	97.09	127.0	69.70	42.8
129.61	368.7	93.49	111.3	63.52	33.0
122.79	299.8	90.82	100.7	56.07	23.0

Boiling point: 156.06 DREISBACH and MARTIN (1949)

Freezing point: −30.82 *ibid.*

Density: (ibid.)

t°	d		
20	1.49500		
25	1.48824		

Refractive index: (ibid.)

t°	n_D		
20	1.55972		
25	1.55709		

IODOBENZENE C_6H_5I

Refractive index: JOSHI and DAS TULI (1951)

t°	n_D	t°	n_D	t°	n_D	t°	n_D
20	1.5714	50	1.5582	65	1.5515	75	1.5468
30	1.5669	55	1.5561	70	1.5492	80	1.5446
40	1.5625	60	1.5537	—	—	—	—

Dielectric constant: PHILIPPE and PIETTE (1955)

t°	ε	t°	ε	
− 0.2	4.556	−65.0	3.085	
10.8	4.593	45.2	3.156	
29.9	4.663	35.1	3.192	
32.4	4.673	31.7	3.213	
45.0	3.155	29.6	4.662	
47.7	3.146	20.0	4.628	
54.5	3.120	+ 9.90	4.521	
60.5	3.101	19.85	4.486	
−75.0	3.050	—	—	

Vapour pressure equations of many fluoro derivatives of toluene, see POTTER and SAYLOR (1951)

Ortho-DICHLOROBENZENE $C_6H_4Cl_2$

Saturated vapour pressure: DREISBACH and SHRADER (1949)

t°	p mm	t°	p mm	
180.48	760	104.94	75.86	
164.65	507.50	97.66	57.04	
147.64	315.52	87.02	37.58	
118.32	123.76	—	—	

Boiling point: 180.48 DREISBACH and MARTIN (1949)

Freezing point: −17.03 DREISBACH and MARTIN (1949)
  −17.02 WITSCHONKE (1954)

Density

t°	d	
20	1.30589	DREISBACH and MARTIN (1949)
25	1.30033	,,

Refractive index

t°	n_D	
20	1 55145	DREISBACH and MARTIN (1949)
25	1.54911	,,
20	1.5505	JOSHI and DAS TULI (1951)
30	1.5461	,,
40	1.5416	,,
50	1.5370	,,
60	1.5324	,,
70	1.5278	,,

Heat of combustion: 706.83 kcal/mol HUBBARD, KNOWLTON and HUFFMAN (1954)

Meta-DICHLOROBENZENE $C_6H_4Cl_2$

Saturated vapour pressure: Dreisbach and Shrader (1949)

$t°$	p mm	$t°$	p mm	
173.00	760	111.49	123.76	
157.37	507.50	98.05	75.86	
140.49	315.52	90.72	57.04	

Boiling point: 173.00 Dreisbach and Martin (1949)

Freezing point: −24.76 *ibid.*

Density (ibid.)

$t°$	d	
20	1.28844	
25	1.28280	

Refractive index (ibid.)

$t°$	n_D	
20	1.54586	
25	1.54337	

Para-DIBROMOBENZENE $C_6H_4Br_2$

Boiling point: 220.40 Dreisbach and Martin (1949)

Melting point: +87.31

Other HALOGEN DERIVATIVES of BENZENE, see: Dreisbach and Shrader (1949) and Dreisbach and Martin (1949)

HEXACHLOROBENZENE C_6Cl_6

HILDENBRAND, KRAMER and STULL (1958)

Melting point: 228.49

Specific heat

$t°$	c_p	$t°$	c_p	$t°$	c_p
−255.15	2.63	−193.15	20.65	−83.15	37.69
238.15	4.53	188.15	21.69	73.15	38.84
248.15	6.34	183.15	22.70	63.15	39.93
243.15	8.03	178.15	23.68	53.15	40.99
238.15	9.56	173.15	24.62	43.15	42.02
233.15	11.00	163.15	26.41	33.15	43.01
228.15	12.36	153.15	28.10	23.15	43.96
223.15	13.65	143.15	29.69	13.15	44.89
218.15	14.90	133.15	31.19	− 3.15	45.78
213.15	16.12	123.15	32.61	+ 6.85	46.65
208.15	17.30	113.15	33.97	16.85	47.48
203.15	18.46	103.15	35.27	25.00	48.11
−198.15	19.57	− 93.15	36.50	+26.85	48.29

BENZYL CHLORIDE C_7H_7Cl

MUMFORD and PHILLIPS (1950)

Density		Viscosity		Surface tension	
$t°$	d	$t°$	$\eta \cdot 10^5$	$t°$	γ
20	1.0993	20	1400	20	37.65
25	1.0945	25	1290	25	36.95

Refractive index: $n_D^{20°} = 1.5391$

α-BROMONAPHTHALENE $C_{10}H_7Br$

Dielectric constant: PHILIPPE and PIETTE (1955)

t°	ε	t°	ε	
Cr.+24.00	5.070	−27.1	2.802	
9.05	5.259	18.0	2.816	
5.95	5.305	− 9.7	2.829	
− 3.0	2.840	+ 3.05	2.852	
37.1	2.788	5.90	2.903	
48.0	2.773	L. 14.45	5.186	
74.4	2.744	20.10	5.115	
−60.2	2.759	+27.15	5.035	

H. HALOGEN DERIVATIVES OF THE CYCLOPARAFFINS

PERFLUOROCYCLOBUTANE C_4F_8

Critical temperature: 115.22° DOUSLIN, MOORE and WADDINGTON (1959)

Critical pressure: 27.412 atm. *ibid.*

Saturated vapour pressure

t°	p mm	t°	p mm	t°	p mm	
Series I		− 42.35	125.7	Series III		
		40.25	142.4			FURUKAWA, McCOSKEY
− 5.27	782.6	40.00	144.6	− 95.80	4.9	and REILLY (1954)
− 2.21	886.2	31.84	226.3	81.34	8.2	
+ 0.47	984.8	26.17	303.3	76.30	10.9	,,
Series II		20.15	406.5	75.99	11.0	,,
		13.65	547.3	66.46	21.7	,,
− 94.00	5.0	9.28	661.9	60.07	35.9	,,
81.22	8.2	− 6.51	743.7	51.56	67.7	,,
71.93	14.7			− 1.22	921.4	,,
57.86	43.4					,,
− 49.56	77.7					
−36.2	193	−19.2	441	− 5.10	801	WHIPPLE (1952)
33.8	219	15.6	519	− 1.05	947	,,
30.0	254	14.3	548	+17.25	1822	,,
26.85	303	10.74	636	+17.70	1868	,,
−25.7	326	− 8.03	714			,,

t°	P atm	t°	P atm	t°	P atm	
− 5.99	1.000	100.00	20.270	115.10	27.347	DOUSLIN, MOORE and WADDINGTON
+30.00	3.607	114.50	27.023	115.20	27.400	,, (1959)
50.00	6.394	114.90	27.238	115.22	27.412	,,
75.00	11.852	115.00	27.294	—	—	,,

Orthobaric densities: DOUSLE, MOORE and WADDINGTON (1959)

t°	d		
	L	V	
30.00	1.4506	—	
50.00	1.3777	—	
75.00	1.2487	—	
100.00	1.0501	0.2382	
115.00	0.7094	0.5490	
115.22	0.6159	0.6159	

Melting point: −40.2180 FURUKAWA, McCOSKEY and REILLY (1954)

Transition points: −131.86; −98.6; −58.32; −56.17 FURUKAWA, McCOSKEY and REILLY (1954)

Heat of melting at −40.20°: 0.6613 kcal/mol *ibid.*

Heat of vaporization at −11.91°: 5.667 kcal/mol *ibid.*

PERFLUOROCYCLOPENTANE C_5F_{10}

Melting point: +10.3 BURGER and CADY (1951)

Transition points I: −154.9 *II:* −157.66 BURGER and CADY (1951)

Density: BURGER and CADY (1951)

t°	d	t°	d	t°	d
22.51	1.6370	17.73	1.6523	13.70	1.6649
21.96	1.6388	16.70	1.6556	12.23	1.6697
21.17	1.6413	15.80	1.6583	11.56	1.6715
20.55	1.6436	15.80	1.6586	11.17	1.6731
18.92	1.6486	14.62	1.6622	10.75	1.6744
18.78	1.6490	14.36	1.6630	10.56	1.6749
18.68	1.6495	13.71	1.6652	—	—

Viscosity: BURGER and CADY (1951)

$t°$	$\eta \cdot 10^5$	$t°$	$\eta \cdot 10^5$	$t°$	$\eta \cdot 10^5$
21.55	748.9	15.84	827.4	12.05	885.7
20.05	767.0	12.56	875.8	10.36	913.9

1,2-DIBROMOCYCLOHEXANE $\quad$ $C_6H_{10}Br_2$

BJELLERUP (1961)
Density

$t°$	d
20	1.7903
25	1.7833

Refractive index

$t°$	Na_D	H_C	H_β
20	1.5529	1.5492	1.5620
25	1.5506	1.5469	1.5598

Heat of combustion at 25° : 867.54 kcal/mol

PERFLUOROCYCLOHEXANE $\quad$ C_6F_{12}

Saturated vapour pressure: ROWLINSON and THACKER (1957)

$t°$	p mm	$t°$	p mm
19.81	169.32	63.16	1139.7
20.61	176.30	65.00	1207.0
25.25	221.74	70.00	1405.8
30.00	278.88	74.00	1579.5
40.00	440.04	109.0	4025
50.00	675.81	121.3	5320
60.00	1014.00	—	—

PERFLUOROMETHYLCYCLOHEXANE　　　　C_7F_{14}

Critical temperature: 213.6° ROWLINSON and THACKER (1957)

Critical pressure: 23 atm. ROWLINSON and THACKER (1957)

Saturated vapour pressure: ROWLINSON and THACKER (1957)

$t°$	p mm	$t°$	p mm	
25.25	107.05	60.00	440.22	
30.00	132.96	70.00	620.18	
40.00	205.58	80.00	851.03	
50.00	304.48	—	—	

Boiling point: 76.3 ROWLINSON and THACKER (1957)

Triple point: −39.0 ROWLINSON and THACKER (1957)

Density at 25°: 1.7870 ROWLINSON and THACKER (1957)

3. OXYGENATED DERIVATIVES OF THE
ALIPHATIC SERIES

A. ALCOHOLS

METHYL ALCOHOL   CH$_4$O

N.B. (p. 302): For the *Cr. P.*: write 59660 instead of 29660.

Saturated vapour pressure: DEVER, FINCH and GRUNWALD (1955)

t°	p mm	t°	p mm	t°	p mm	t°	p mm
13.88	69.92	19.41	94.62	24.84	126.1	29.84	162.8
14.60	72.81	19.83	97.65	25.13	127.9	30.57	169.0
15.37	75.81	20.34	99.56	25.54	130.6	30.77	170.1
15.70	77.29	20.91	102.7	26.11	134.5	31.32	175.3
16.34	80.25	21.41	105.3	26.34	136.0	31.64	178.0
16.73	81.93	21.84	107.7	27.09	141.7	32.09	182.1
17.27	84.36	22.36	110.8	27.27	143.0	32.61	186.7
17.78	86.64	22.75	112.9	28.22	150.4	33.45	194.6
18.28	89.00	23.84	119.8	28.52	152.1	34.11	200.9
18.83	91.73	24.14	121.5	29.07	156.6	—	—

t°	p mm	
21	102.735	COLMANT (1954)
20	97.35	,,
19	92.22	,,
18	87.32	,,

t°	p mm	t°	p mm	
11.9	62.2	37.60	234.9	KLYUEVA, MISHCHENKO and FEDOROV
14.69	72.6	39.76	259.6	,, (1960)
17.72	85.8	42.69	297.9	,,
22.06	108.1	45.39	337.4	,,
24.93	126.3	48.53	386.7	,,
30.15	164.8	50.21	413.3	,,
34.59	204.0			

Boiling point: 64.65 COLMANT (1954)

Freezing point: −97.8 GARRETT and WOODRUFF (1951)

Critical solution point: (with CS_2) 34.95 DE BROUCKERE and GILLET (1935)

                      (with C_6H_{12}) 46.20 DE BROUCKERE and GILLET (1935)

Constants of state

Compressibility of the vapour: FOZ, MORCILIO *et al.* (1954)

Density of the liquid

t°	d	
15	0.79609	PARIAUD (1951)
18	0.7932	GREEN and VENER (1955)
20	0.7913	HAMMOND, HOWARD and Mc ALLISTER (1958)
20	0.79141	DAVIDSON (1957)
20	0.7916	COLMANT (1954)
25	0.78653	KRETSCHMER and WIEBE (1954)

Compressibility at $0°$: $\beta_0 = 108.3 \cdot 10^{-6}$ MCKINNEY, SKINNER and STAVELEY (1959)

Viscosity at $20°$: $\eta \cdot 10^5 = 592$ COLMANT (1954)

Surface tension: KOEFOED and VILLADSEN (1958)

t°	γ	
25.0	22.28	

Refractive index

t°	n_D	
18	1.32941	GREEN and VENER (1955)
20	1.3287	COLMANT (1954)
20	1.3287	GARRETT and WOODRUFF (1951)

Dielectric constant: DAVIDSON (1957)

t°	ε	t°	ε	t°	ε
−96.56	73.08	−68.56	59.85	−13.16	40.85
92.46	70.91	60.86	56.51	11.16	40.48
91.16	70.52	50.06	52.50	+ 1.04	37.68
82.26	65.64	40.46	49.19	+ 6.34	36.45
−79.66	65.10	−22.56	43.52	+21.04	33.42

Magnetic susceptibility at $20°$: $- 0.664 \cdot 10^{-6}$ VON RAUTENFELD, STEURER (1942)

METHANOL D   CH₃OD

Density at 20°: 0.81252 DAVIDSON (1957)

Dielectric constant: DAVIDSON (1957)

$t°$	ε	$t°$	ε	$t°$	ε	$t°$	ε
−98.86	70.99	−83.06	65.23	−46.16	50.24	+ 0.44	36.41
96.86	72.73	76.16	62.00	35.16	46.28	5.24	35.44
94.66	71.31	67.46	57.93	20.66	42.16	12.64	33.89
92.36	70.15	63.46	56.81	7.86	38.49	+24.34	31.68
−88.86	68.21	−55.26	53.86	− 0.06	36.59	—	—

ETHYL ALCOHOL   C₂H₆O

Saturated vapour pressure: 43.63 mm at 20° HUET, PHILIPPE and BONO (1953)
         173.09 mm at 45° BROWN and EWALD (1951)
         438.42 mm at 65°

Boiling point: 78.30 BROWN and EWALD (1951)
     78.30 HUET, PHILIPPE and BONO (1953)
     78.30 GRIFFITHS (1952)
     78.32 JONES, SCHOENBORN and BONNER (1942)

Orthobaric densities: COSTELLO and BOWDEN (1958)

$t°$	d		
	L	**V**	
0	0.8063	0.0000	
20	0.7894	0.0001	
40	0.7722	0.0003	
60	0.7541	0.0008	
80	0.7348	0.0017	
100	0.7157	0.0035	
120	0.6925	0.0066	
140	0.6631	0.0115	
160	0.6329	0.0192	
180	0.5984	0.0312	
200	0.5568	0.0508	

Density

$t°$	d	
0	0.80624	JONES, SCHOENBORN and COLBURN (1942)
20	0.7893	JONES, SCHENTOWN and COLLIN (1943)
25	0.78508	GRIFFITHS (1952)
25	0.78511	BROWN and EWALD (1951)

Compressibility at 0° : $\beta_0 = 100.0 \cdot 10^{-6}$ McKINNEY, SKINNER and STAVELEY (1959)

Refractive index

t°	n_D	
9.87	1.36536	SMITH and BONNER (1952)
14.74	1.36342	,,
19.97	1.36126	,,
25.00	1.35929	,,
29.95	1.35729	,,
25	1.35929	BROWN and FOCH (1955)
25	1.3596	BROWN and EWALD (1951)

Magnetic susceptibility at 20°: $- 0.734 \cdot 10^{-6}$ VON RAUTENFELD and STEURER (1942)

n-PROPYL ALCOHOL C_3H_8O

(See also Addenda, p. 438)

Orthobaric densities: COSTELLO and BOWDEN (1958)

t°	d		
	L	V	
0	0.8193	0.0000	
20	0.8035	0.0001	
40	0.7875	0.0002	
60	0.7700	0.0004	
80	0.7520	0.0010	
100	0.7325	0.0023	
120	0.7110	0.0044	
140	0.6875	0.0081	
160	0.6600	0.0138	
180	0.6285	0.0225	
200	0.5920	0.0353	
220	0.5485	0.0556	

Saturated vapour pressure: MATHEWS and McKETTA (1961)

t°	p mm	
70.74	252.2	
86.84	505.2	
97.14	758.0	
104.94	1010.4	
111.34	1262.2	

Second virial coefficient: Cox (1961)

t°	p mm	$-B_p$	
105.0	347–508	913	
120.0	372–560	781	
135.0	375–544	669	
150.0	407–623	606	

Viscosity: KHALIBOV (1944)

t°	$\eta \cdot 10^5$	.
20	2237	
40	1391	
60	881.6	
80	631.5	
90	535.5	

Magnetic susceptibility at 20° : $-0.755 \cdot 10^{-6}$ VON RAUTENFELD, STEURER (1942)

Iso-PROPYL ALCOHOL C_3H_8O

(See also Addenda, p. 439)

Second virial coefficient: Cox (1961)

p mm	t°	$-B_p$	
357–605	105.0	867	
381–755	120.0	700	
382–624	135.0	599	
403–523	150.0	529	

Saturated vapour pressure: FOZ, MORCILIO et al. (1954)

t°	p mm	t°	p mm	t°	p mm
81.61	742.4	95.24	1250.9	122.71	3087.3
84.85	843.2	97.53	1357.9	130.46	3871.4
86.96	916.8	99.04	1430.9	136.93	4647.2
89.07	994.9	100.55	1507.9	142.64	5299.5
91.79	1102.4	100.94	1536.8	147.63	6198.7
93.50	1174.4	113.33	2312.1	—	—

Density

t°	d	
25	0.78083	Kretschmer and Wiebe (1954)
25	0.78091	Starobinetz G. L. and K. C. (1954)
55	0.7532	,,

Surface tension: Starobinetz G. L. and K. C. (1951)

t°	γ	
55	19.05	

Dielectric constant: Starobinetz G. L. and K. C. (1951)

t°	ε	
55	14.330	

Heat of combustion at 25°: -479.23 cal/mol Parks, Manchester and Vaughan (1954)

n-BUTYL ALCOHOL $\quad$ $C_4H_{10}O$

(See also Addenda, p. 440)

Critical constants: Singh and Shemilt (1955)

Temperature: 286.95°

Pressure: 48.60 atm

Density: 0.2700

Orthobaric densities: Singh and Shemilt (1955)

t°	d_V	d_L	
155.8	0.0079	0.70520	
173.3	0.012494	0.67059	
183.6	0.01587	0.62478	
198.9	0.02106	0.61920	
212.0	0.02775	0.59305	
232.4	0.04280	—	
237.3	—	0.5359	
244.6	0.05516	0.51993	
260.6	0.07733	0.48589	
268.9	0.09480	0.45740	
272.25	0.1023	0.43200	
276.45	0.1300	0.42370	
283.94	0.1681	0.3620	
285.72	0.2402	0.3620	

Second virial coefficient: Cox (1961)

p mm	t°	$-B_p$	
411–496	120.0	1086	
462–557	135.0	929	
417–558	150.0	790	
412–534	166.0	634	

Boiling point: 117.4 Teitelbaum, Gortalova and Sidorova (1951)
117.9 Mumford and Phillips (1950)

Density at 20°: 0.8097 Pariaud (1951)
0°: 0.82461 McKinney, Skinner and Staveley (1959)

Compressibility at 0°: $\beta_0 = 82.03 \cdot 10^{-6}$ McKinney and Staveley (1959)

Surface tension: Teitelbaum, Gortalova and Sidorova (1951)

t°	γ	
15	24.90	
20	24.52	
25	23.98	
30	23.51	

Heat of combustion (liquid) at 25°: 639.31 kcal/mol Skinner and Snelson (1960)

Iso-BUTYL ALCOHOL $\quad$ C$_4$H$_{10}$O

(See also Addenda, p. 441)

Orthobaric densities: Costello and Bowden (1958)

t°	d_L	d_V	t°	d_L	d_V
−60	0.8613	—	60	0.7692	0.0006
−40	0.8464	—	80	0.7510	0.0010
−20	0.8314	—	100	0.7313	0.0018
0	0.8167	—	120	0.7115	0.0032
+20	0.8021	0.0002	140	0.6890	0.0056
40	0.7858	0.0003	160	0.6643	0.0100

Second virial coefficient: Cox (1961)

p mm	t°	$-B_p$	
405–490	120.0	1070	
525	135.0	930	
565	150.0	811	
420–520	166.0	642	

Density: 20°: 0.8021 TEITELBAUM *et al.* (1957)

       55°: 0.7726 STAROBINETZ G. L. and K. C. (1951)

Surface tension: at 55°: 20.20 STAROBINETZ G. L. and K. C. (1951)

t°	γ	
15	23.08	TEITELBAUM *et al.* (1951)
20	22.73	
30	22.04	

Dielectric constant: at 55°: 13.177 STAROBINETZ G. L. and K. C. (1951)

Heat of combustion: 19.11 cal/gr STAROBINETZ G. L. and K. C. (1951)

Heat of combustion (liquid) at 25°: 637.79 cal/mol SKINNER and SNELSON (1960)

<h3 align="center">Sec.-BUTYL ALCOHOL $C_4H_{10}O$</h3>

(See also Addenda, p. 442)

Vapour pressure: BERMAN and McKETTA (1962)

t°	p mm	
66.76	189.78	
82.05	379.63	
91.95	568.46	
99.34	754.70	
105.34	937.63	

Latent heat of vaporization (ibid.)

t°	cal/mol	
66.76	10824	
82.05	10350	
91.95	10014	
99.34	9753	

Second virial coefficient: Cox (1961)

p mm	t°	−B_p	
418–482	105.0	1171	
457–529	120.0	999	
420–549	135.0	853	
424–573	150.0	705	

Heat of combustion: 19.56 cal/gr. Teitelbaum *et al.* (1957)

Heat of combustion (liquid) at 25°: 635.91 kcal/mol Skinner and Snelson (1960)

Tert.-BUTYL ALCOHOL $C_4H_{10}O$

(See also Addenda, p. 443)

Orthobaric densities: Costello and Bowden (1958)

t°	d_L	d_V	
40	0.7652	0.0007	
60	0.7429	0.0013	
80	0.7212	0.0024	
100	0.6974	0.0042	
120	0.6715	0.0075	
140	0.6450	0.0159	

Second virial coefficient: Cox (1961)

p mm	t°	−B_p	
400–543	105.0	962	
403–584	120.0	830	
422–548	135.0	673	
421–575	150.0	549	

Boiling point: 82.8 Westwater (1955)

Melting point: 25.5 Costello and Bowden (1958)

25.60 De Vries and Soffer (1951). The sample was dehydrated by calcium hydrate.

Density at 20°: 0.7873 Westwater (1955)

Refractive index: $n_D^{20°} = 1.38695$ Westwater (1955)

N.B. (pp. 324-5) The data of Brown of Smith (1962): 27°: − 0.77838 n_D: 1.38401 do not agree with the former.

Dielectric constant: PHILIPPE and PIETTE (1955)

t°	ε	t°	ε	
+40.00	9.66	− 82.0	2.121	
35.50	10.35	− 149.0	2.103	
30.00	11.23	+ 14.6	2.134	
29.10	11.37	+ 20.6	2.198	
23.90	12.45	+ 23.8	2.403	
13.80	2.127	+ 25.6	2.694	
− 8.0	2.198	+ 25.6	3.287	
−30.0	2.158	L.+ 25.6	6.391	

Heat of combustion (liquid) at 25°: 631.92 kcal/mol SKINNER and SNELSON (1960)

n-AMYL ALCOHOL $C_5H_{12}O$

Orthobaric densities: COSTELLO and BOWDEN (1958)

t°	d_L	d_V	
−60	0.8730	—	
−40	0.8581	—	
−20	0.8430	—	
0	0.8278	—	
+20	0.8133	0.0001	
40	0.7981	0.0001	
60	0.7834	0.0004	
80	0.7680	0.0006	
100	0.7515	0.0010	
120	0.7356	0.0016	
140	0.7184	0.0028	
160	0.6983	0.0047	
180	0.6754	0.0077	

Boiling point: 138.00 *dt/dp (10 mm):* 0.37 SIMON (1929)

Freezing point: −78.5 *ibid.*

Density

t°	d	
0	0.82897	SIMON (1929)
15	0.81837	,,
30	0.80764	,,

Refractive index (ibid.)

t°	He_red	H_α	Na_D	He_γ	He_gr	H_β	He_viol	H_γ
15	1.40980	1.40965	1.41173	1.41185	1.41580	1.41674	1.41990	1.42111
25	1.40573	1.40604	1.40815	1.40820	1.41212	1.41316	1.41621	1.41744

Sec.-AMYL ALCOHOL $C_5H_{12}O$

Costello and Bowden (1958)

Boiling point: 119.0°/758 mm

Orthobaric densities

t°	d_L	d_V	t°	d_L	d_V
−40	0.8549	—	+40	0.7919	0.0003
−20	0.8402	—	60	0.7742	0.0006
0	0.8246	—	80	0.7551	0.0010
+20	0.8089	0.0001	100	0.7304	0.0017

DIMETHYL-ETHYLCARBINOL $C_5H_{12}O$

Dielectric constant: Philippe and Piette (1955)

t°	ε	t°	ε	
+20.00	5.924	− 80.0	2.339	
15.20	6.201	100.5	2.340	
10.50	6.536	146.0	2.187	
− 9.0	2.630	−152.0	2.184	
44.5	2.374	135.0	2.220	
−59.0	2.344	−129.0	2.298	

n-HEXYL ALCOHOL $C_6H_{14}O$

Orthobaric densities: Costello and Bowden (1958)

t°	d_L	d_V	
− 20	0.8503	—	
0	0.8359	—	
+ 20	0.8217	0.0001	
40	0.8076	0.0002	
60	0.7924	0.0003	
80	0.7766	0.0005	
100	0.7599	0.0007	
120	0.7432	0.0012	
140	0.7247	0.0020	
160	0.7056	0.0029	
180	0.6850	0.0048	
200	0.6638	0.0080	
220	0.6406	0.0131	
240	0.6163	0.0207	

Boiling point: 157.5°/761 mm COSTELLO and BOWDEN (1958)

Density at 0°: 0.83284 McKINNEY, SKINNER and STAVELEY (1959)

Compressibility at 0°: $\beta_0 = 75.63 \cdot 10^{-6}$ McKINNEY, SKINNER and STAVELEY (1959)

DIETHYLETHANOL $C_6H_{14}O$

Heat of combustion at 25°: 639.3 cal/mol THE DOW CHEMICAL COMPANY (1956)

DIETHYLMETHYLCARBINOL $C_6H_{14}O$

Dielectric constant: PHILIPPE and PIETTE (1955)

t°	ε	t°	ε	
20.00	4.322	−65.1	2.595	
9.30	4.098	46.1	2.682	
− 9.0	3.741	27.8	2.849	
22.5	3.509	25.2	2.877	
24.3	3.474	−23.9	2.900	
36.2	2.765	+ 0.30	3.915	
54.9	2.627	18.80	4.297 ·	
−75.0	2.580	—	—	

Iso-HEXYL ALCOHOL $C_6H_{14}O$

Orthobaric densities: COSTELLO and BOWDEN (1958)

t°	d_L	d_V	
− 20	0.8593	—	
0	0.8446	—	
+ 20	0.8292	—	
40	0.8142	0.0002	
60	0.7983	0.0003	
80	0.7810	0.0005	
100	0.7632	0.0010	
120	0.7448	0.0015	
140	0.7245	0.0025	
160	0.7040	0.0044	
180	0.6837	0.0070	
200	0.6620	0.0109	
220	0.6380	0.0178	

Boiling point: 146.2°/758 mm COSTELLO and BOWDEN (1958)

n-HEPTYL ALCOHOL $C_7H_{16}O$

The data of BILTERYS (1935), DEFFET (1935) and SHERRILL (1930) do not agree.

TRIETHYLCARBINOL $C_7H_{15}O$

Dielectric constant: PHILIPPE and PIETTE (1955)

$t°$	ε	$t°$	ε	
36.65	3.419	−49.8	2.653	
33.60	3.376	19.7	2.866	
27.40	3.279	14.1	2.925	
23.55	3.217	−12.4	2.922	
+13.10	3.039	+ 5.95	2.912	
− 1.1	2.781	12.00	3.020	
9.6	2.612	16.30	3.093	
14.7	2.504	18.85	3.140	
26.4	2.812	24.85	3.239	
38.1	2.722	33.05	3.369	
61.2	2.601	40.35	3.462	
−74.8	2.553	44.50	3.516	
—	—	48.70	3.562	

n-DECYL ALCOHOL $C_{10}H_{22}O$

Boiling point: 231°/759 mm COSTELLO and BOWDEN (1958)

Orthobaric densities *(ibid.)*

$t°$	d_L	d_V	$t°$	d_L	d_V
20	0.8260	—	160	0.7224	0.0009
40	0.8127	—	180	0.7053	0.0013
60	0.7998	0.0001	200	0.6883	0.0021
80	0.7858	0.0002	220	0.6708	0.0030
100	0.7705	0.0003	240	0.6535	0.0048
120	0.7550	0.0004	260	0.6350	0.0071
140	0.7387	0.0007	280	0.6127	0.0105

n-DODECYL ALCOHOL $C_{12}H_{16}O$

Boiling point: 114°/20 mm COSTELLO and BOWDEN (1958)

Orthobaric densities (ibid.)

t°	d_L	d_V	t°	d_L	d_V
40	0.8196	—	180	0.7144	0.0010
60	0.8057	0.0001	200	0.6982	0.0013
80	0.7920	0.0002	220	0.6810	0.0021
100	0.7774	0.0002	240	0.6635	0.0028
120	0.7622	0.0003	260	0.6457	0.0047
140	0.7468	0.0005	280	0.6275	0.0069
160	0.7307	0.0007	300	0.6097	0.0099

Dielectric constant: PHILIPPE and PIETTE (1955)

t°	ε	t°	ε
42.15	4.928	−62.0	2.709
25.05	5.703	49.0	2.730
22.15	5.861	26.1	2.781
19.65	5.157	− 3.8	2.855
15.30	4.752	+ 8.85	3.139
13.20	4.609	15.00	3.730
3.60	2.965	22.35	5.537
− 6.9	2.839	28.20	5.548
15.5	2.812	34.50	5.252
37.1	2.754	50.05	4.620
−74.2	2.695	—	—

n-TETRADECYL ALCOHOL $C_{14}H_{30}O$

COSTELLO and BOWDEN (1958)

Boiling point: 170°/20 mm

Orthobaric densities

t°	d_L	d_V	t°	d_L	d_V
40	0.8227	—	180	0.7188	0.0009
60	0.8079	0.0001	200	0.7032	0.0015
80	0.7931	0.0002	220	0.6865	0.0022
100	0.7784	0.0003	240	0.6700	0.0032
120	0.7636	0.0004	260	0.6534	0.0047
140	0.7488	0.0005	280	0.6362	0.0064
160	0.7340	0.0006	300	0.6178	0.0102

n-HEXADECYL ALCOHOL $C_{16}H_{34}O$

COSTELLO and BOWDEN (1958)

Orthobaric densities

$t°$	d_L	d_V	
60	0.8105	—	
80	0.7971	—	
100	0.7830	0.0001	
120	0.7684	0.0002	
140	0.7537	0.0003	
160	0.7387	0.0004	
180	0.7233	0.0006	
200	0.7082	0.0008	
220	0.6928	0.0010	
240	0.6770	0.0016	
260	0.6607	0.0023	
280	0.6454	0.0033	
300	0.6288	0.0049	

Boiling point: 190°/20 mm

Melting point: 49.2°

n-OCTADECYL ALCOHOL $C_{18}H_{38}O$

COSTELLO and BOWDEN (1958)

Orthobaric densities

$t°$	d_L	d_V	
80	0.7973	—	
100	0.7839	0.0001	
120	0.7694	0.0001	
140	0.7545	0.0002	
160	0.7398	0.0003	
180	0.7251	0.0005	
200	0.7103	0.0006	
220	0.6956	0.0009	
240	0.6808	0.0012	
260	0.6661	0.0018	
280	0.6498	0.0025	
300	0.6316	0.0035	

Boiling point: 217° (17 mm)

Melting point: 59°

POLYALCOHOLS

ETHYLENE GLYCOL $C_2H_6O_2$

Boiling point: 197.1°/750 mm COSTELLO and BOWDEN (1958)

197.90°/760 mm; *dt/dp (10 mm):* 0.50 CRUTZEN, JOST and SIEG (1957)

Freezing point: −13.0 COSTELLO and BOWDEN (1958)

Density at 20°: 1.11369 CRUTZEN, JOST and SIEG (1957)

Refractive index at 20°: 1.4313 CRUTZEN, JOST and SIEG (1957)

Orthobaric densities

$t°$	d_L	d_V	$t°$	d_L	d_V
0	1.126	—	160	1.007	0.001
20	1.113	—	180	0.9892	0.0013
40	1.100	—	200	0.9708	0.0018
60	1.086	—	220	0.9503	0.0027
80	1.071	—	240	0.9304	0.0041
100	1.056	—	260	0.9103	0.0063
120	1.041	—	280	0.8892	0.0098
140	1.024	0.001	—	—	—

KETELAAR and VAN MEURS (1957) have measured the *density* and *dielectric constant* of 1,2-ETHANEDIOL, 1,3-PROPANEDIOL, 1,4-BUTANEDIOL and 1,5-PENTANEDIOL at 20°, 45° and 70°.

WATSON, COOPE and BARNWELL (1951) have measured n and α of the three 2,3-BUTANEDIOLS.

MANNITOL $C_6H_{14}O_6$.

Specific heat: SPAGHT, THOMAS and PARKS (1932)

$t°$	c_p	$t°$	c_p	$t°$	c_p	$t°$	c_p
30	0.321	80	0.373	130	0.425	170	—
40	0.331	90	0.384	140	0.435	180	0.720
50	0.341	100	0.394	150	0.446	190	0.721
60	0.352	110	0.404	160	0.456	200	0.723
70	0.363	120	0.415	—	—	—	—

ERYTHRITOL $C_6H_{14}O_6$

Specific heat: SPAGHT, THOMAS and PARKS (1932)

$t°$	c_p	$t°$	c_p	$t°$	c_p	$t°$	c_p
30	0.334	70	0.383	100	0.421	130	0.683
40	0.345	80	0.396	110	0.434	140	0.688
50	0.357	90	0.408	120	—	150	0.693
60	0.370	—	—	—	—	—	—

B. ETHERS and ACETALS

DIETHYL ETHER $C_4H_{10}O$

Surface tension at 25.0°: 16.50 dyn/cm KOEFOED and VILLADSEN (1958)

Magnetic susceptibility at 20°: $-0.758 \cdot 10^{-6}$ VON RAUTENFELD and STEURER (1942)

MUMFORD and PHILLIPS (1950) as well as JUREK, HUBIK and VECERA (1960) measured the *refractive index* of many other mixed ETHERS

DI-*n*-BUTYL ETHER $C_8H_{18}O$

Dielectric constant: $\varepsilon^{20°} = 3.0922$ MECKE and KLINGENBERG (1961)

DI-*tert.*-BUTYL ETHER $C_8H_{18}O$

SMUTNY and BONDI (1961)

Saturated vapour pressure

$t°$	p mm	$t°$	p mm	
4.0	9.8	30.0	42.3	
14.0	18.4	34.0	50.8	
18.0	22.4	38.0	59.2	
22.0	28.3	109.0	760.0	
26.0	34.5	—	—	

Density at 20°: 0.7622

Refractive index $n_D^{20°}$: 1.3946

Viscosity

$t°$	$\eta \cdot 10^5$	
−53.9	6370	
−40.0	4109	
+20.0	1068	
+50.0	722	
+60.0	636	
+98.9	427	

Heat of combustion (at constant volume) at 25°: 1268.7 kcal/mol

METHYL-*tert*.-BUTYL ETHER $C_5H_{12}O$

Smutny and Bondi (1961)

Density at 20° : 0.7418

Viscosity

$t°$	$\eta \cdot 10^5$	
−53.9	1332	
−40	1028	
+20	471	
+50	367	

Heat of combustion (at constant volume) at 25°: 801.5 kcal/mol

Iso-PROPYL-*tert*.-BUTYL ETHER $C_7H_{16}O$

Smutny and Bondi (1961)

Viscosity

$t°$	η	
−53.9	2.734	
−40	1.949	
+20	0.669	
+50	0.491	
+60	0.449	

Heat of combustion (at constant volume) at 25°: 1108.9 kcal/mol

METHYLAL $C_3H_8O_2$

Saturated vapour pressure: NICOLINI (1951)

t°	p mm	t°	p mm	t°	p mm
0	130.7	15	261.5	30	483.5
5	166.0	20	325.1	35	584.5
10	209.4	25	397.8	—	—

Boiling point: 42.55°/766.6 mm NICOLINI (1951)

Refractive index: $n_D^{15°} = 1.3561$ NICOLINI (1951)

Dielectric constant: PHILIPPE and PIETTE (1955)

t°	ε	t°	ε	
20.00	2.645	−164.0	2.356	
0.0	2.624	146.0	2.371	
− 48.0	2.576	120.5	2.383	
75.5	2.551	115.0	2.395	
108.0	2.543	102.5	2.544	
140.0	2.372	− 75.0	2.556	
153.0	2.364	—	—	

N.B. (p. 351) Suppress ε of PIETTE (1947).

NICOLINI (1951) also measured the *saturated vapour pressure* of many other ETHERS and ACETALS.

ETHYLAL $C_5H_{12}O_2$

Saturated vapour pressure: NICOLINI (1951)

t°	p mm	t°	p mm	t°	p mm
0	17.7	30	85.1	55	244.6
5	23.5	35	106.8	60	295.0
10	31.0	40	133.5	65	353.7
15	40.6	45	164.7	70	420.8
20	52.7	50	201.1	75	499.0

Boiling point: 87.9 NICOLINI (1951)

Refractive index: NICOLINI (1951)

t°	n_D	
17	1.3759	
21	1.3742	

Dielectric constant: PHILIPPE and PIETTE (1955)

t°	ε	t°	ε	
20.00	2.527	−137.5	2.203	
0.0	2.528	111.0	2.214	
− 26.5	2.529	93.0	2.221	
46.0	2.531	77.0	2.234	
71.5	2.537	68.0	2.291	
86.0	2.223	67.0	2.425	
121.0	2.212	66.0	2.491	
−152.0	2.198	59.0	2.532	
—	—	− 31.0	2.533	

N.B. (p. 352) Suppress ε of PIETTE (1947).

DIMETHYL ACETAL $C_4H_{10}O_2$

NICOLINI (1951)

Saturated vapour pressure

t°	p mm	t°	p mm	t°	p mm
0	50.3	25	171.2	45	387
5	65.4	30	212.2	50	464.4
10	84.4	35	261.3	55	553.5
15	107.9	40	320	60	655.2
20	136.8	—	—	—	—

Boiling point: 64.3°/760 mm

Refractive index: $n_D^{21°} = 1.3670$

DIETHYL ACETAL $C_6H_{14}O_2$

NICOLINI (1951)

Saturated vapour pressure

t°	p mm	t°	p mm	t°	p mm
0	7.9	25	34.1	50	112.6
5	10.9	30	44.0	55	138.2
10	14.7	35	56.5	60	168.8
15	19.7	40	71.9	65	205.6
20	26.1	45	90.5	—	—

Boiling point: 103.6°/760 mm

Refractive index: $n_D^{22°} = 1.3812$

C. ALDEHYDES

SMITH and BONNER (1951) give the *density, refractive index* and *vapour pressure* of
ACETALDEHYDE, PROPIONALDEHYDE and *n*-BUTYRALDEHYDE.

VALERALDEHYDE, see Addenda, p. 445

D. KETONES

ACETONE C_3H_6O

Saturated vapour pressure: DREISBACH and SHRADER (1949)

$t°$	p mm	
44.81	507.50	
32.55	315.52	

Boiling point: 56.20 DREISBACH and SHRADER (1949)
              56.20 GRIFFITHS (1952)

Melting point: —95.35 DREISBACH and MARTIN (1949)

Density and Viscosity

$t°$	d	
20	0.79079	DREISBACH and MARTIN (1949)
25	0.78508	,,
25	0.78507	GRIFFITHS (1952)
25	0.78501	BROWN and FOCH (1955)

$t°$	d	$\eta \cdot 10^5$	
20	0.7905	3218	ZINOV and ROSOLOVSKI (1960)
10	0.8015	3554	,,
0	0.8125	3939	,,
—10	0.8237	4379	,,
—20	0.8343	4877	,,
—30	0.8453	5435	,,

Refractive index

t°	n_D	
25	1.35599	BROWN and FOCK (1955)
20	1.35880	DREISBACH and MARTIN (1949)
25	1.35609	,,

Specific magnetic susceptibility at 20°: $-0.569 \cdot 10^{-6}$ VON RAUTENFELD and STEURER (1942)

METHYL ETHYL KETONE C_4H_8O

Boiling point: 79.6   KYLE and REED (1958)
                79.58 RANDALL and McKENNA (1951)

Melting point: -83.36 RANDALL and McKENNA (1951)

Density at 25°: 0.7995   KYLE and REED (1958)
                 0.79948 RANDALL and McKENNA (1951)

Refractive index $n_D^{25°}$: 1.3761 KYLE and REED (1958)

Heat capacity of the vapour, heat of vaporization and *second virial coefficient:* NICKERSON, KOBE and McKETTA (1961)

METHYL PROPYL KETONE $C_5H_{10}O$

Boiling point: 102.4 POMERANTZ, FOOKSON *et al.* (1954)

Density and Refractive index: (*ibid.*)

t°	d	n_D	
20	0.8095	1.3903	

Heat capacity of the vapour, heat of vaporization and *second virial coefficient:* NICKERSON, KOBE and McKETTA (1961)

METHYL iso-BUTYL KETONE $C_6H_{12}O$

Boiling point: 116.2 FUGE, BOWDEN and JONES (1952)
                115.91 KARR, BOWES and SCHEIBEL (1951)

Saturated vapour pressure: FUGE, BOWDEN and JONES (1952)

t°	p mm	t°	p mm	
21.7	16.5	70.0	162.0	
32.7	29.5	80.1	240.0	
41.5	47.0	90.9	348.0	
50.2	69.5	116.2	760.0	
60.8	112.5	—	—	

Density

t°	d	
20.0	0.8007	FUGE, BOWDEN and JONES (1952)
40.0	0.7823	,,
60.0	0.7642	,,
80.0	0.7442	,,
100.0	0.7249	,,
25.0	0.7960	KARR, BOWES and SCHEIBEL (1951)

Viscosity at 25°: $\eta \cdot 10^5 = 542$ KARR, BOWES and SCHEIBEL (1951)

Surface tension γ at 20°: 23.9 FUGE, BOWDEN and JONES (1952)

Refractive index: n_D at 25° = 1.3937 KARR, BOWES and SCHEIBEL (1951)
1.3943 FUGE, BOWDEN and JONES (1952)

DIETHYL KETONE $C_5H_{10}O$

Saturated vapour pressure: DREISBACH and SHRADER (1949)

t°	p mm	t°	p mm	
88.91	507.50	51.24	123.76	
75.04	315.52	36.36	75.86	

Boiling point: 101.70 DREISBACH and MARTIN (1949)

Melting point: −39.50 *ibid.*

Density and Refractive index: (ibid.)

t°	d	n_D	
20	0.81440	1.39240	
25	0.80953	1.39003	

E. OXIDES

CARBON MONOXIDE   CO

(See also Addenda, p. 446)

Saturated vapour pressure: MICHELS, WASSENAAR and ZWIETERING (1952)

t°	P atm	t°	P atm	t°	P atm	t°	P atm
−179.899	3.1461	−168.015	7.7092	−156.823	15.1905	−143.275	30.0316
178.351	3.5823	164.335	9.7762	153.766	17.9113	142.009	31.8405
176.914	4.0237	164.332	9.7789	150.441	21.2562	141.247	32.9704
171.876	5.8973	160.666	12.2094	148.160	23.7927	−140.555	34.0299
−170.069	6.7016	−156.825	15.1898	−145.569	26.9634	—	—

Compressibility of the vapour at 0°: GOIG (1929)

p	pv	p	pv	p	pv	p	pv
53.58	0.9754	69.04	0.9721	84.18	0.9702	104.63	0.9708
56.68	0.9748	69.22	0.9722	85.92	0.9701	107.99	0.9714
59.70	0.9737	70.39	0.9717	87.78	0.9700	110.68	0.9721
62.98	0.9731	73.20	0.9714	89.54	0.9700	113.73	0.9724
64.72	0.9730	75.20	0.9712	92.42	0.9703	117.38	0.9734
66.00	0.9727	78.24	0.9706	93.05	0.9702	119.87	0.9738
66.04	0.9727	78.38	0.9706	95.27	0.9704	120.49	0.9740
67.57	0.9722	81.76	0.9705	97.40	0.9703	126.87	0.9755
67.61	0.9723	83.35	0.9703	101.90	0.9707	127.67	0.9760

Compressibility of the vapour: between 0 and 150° and up to 3000 atm MICHELS, LUPTON *et al.* (1952)

Melting curve: CLUSIUS, PIESBERGEN and VARDE (1960)

t°	P atm	t°	P atm	
−199.579	247.7	−203.397	71.5	
200.092	224.1	203.627	61.9	
200.544	202.2	203.842	52.2	
201.088	178.0	204.112	40.8	
201.688	149.5	204.331	30.0	
202.248	124.7	204.538	21.8	
202.761	100.9	204.777	10.4	
− 203.048	87.4	−205.011	0.15	

Transition under high pressure: STEVENSON (1957)

CARBON DIOXIDE CO_2

Saturated vapour pressure: MICHELS, WASSENAAR *et al.* (1950)

$t°$	P atm	$t°$	P atm	$t°$	P atm	$t°$	P atm
−56.037	5.2339	−45.868	7.9409	−19.243	19.895	+ 0.015	34.404
55.496	5.3578	39.239	10.197	12.360	24.424	1.036	35.345
54.898	5.4955	31.502	13.392	5.404	29.726	2.021	36.268
54.280	5.6430	26.245	15.950	1.677	32.889	3.015	37.222
−52.495	6.0825	−21.176	18.742	− 0.771	33.694		

GIAUQUE and EGAN (1937) (The authors give: 0°C = 273.10 K)

$t°$	p mm	$t°$	p mm	$t°$	p mm	$t°$	p mm
−118.904	11.32	−106.396	51.86	−94.531	179.94	−80.437	643.36
114.697	19.40	102.409	80.39	90.767	257.75	78.118	779.62
110.503	32.21	98.412	122.20	85.744	407.18	77.269	835.30

Boiling point (theoretical) of the supercooled liquid: −88.46 at 760 mm CLARK and DIN (1950)

Triple point: −56.603 AMBROSE (1956)

Transition under high pressure: STEVENSON (1957)

Vapour phase

Compressibility (PV-values in Amagat units): McCORMACK and SCHNEIDER (1950)

P atm	1	10	20	30	40	50
$t°$						
0	1.00000	0.93402	0.85199	0.75058	—	—
50	1.18676	1.14422	1.09478	1.04257	0.99238	0.92619
100	1.37249	1.34314	1.30998	1.27623	1.24189	1.20697
150	1.55778	1.53732	1.51459	1.49186	1.46913	1.44640
200	1.74285	1.72907	1.71377	1.69846	1.68315	1.66785
300	2.11244	2.10696	2.10086	2.09476	2.08867	2.08257
400	2.48165	2.48101	2.48031	2.47960	2.47889	2.47818
500	2.85065	2.85310	2.85583	2.85855	2.86128	2.86400
600	3.21959	3.22449	3.22993	3.23537	3.24081	3.24625

Compressibility: deviation from the law of BOYLE.

A_0^1: 0.00668 BATUECAS and GARCIA MALDE (1953)

A_0^1: 0.00683 BATUECAS and GUTIERREZ LOSA (1954)

Compressibility under high pressure: STEVENSON (1957)

Second virial coefficient

$t°$	B (ml/mol)	
25	125.7	PEREZ MASIA and DIAZ PENA (1958)
30	119.3	,,
50	104.3	,,
75	85.1	,,
100	73.9	,,
125	59.4	,,
150	52.6	,,
+30	127	COOK (1957)
0	168	,,
−25	204	,,
−40	266	,,
−50	302	,,
−60	310	,,

Viscosity: $\eta \cdot 10^6$: 148.3 at 25° BUDDENBERG and WILKE (1951)

Dielectric constant: YASUMI, OKABAYASHI and KOMOOKA (1958)

$t°$	ε	$t°$	ε	$t°$	ε	$t°$	ε
24.28	1.02486	116.87	1.12444	350.40	1.41189	549.90	1.69318
61.20	1.06343	231.23	1.25991	470.70	1.57801	595.89	1.76244

Thermic conductivity in the critical region: MICHELS, SENGERS and VAN DER GULIK (1962)

Specific heat: GIAUQUE and EGAN (1937) (The authors give 0°C = 273.10°K)

$t°$	c_p	$t°$	c_p	$t°$	c_p	$t°$	c_p
−257.58	0.606	−233.67	4.603	−191.16	8.703	−137.36	10.88
255.80	0.825	229.91	5.195	185.65	8.984	131.96	11.08
254.05	1.081	225.48	5.794	180.39	9.189	126.62	11.27
251.35	1.419	220.99	6.326	175.17	9.421	121.43	11.45
249.85	1.791	216.93	6.765	169.84	9.671	116.38	11.64
247.46	2.266	212.24	7.269	164.54	9.893	111.10	11.84
245.38	2.676	211.84	7.302	159.19	10.07	105.48	12.07
243.18	3.069	206.86	7.707	153.86	10.27	99.74	12.32
240.31	3.555	201.88	8.047	148.52	10.44	93.88	12.57
−237.11	4.063	−196.63	8.370	−142.92	10.69	88.52	12.82
						− 83.32	13.05

Specific heat: MICHELS and STRIJLAND (1952)

d	t°	c_v	d	t°	c_v	d	t°	c_v
135.0	23.512	51.04	185.3	23.530	41.18	230.2	24.056	35.88
in	25.077	50.48		24.731	41.55		24.053	35.65
Ama-	26.249	31.92		28.742	48.66		26.891	38.46
gat	27.430	12.67		29.227	48.27		28.145	40.12
units	28.498	12.18		29.494	42.14		29.358	43.86
	33.799	11.24		30.301	26.70		30.458	42.47
	39.292	10.51		31.103	15.46		30.573	35.76
				34.158	13.21		31.676	17.21
				39.299	12.12		33.945	13.76
							39.334	12.04
							39.322	12.19
269.6	24.142	34.25	338.8	24.077	30.82	413.5	24.765	10.50
	26.941	36.73		25.114	31.14		29.925	10.45
	28.201	38.66		26.043	30.72		34.688	10.53
	29.405	41.51		27.072	19.03		39.395	10.58
	30.168	41.04		28.282	12.42			
	30.614	26.44		29.831	12.13			
	31.142	16.75		29.894	12.01			
	31.729	15.91		34.615	11.52			
	32.848	14.92		39.445	11.28			
	39.193	12.76						

G. FATTY ACIDS

FORMIC ACID CH_2O_2

Specific magnetic susceptibility at 20° : $-0.428 \cdot 10^{-6}$ VON RAUTENFELD and STEURER (1942)

ACETIC ACID $C_2H_4O_2$

Saturated vapour pressure: DREISBACH and SHRADER (1949)

t°	p mm	t°	p mm	t°	p mm
91.13	315.52	66.07	123.76	55.75	77.86

Orthobaric densities: COSTELLO and BOWDEN (1958)

t°	d_L	d_V	t°	d_L	d_V
20	1.0491	0.0001	160	0.8829	0.0089
40	1.0284	0.0002	180	0.8555	0.0137
60	1.0060	0.0005	200	0.8265	0.0205
80	0.9835	0.0010	220	0.7941	0.0302
100	0.9599	0.0018	240	0.7571	0.0433
120	0.9362	0.0033	260	0.7136	0.0617
140	0.9091	0.0055	280	0.6629	0.0883

Boiling point: 117.72 DREISBACH and SHRADER (1949)

Freezing point: 16.56 BROWN and EWALD (1950) and LOUGUININE (1900)

16.52 DREISBACH and MARTIN (1949)

Density and Refractive index

t°	d	n_D	
20	1.04923	1.37160	DREISBACH and MARTIN (1949)
25	1.04365	1.36995	,,

Dielectric constant: PHILIPPE and PIETTE (1955)

	t°	ε	t°	ε		t°	ε
L.	20.00	6.203	−61.5	2.486		−10.0	2.665
	18.00	6 194	50.0	2.496		+ 1.4	2.761
	15.00	6 165	44.5	2.502		15.5	3.16
C.	1.0	2.792	35.5	2.535	L.	15.5	4.12
	−48.5	2.526	31.5	2.610		15.5	4.92
	−79.0	2.456	−19.5	2.646		—	—

Heat of combustion at 25°: 208.7 kcal/mol DOW CHEMICAL COMPANY (1956)

Specific magnetic susceptibility at 20°: $-0.534 \cdot 10^{-6}$ VON RAUTENFELD and STEURER (1942)

DEUTERO ACETIC ACID $C_2D_4O_2$

Saturated vapour pressure: POTTER JR and RITTER (1954)

t°	p mm	t°	p mm	t°	p mm	t°	p mm
24.34	15.6	65.11	118.2	90.10	315.2	114.86	721.0
30.42	22.0	69.85	144.2	94.95	374.0	116.61	761.3
40.27	37.1	74.83	176.6	99.89	443.8	118.88	815.7
50.27	60.7	75.32	179.6	103.97	508.9	119.52	832.3
55.39	77.1	80.18	217.0	104.73	522.0	121.21	876.0
60.04	94.8	84.82	258.8	109.80	615.3	122.44	908.7
60.06	95.1	89.92	312.8	114.59	715.3	124.39	962.3

Boiling point: 116.53 *ibid.*

Density: (ibid.)

t°	d	t°	d	t°	d	t°	d
28.70	1.1091	49.81	1.0833	74.80	1.0528	99.98	1.0213
29.86	1.1075	54.85	1.0772	79.77	1.0466	105.05	1.0148
34.84	1.1013	59.40	1.0716	84.98	1.0402	109.51	1.0090
39.75	1.0956	64.77	1.0650	89.90	1.0340	113.32	1.0041
44.52	1.0898	69.88	1.0588	94.85	1.0278	—	—

PROPIONIC ACID $C_3H_6O_2$

Saturated vapour pressure: DREISBACH and SHRADER (1949)

t°	p mm	t°	p mm	t°	p mm
128.34	507.50	90.73	123.76	76.75	66.39
114.62	315.52	79.68	75.86	72.39	57.04

Boiling point: 140.80 DREISBACH and MARTIN (1949)

Melting point: −20.83 *ibid.*

Density and Refractive index: (ibid.)

t°	d	n_D
20	0.99336	1.38650
25	0.98797	1.38430

n-BUTYRIC ACID $C_4H_8O_2$

Saturated vapour pressure: JASPER and MILLER (1955)

t°	p mm	t°	p mm	t°	p mm	t°	p mm
20	0.77	60	9.80	100	73.80	130	247.00
30	1.60	70	16.80	110	112.40	140	357.20
40	3.00	80	28.00	120	166.70	150	509.10
50	5.50	90	45.30	—	—	—	—

Orthobaric densities: COSTELLO and BOWDEN (1958)

t°	d_L	d_V	t°	d_L	d_V
0	0.9767	—	140	0.8399	0.0025
20	0.9572	0.0002	160	0.8193	0.0040
40	0.9380	0.0003	180	0.7973	0.0060
60	0.9182	0.0004	200	0.7740	0.0095
80	0.8990	0.0007	220	0.7490	0.0148
100	0.8796	0.0011	240	0.7221	0.0240
120	0.8600	0.0016	260	0.6911	0.0375

Boiling point: 162.1°/763 mm COSTELLO and BOWDEN (1958)

Freezing point: −5.4 COSTELLO and BOWDEN (1958)

Refractive index: n_D at 24.8° = 1.3954 JASPER and MILLER (1955)

Iso-BUTYRIC ACID $C_4H_8O_2$

Boiling point: 154.0°/761 mm COSTELLO and BOWDEN (1958)

N.B. (p. 389) *Saturated vapour pressure*, 5th column, t°: 143.0 should read 140.3

Orthobaric densities: COSTELLO and BOWDEN

t°	d_L	d_V	t°	d_L	d_V
−60	1.024	—	+100	0.8680	0.0012
−40	1.006	—	120	0.8472	0.0020
−20	0.9870	—	140	0.8266	0.0030
0	0.9680	0.0001	160	0.8044	0.0049
+20	0.9485	0.0002	180	0.7808	0.0077
40	0.9285	0.0003	200	0.7560	0.0122
60	0.9086	0.0005	220	0.7283	0.0190
+80	0.8886	0.0008	+240	0.6982	0.0300

n-VALERIC ACID $C_5H_{10}O_2$

Boiling point: 187.0° at 760 mm COSTELLO and BOWDEN (1958)

Orthobaric densities

t°	d_L	d_V	t°	d_L	d_V
−40	0.9894	—	+120	0.8478	0.0012
−20	0.9720	—	140	0.8292	0.0017
0	0.9547	—	160	0.8102	0.0025
+20	0.9374	0.0001	180	0.7900	0.0040
40	0.9199	0.0002	200	0.7686	0.0066
60	0.9020	0.0003	220	0.7462	0.0103
80	0.8845	0.0005	240	0.7213	0.0150
+100	0.8663	0.0008	+260	0.6938	0.0210

Iso-VALERIC ACID $C_5H_{10}O_2$

Boiling point: 175.2°/750 mm COSTELLO and BOWDEN (1958)

Orthobaric densities: *(ibid.)*

$t°$	d_L	d_V	$t°$	d_L	d_V
−20	0.9804	—	+120	0.8362	0.0013
−40	0.9627	—	140	0.8174	0.0021
0	0.9450	0.0001	160	0.7980	0.0032
+20	0.9270	0.0002	180	0.7772	0.0050
40	0.9091	0.0003	200	0.7550	0.0076
60	0.8911	0.0004	220	0.7310	0.0117
80	0.8732	0.0006	240	0.7057	0.0185
+100	0.8548	0.0008	+260	0.6785	0.0285

n-CAPROIC ACID $C_6H_{10}O_2$

Boiling point: 205.3 MUMFORD and PHILLIPS (1950)
205.1°/767 mm COSTELLO and BOWDEN (1958)

Orthobaric densities: *(ibid.)*

$t°$	d_L	d_V	$t°$	d_L	d_V
0	0.9414	—	160	0.8040	0.0022
20	0.9243	—	180	0.7857	0.0032
40	0.9078	—	200	0.7662	0.0047
60	0.8905	0.0003	220	0.7464	0.0068
80	0.8738	0.0005	240	0.7250	0.0105
100	0.8569	0.0007	260	0.7021	0.0160
120	0.8396	0.0010	280	0.6778	0.0244
140	0.8220	0.0015	—	—	—

Freezing point: −4.0 COSTELLO and BOWDEN (1958)

Density: $d^{25} = 0.9230$ MUMFORD and PHILLIPS (1950)

Viscosity, Surface tension and Refractive index: *(ibid.)*

$t°$	$\eta \cdot 10^4$	γ	n_D
20	3.22	28.05	1.4162
25	2.87	27.55	

Iso-CAPROIC ACID $C_6H_{10}O_2$

COSTELLO and BOWDEN (1958)

Boiling point: 201°/761 mm

Orthobaric densities

$t°$	d_L	d_V	$t°$	d_L	d_V
− 20	0.9535	—	+140	0.8191	0.0015
0	0.9371	—	160	0.8011	0.0022
+ 20	0.9209	0.0001	180	0.7824	0.0032
40	0.9041	0.0002	200	0.7634	0.0047
60	0.8876	0.0003	220	0.7438	0.0068
80	0.8704	0.0005	240	0.7230	0.0105
100	0.8537	0.0007	260	0.7011	0.0160
+120	0.8367	0.0010	+280	0.6744	0.0214

n-CAPRYLIC ACID $C_8H_{16}O_2$

COSTELLO and BOWDEN (1958)

Boiling point: 237.5°/763 mm

Melting point: 16.5

Orthobaric densities

$t°$	d_L	d_V	$t°$	d_L	d_V
20	0.9090	—	180	0.7776	0.0017
40	0.8930	—	200	0.7604	0.0027
60	0.8767	0.0002	220	0.7420	0.0042
80	0.8605	0.0003	240	0.7232	0.0060
100	0.8442	0.0005	260	0.7030	0.0085
120	0.8280	0.0007	280	0.6812	0.0130
140	0.8118	0.0009	300	0.6567	0.0195
160	0.7946	0.0012	—	—	—

n-CAPRIC ACID $C_{10}H_{20}O_2$

COSTELLO and BOWDEN (1958)

Boiling point: 158°/17 mm

Melting point: 30.7

Orthobaric densities

$t°$	d_L	d_V	$t°$	d_L	d_V
40	0.8817	—	180	0.7768	0.0013
60	0.8670	—	200	0.7606	0.0020
80	0.8520	—	220	0.7440	0.0027
100	0.8373	0.0002	240	0.7269	0.0038
120	0.8224	0.0003	260	0.7090	0.0055
140	0.8079	0.0005	280	0.6902	0.0081
160	0.7925	0.0008	300	0.6695	0.0118

n-LAURIC ACID $C_{12}H_{24}O_2$

COSTELLO and BOWDEN (1958)

Boiling point: 179°/18 mm

Melting point: 43.5

Orthobaric densities

t°	d_L	d_V	t°	d_L	d_V
60	0.8598	—	200	0.7580	0.0013
80	0.8454	—	220	0.7422	0.0019
100	0.8311	0.0002	240	0.7265	0.0026
120	0.8168	0.0002	260	0.7096	0.0037
140	0.8024	0.0005	280	0.6926	0.0052
160	0.7879	0.0007	300	0.6750	0.0073
180	0.7730	0.0009	—	—	—

n-MYRISTIC ACID $C_{14}H_{28}O_2$

COSTELLO and BOWDEN (1958)

Boiling point: 200°/20 mm

Melting point: 53.9

Orthobaric densities

t°	d_L	d_V	t°	d_L	d_V
60	0.8573	—	200	0.7588	0.0010
80	0.8434	—	220	0.7434	0.0014
100	0.8294	—	240	0.7281	0.0019
120	0.8156	0.0002	260	0.7121	0.0027
140	0.8015	0.0003	280	0.6956	0.0037
160	0.7878	0.0005	300	0.6780	0.0051
180	0.7733	0.0007	—	—	—

n-PALMITIC ACID $C_{16}H_{32}O_2$

COSTELLO and BOWDEN (1958)

Boiling point: 219°/17 mm

Melting point: 62.3

Orthobaric densities

t°	d_L	d_V	t°	d_L	d_V
80	0.8414	—	200	0.7590	0.0008
100	0.8278	—	220	0.7441	0.0011
120	0.8141	0.0002	240	0.7290	0.0015
140	0.8002	0.0003	260	0.7131	0.0021
160	0.7870	0.0004	280	0.6972	0.0027
180	0.7730	0.0006	300	0.6803	0.0039

n-STEARIC ACID $C_{18}H_{36}O_2$

Boiling point: 235°/20 mm COSTELLO and BOWDEN (1958)

Melting point: 69.2   ,,
            69.4 MEDARD and THOMAS (1952)

Orthobaric densities: COSTELLO and BOWDEN (1958)

$t°$	d_L	d_V	$t°$	d_L	d_V
80	0.8377	—	200	0.7579	0.0006
100	0.8247	—	220	0.7437	0.0008
120	0.8117	—	240	0.7292	0.0010
140	0.7988	0.0002	260	0.7143	0.0014
160	0.7856	0.0003	280	0.6991	0.0020
180	0.7720	0.0004	300	0.6831	0.0029

Refractive index: n_D at 20° = 1.4334 MEDARD and THOMAS (1952)

Heat of combustion at constant pressure: 9519 cal/mol   ,,

OLEIC ACID $C_{18}H_{30}O_2$

N.B. (p. 404): HOERR and HARWOOD (1953) do not agree with BERTRAM (1927)

CITRIC ACID MONOHYDRATE $C_6H_8O_7.H_2O$

(See also Addenda, p. 446)

Heat capacity: EVANS, HOARE and MELIA (1962)

J. ESTERS

ETHYL FORMATE $C_3H_6O_2$

MUMFORD and PHILLIPS (1950)

Boiling point: 54.3

Density, Viscosity and Refractive index

$t°$	d	$\eta \cdot 10^5$	n_D
20	0.9237	402	1.3599
25	0.9173	382	

PROPYL FORMATE $C_4H_8O_2$

B. E. (1959)

Boiling point: —80.85

Freezing point: —92.9

Density

t°	d	
0	0.92831	
15	0.91109	
30	0.89406	

Refractive index at 15° and *dn/dt*

He$_r$	H$_C$	Na$_D$	He$_y$	He$_g$	H$_\beta$	He $_{viol}$	H$_\gamma$
1.37672	1.3772	1.37898	1.37908	1.38261	1.38372	1.38647	1.38770
0.00048	0.00048	—	0.00048	0.00048	0.00047	0.00048	0.00051

Viscosity

t°	$\eta \cdot 10^5$	
15	544	
30	460	

Surface tension

t°	γ	
15	25.14	
20	24.49	
30	23.28	

METHYL ACETATE $C_3H_6O_2$

N.B. (p. 414): Instead of CHADWELL (1925) it should be RICHARD and CHADWELL (1925)

Boiling point: 56.9 MUMFORD and PHILLIPS (1950)

Density: (ibid.)

t°	d	
20	0.9342	
25	0.9279	

Viscosity: (ibid.)

t°	$\eta \cdot 10^5$	
20	385	
25	364	

Surface tension: (ibid.)

t°	γ	
20	24.8	
25	24.1	

Refractive index: (ibid.)

t°	n_D	
20	1.3614	

Specific magnetic susceptibility at 20°: $-0.576 \cdot 10^{-6}$ VON RAUTENFELD and STEURER (1942)

ETHYL ACETATE $C_4H_8O_2$

Boiling point: 77.15 MUMFORD and PHILLIPS (1950)

Freezing point: -39.50 *ibid.*

Density: (ibid.)

t°	d	
20	0.9007	
25	0.8946	

Refractive index: (ibid.)

t°	n_D	
25	1.3728	

Viscosity: (ibid.)

t°	$\eta \cdot 10^5$	
20	452	
25	425	

Specific magnetic susceptibility at 20°: $-0.611 \cdot 10^{-6}$ VON RAUTENFELD and STEURER (1942)

Dielectric constant: PHILIPPE and PIETTE (1955)

t°	ε	t°	ε
+ 20.00	6.002	−144.5	2.471
− 13.5	6.717	140.5	2.476
43.5	7.461	135.0	2.478
78.0	8.540	124.0	2.483
84.0	8.817	107.5	2.498
111.0	2.490	98.0	2.532
136.5	2.482	93.0	2.737
170.0	2.457	91.0	3.030
−155.0	2.465	− 45.0	7.502

n-PROPYL ACETATE $C_5H_{10}O_2$

Boiling point: 101.70 *dt/dp (10 mm):* 0.43 B. E. (1959)
101.4 PICK, HALA and FRIED (1959)

Density

t°	d	
0	0.91024	B. E. (1959)
15	0.89377	,,
30	0.87716	,,
20	0.88827	PICK, HALA and FRIED (1959)

Refractive index at 15°

	He$_r$	H$_C$	Na$_D$	He$_y$	H$_\beta$	He$_{gr}$	He $_{viol}$	H$_\gamma$	
	1.38434	1.38460	1.38656	1.38666	1.39013	1.39114	1.39390	1.39511	B. E. (1959)
dn/dt	0.00049	0.00049	—	0.00048	0.00047	0.00048	0.00047	0.00048	

Viscosity

t°	$\eta \cdot 10^5$	
15	619	B. E. (1959)
20	510	,,

Surface tension

t°	γ	
15.475	24.81	B. E. (1959)
20	24.27	,,
30	23.10	,,

Dielectric constant

t°	ε	
20	5.604	LAFONTAINE (1958)

Specific magnetic susceptibility at 20°: $-0.642 \cdot 10^{-6}$ VON RAUTENFELD and STEURER (1942)

n-BUTYL ACETATE $C_6H_{12}O_6$

Boiling point: 126.52   *dt/dp* (10 mm): 0.46   B.E. (1959)
          126.09   KLIMENT, FRIED and PICK (1964)

Density

t°	d		t°	d	
0	0.90163	B.E. (1959)	20	0.88152	KLIMENT, FRIED and
15	0.88652				PICK (1964)
30	0.87129				

Refractive index at 15° and *dn/dt:* B.E. (1959)

He_r	H_C	Na_D	He_y	He_gr	H_β	He viol	H_γ
1.39403	1.39437	1.39636	1.39646	1.40022	1.40120	1.40409	1.40511
0.00046	0.00046	—	0.00047	0.00048	0.00047	0.00048	0.00046

n_D at 20°: 1.391;   at 45°: 1.3823   KLIMENT, FRIED and PICK (1964)

Viscosity and *Surface tension:* B.E. (1959)

t°	$\eta \cdot 10^5$	γ	
15	770	25.66	
20	—	25.09	
30	628	23.98	

Dielectric constant ε at 20°: 128   LAFONTAINE (1958)

Saturated vapour pressure: KLIMENT, FRIED and PICK (1964)

t°	p (mm)	t°	p (mm)	t°	p (mm)	t°	p (mm)
59.74	69.08	71.70	115.30	89.58	231.50	113.62	521.20
62.53	78.20	75.88	136.90	95.06	281.60	120.62	645.45
65.52	89.08	80.49	164.20	100.53	340.20	126.09	760.00
67.96	98.70	84.21	189.50	107.07	423.40		

METHYL PROPIONATE $C_4H_8O_2$

B. E. (1959)

Boiling point: 79.76 *dt/dp (10 mm):* 0.42

Freezing point: −87.5

Density

t°	d
0	0.93890
15	0.92112
30	0.90337

Viscosity

t°	$\eta \cdot 10^5$
15	477
30	405

Surface tension

t°	γ
15	25.56
20	24.86
30	23.57

Refractive index: n at 15° and *dn/dt*

He$_r$	H$_C$	Na$_D$	He$_y$	He$_{gr}$	H$_\beta$	He $_{viol}$	H$_\gamma$
1.37716	1.37744	1.37930	1.37940	1.38284	1.38380	1.38660	1.38765
0.00050	0.00050	—	0.00049	0.00050	0.00050	0.00053	0.00053

Dielectric constant

t°	ε	
20	6.206	LAFONTAINE (1958)

n-PROPYL PROPIONATE   C$_6$H$_{12}$O$_2$

B. E. (1959)

Boiling point: 123.20 *dt/dp (10 mm):* 0.43

Freezing point: −75.9

Density

t°	d	
0	0.90227	
15	0.88661	
30	0.87085	

Viscosity

t°	$\eta \cdot 10^5$	
15	712	
30	586	

Surface tension

t°	γ	
15	25.28	
20	24.68	
30	23.65	

Refractive index: n at 15° and *dn/dt*

He$_r$	H$_\alpha$	Na$_D$	He$_y$	He$_{gr}$	H$_\beta$	He $_{viol}$	H$_\gamma$
1.39295	1.39330	1.39530	1.39540	1.39900	1.39997	1.40297	1.40424
0.00046	0.00046	—	0.00047	0.00048	0.00046	0.00051	0.00051

Dielectric constant

t°	ε	
20	5.249	LAFONTAINE (1958)

n-BUTYL PROPIONATE $C_7H_{14}O_2$

B. E. (1959)

Boiling point: 146.50 *dt/dp (10 mm):* 0.48

Density

t°	d	
0	0.89609	
15	0.88136	
30	0.86664	

Viscosity

t°	$\eta \cdot 10^5$	
15	875	
30	712	

Surface tension

t°	γ	
15	25.74	
20	25.26	
30	24.23	

Refractive index: n at 15° and *dn/dt*

He$_r$	H$_C$	Na$_D$	He$_y$	He$_g$	H$_\beta$	He $_{viol}$	H$_\gamma$
1.40084	1.40135	1.40324	1.40334	1.40704	1.40823	1.41108	1.41223
0.00044	0.00047	—	0.00046	0.00046	0.00047	0.00049	0.00046

Dielectric constant

t°	ε	
20	4.838	LAFONTAINE (1958)

n-AMYL PROPIONATE $\qquad$ C$_8$H$_{16}$O$_2$

B. E. (1959)

Boiling point: 168.75 *dt/dp (10 mm):* 0.50

Density

t°	d	
0	0.89136	
15	0.87738	
30	0.86347	

Viscosity

t°	$\eta \cdot 10^5$	
15	1104	
30	880	

Surface tension

t°	γ	
15	26.46	
20	25.98	
30	24.94	

Refractive index: n at 15° and *dn/dt*

He_r	H_C	D	He_y	He_gr	H_β	He viol	H_γ
1.40750	1.40783	1.40995	1.41005	1.41379	1.41495	1.41773	1.41951
0.00043	0.00043	—	0.00045	0.00044	0.00045	0.00044	0.00050

Dielectric constant

$t°$	ε	
20	4.552	LAFONTAINE (1958)

ETHYL BUTYRATE $C_6H_{12}O_2$

MUMFORD and PHILLIPS (1950)

Boiling point: 121.4

N.B. (p. 428): *Freezing point:* −98.0 instead of −100.8 B. E.

Density, *Viscosity* and *Refractive index*

$t°$	d	$\eta \cdot 10^5$	n_D	
20	0.8794	672	1.3922	
25	0.8742	627		

METHYL *n*-CAPROATE $C_7H_{14}O_2$

N.B. (p. 435): *Freezing point:* −68.1 instead of −71.0 B. E.

ETHYL *n*-CAPROATE $C_8H_{16}O_2$

SIMON (1929)

Boiling point: 167.85

Freezing point: −67.5

Density   *Viscosity*

$t°$	d	$t°$	$\eta \cdot 10^5$	
0	0.88956	15	1098	
15	0.87583	30	871	
30	0.86196			

Refractive index

t°	He$_r$	H$_C$	Na$_D$	He$_y$	He$_g$	H$_\beta$	He$_{viol}$	H$_\gamma$
15	1.40738	1.40763	1.40971	1.40985	1.41382	1.41480	1.41796	1.41907
25	1.40317	1.40342	1.40544	1.40559	1.40957	1.41055	1.41363	1.41475
dn/dt	0.000421	0.000421	0.000427	0.000426	0.000425	0.000425	0.000433	0.000432

METHYL ETHYL CARBONATE $C_4H_8O_3$

Dielectric constant: PHILIPPE and PIETTE (1955)

t°	ε	t°	ε
+16.00	2.984	−55.0	2.651
−110.5	2.450	55.0	2.717
103.0	2.453	55.0	2.821
77.0	2.478	55.0	2.925
68.0	2.484	36.5	2.985
63.5	2.498	−10.0	2.985
59.0	2.508	+20.00	2.985
58.0	2.560	30.00	2.985
−56.0	2.573	40.00	2.984

DIETHYL CARBONATE $C_5H_{10}O_3$

Dielectric constant: PHILIPPE and PIETTE (1955)

t°	ε	t°	ε
+ 20.0	2.820	−80.0	2.302
− 2.5	2.818	72.0	2.815
+ 11.0	2.820	55.0	2.820
− 23.0	2.818	50.0	2.819
39.0	2.816	−47.0	2.818
86.0	2.825	0.00	2.818
110.0	2.274	+20.00	2.820
160.0	2.234	30.00	2.820
139.0	2.250	40.00	2.819
− 95.0	2.289	50.00	2.817

ETHYL ORTHOFORMATE $C_7H_{16}O_3$

B. E. (1959)

Boiling point: 146.40 *dt/dp (10 mm):* 0.46

Density

t°	d
0	0.91262
15	0.89755
30	0.88258

Viscosity

t°	$\eta \cdot 10^5$	
15	790	
30	634	

Surface tension

t°	γ	
15	24.08	
20	23.56	
30	22.54	

Refractive index n at 15° and *dn/dt*

He$_r$	H$_C$	Na$_D$	He$_y$	He$_g$	H$_\beta$	He $_{viol}$	H$_\gamma$
1.39105	1.39129	1.3932	1.39330	1.39673	1.39752	1.40025	1.40150
0.00046	0.00046	—	0.00046	0.00046	0.00044	0.00046	0.00046

Dielectric constant

t°	ε	
20	4.779	LAFONTAINE (1958)

Numerous other esters, see MUMFORD and PHILLIPS (1950).

α-ACETOXYPROPIONATES: see REHBERG and DIXON (1950)

GLYCERIDES: see CROWE and SMYTH (1950).

DIESTERS

Name	Authors	d				ε			
		20°	45°	70°	95°	20°	45°	70°	95°
ETHYL OXALATE	KETELAAR and v. MEURS (1957)	1.0791	1.0499	1.0202	0.9907	8.266	7.622	7.085	6.608
ETHYL MALONATE	,,	1.0552	1.0285	1.0018	—	7.908	7.234	6.671	—
ETHYL SUCCINATE	,,	1.0404	1.0150	0.9891	—	6.098	5.724	5.317	—

N.B. (p. 448): *Density*, 2nd column, last line: d: 1.08829 should read 0.98829.

LACTATES: see REHBERG and DIXON (1950)

d-DIMETHYLTARTRATE and dl-DIMETHYLTARTRATE $C_6H_{10}O_5$

CROWELL and JONES Jr (1954)

Melting point: 48°   89°

Saturated vapour pressure

$t°$	$10^3 p$ mm	$t°$	$10^3 p$ mm	$t°$	$10^3 p$ mm	$t°$	$10^3 p$ mm
solid		**liquid**		**solid**		**liquid**	
35.4	3.02	49.5	22.6	42.5	1.98	91.8	621
40.4	6.16	55.8	39.1	49.5	5.33		
44.2	10.23	63.3	73.5	55.8	11.65		
		85.2	381	65.6	39.6		
		91.8	625	72.9	90.0		
				85.2	275		

Heat of sublimation:
     27.01 kcal/mol   27.19 kcal/mol

Heat of vaporization (liquid):
     18.26   kcal/mol   18.26 kcal/mol

Heat of fusion:
     8.75 kcal/mol   8.93 kcal/mol

4. OXYGENATED DERIVATIVES OF THE AROMATIC SERIES

A. ALCOHOLS AND PHENOLS

COSTELLO and BOWDEN (1958)

BENZYL ALCOHOL C_7H_8O

Boiling point: 205°/754 mm

Freezing point: − 15.5

Orthobaric densities

BENZHYDROL $C_{13}H_{14}O$

180°/20 mm

68

$t°$	d_L	d_V	$t°$	d_L	d_V
0	1.061	—	80	1.054	—
20	1.045	—	100	1.038	—
40	1.030	—	120	1.022	—
60	1.014	—	140	1.006	—
80	0.9988	0.0003	160	0.9900	0.0003
100	0.9818	0.0003	180	0.9740	0.0004
120	0.9646	0.0005	200	0.9580	0.0006
140	0.9464	0.0007	220	0.9420	0.0009
160	0.9288	0.0011			
180	0.9108	0.0016			
200	0.8914	0.0024			
220	0.8723	0.0038			
240	0.8520	0.0061			
260	0.8319	0.0089			
280	0.8100	0.0136			

PHENOL C_6H_6O

Boiling point: 181.8   FRIED and PICK (1961)
181.839 ANDON, BIDDISCOMBE *et al.* (1960)

dt/dp (10 mm): 0.4788 ANDON, BIDDISCOMBE *et al.* (1960)

Freezing point: 40.90 PERRIN (1962)
40.84 ANDON, BIDDISCOMBE *et al.* (1960)
40.6   FRIED and PICK (1961)

Density

t°	d	$\eta \cdot 10^5$	ε	
41.5	1.0571	320.0	11.78	SURYANANAYANA and
42.3	1.0565	308.8	11.72	SOMASUNDARAM (1959)
49.8	1.0503	228.7	11.10	
50.6	1.0497	221.9	11.03	
58.1	1.0430	171.2	10.48	
60.7	1.0406	157.5	10.32	
64.8	1.0371	137.5	10.03	
65.4	1.0366	135.0	9.98	
65.5	1.0365	134.4	9.97	
65.9	1.0361	132.5	9.95	
45.0	1.0543	—	—	FRIED and PICK (1961)

Refractive index n_D at $25° = 1.5404$ FRIED and PICK (1961)

Heat of vaporization at $25°$: 16410 cal/mol ANDON, BIDDISCOMBE *et al.* (1960)

Heat of combustion of the crystals: 729.80 cal/mol ANDON, BIDDISCOMBE *et al.* (1960)

o, m and *p*-CRESOL C_7H_8O

	o	*m*	*p*	
Boiling point	191.003	202.231	201.940	ANDON, BIDDISCOMBE, *et al.* (1960)
dt/dp (10 *mm*)	0.5021	0.5007	0.4985	,,
Freezing point	30.97	12.16	34.65	,,
,,	30.85	11.95	34.55	PERRIN (1962)
,, (metastable)			32.85	,,
Heat of vaporization	18170	14750	17670	cal/mol (crystals)
at 25°				ANDON, BIDDISCOMBE *et al.* (1960)
Heat of combustion	882.72	885.25	883.99	kcal/mol ,, ,,

2,3-XYLENOL $C_8H_{10}O$

ANDON, BIDDISCOMBE *et al.* (1960)
Saturated vapour pressure

t°	p mm	t°	p mm	t°	p mm
C. 9.91	0.0045	24.71	0.0273	39.54	0.130
14.70	0.0080	29.58	0.0432	44.81	0.224
19.70	0.0145	35.19	0.0760	49.88	0.397

L. 149.346	99.79	200.752	500.88	215.091	727.03
160.940	150.35	204.000	546.36	215.646	737.18
169.634	200.30	207.544	599.68	216.144	746.41
176.314	247.24	210.612	649.12	216.987	762.16
182.500	298.37	213.454	697.75	217.323	768.59
187.374	344.43	214.137	709.89	217.928	780.14
192.094	394.33	214.768	721.19	218.467	790.54
196.778	449.43	—	—	—	—

Boiling point: 216.870 *dt/dp (10 mm):* 0.5309

Freezing point: 72.53

Heat of vaporization at 25°: 20080 cal/mol

Heat of combustion: 1036.33 kcal/mol

2,4-XYLENOL   C$_8$H$_{10}$O

ANDON, BIDDISCOMBE *et al.* (1960)

Saturated vapour pressure

t°	p mm	t°	p mm	
L. 9.73	0.0228	29.91	0.151	(supercooled)
14.94	0.0380	35.16	0.231	,,
20.13	0.0621	39.41	0.328	,,
24.87	0.0961	44.86	0.503	,,

t°	p mm	t°	p mm	t°	p mm
L. 144.382	98.97	194.795	496.45	209.314	729.44
156.053	150.19	198.444	548.41	209.847	739.41
164.129	197.18	201.747	599.13	210.450	750.83
171.241	247.90	204.809	649.43	210.951	760.42
176.700	293.69	207.513	696.56	211.453	770.06
182.116	345.61	208.299	710.79	211.888	778.59
186.619	394.21	208.898	721.74	212.320	787.06
191.348	451.02	—	—	—	—

Boiling point: 210.931 *dt/dp (10 mm):* 0.5206

Freezing point: 24.52

Heat of vaporization at 25°: 15740 cal/mol (liquid)

Heat of combustion: 1039.31 kcal/mol

2,5-XYLENOL　　　　　　C₈H₁₀O

ANDON, BIDDISCOMBE *et al.* (1960)

Saturated vapour pressure

t°	p mm	t°	p mm		
C.　9.43	0.0045	35.33	0.0944		
15.01	0.0091	39.41	0.146		
19.90	0.0164	44.79	0.259		
24.82	0.0296	49.45	0.396		
29.83	0.0513	—	—		

t°	p mm	t°	p mm	t°	p mm
L.　143.924	97.43	191.460	451.10	209.138	722.68
154.805	144.27	194.984	497.38	209.556	730.36
164.433	199.40	198.830	552.06	210.117	740.79
171.549	250.33	201.834	598.06	210.711	751.99
176.902	295.23	204.603	643.08	211.232	761.91
182.455	348.48	207.748	697.47	211.736	771.59
187.328	401.35	208.661	713.92	—	—

Boiling point: 211.132 *dt/dp (10 mm):* 0.5233

Freezing point: 74.77

Heat of vaporization at 25° : 20310 cal/mol (**solid**)

Heat of combustion: 1035.04 kcal/mol

2,6-XYLENOL　　　　　　C₈H₁₀O

ANDON, BIDDISCOMBE *et al.* (1960)

Saturated vapour pressure

t°	p mm	t°	p mm		
4.75	0.0195	24.67	0.175		
9.46	0.0336	30.20	0.299		
14.98	0.0624	34.98	0.487		
19.78	0.104	39.66	0.752		

t°	p mm	t°	p mm	t°	p mm
L.　144.798	148.61	184.792	499.01	199.432	730.36
153.385	197.43	188.694	553.93	199.983	740.47
160.624	248.11	191.754	600.37	200.450	749.17
166.759	298.92	194.810	649.67	201.059	760.56
171.831	347.08	196.676	681.38	201.616	771.12
176.276	394.26	198.414	711.94	202.519	788.44
180.369	442.14	198.937	721.38	203.525	808.10

Boiling point: 201.030 *dt/dp (10 mm):* 0.5302

Freezing point: 45.56

Heat of vaporization at 25°: 18070 cal/mol **(solid)**

Heat of combustion: 1037.25 kcal/mol

3,4-XYLENOL $C_8H_{10}O$

Saturated vapour pressure: ANDON, BIDDISCOMBE *et al.* (1960)

t°	p mm	t°	p mm	t°	p mm
C. 9.89	0.0022	24.88	0.0138	39.67	0.0704
14.78	0.0040	29.80	0.0243	44.76	0.121
19.98	0.0077	34.86	0.0422	49.36	0.191

t°	p mm	t°	p mm	t°	p mm
L. 171.933	152.57	211.126	502.91	225.276	728.71
180.131	200.29	214.126	545.32	225.928	740.84
186.548	245.64	217.587	597.79	226.392	749.46
193.380	302.79	220.898	651.67	226.921	759.38
197.879	346.04	223.649	699.26	227.397	768.62
202.370	393.98	224.292	710.79	228.487	789.73
207.376	453.62	224.799	720.03	228.899	797.85

Boiling point: 226.947 *dt/dp (10 mm):* 0.5257 ANDON, BIDDISCOMBE *et al.* (1960)

Freezing point: 65.00 NYVLT and ERDOS (1959)
65.08 JAGER, BIROS and ERDOS (1955)
65.09 ANDON, BIDDISCOMBE *et al.* (1960)

Velocity of crystallization: I: 10.05 cm/min. at 40°   JAGER BIROS and ERDOS
II: 79.79 cm/min. at 40°   ,,   (1955)

Heat of vaporization at 25°: 20490 cal/mol ANDON, BIDDISCOMBE *et al.* (1960)

Heat of combustion: 1036.07 kcal/mol ANDON, BIDDISCOMBE *et al.* (1960)

Heat of sublimation: I 17820 cal/mol JAGER, BIROS and ERDOS (1955)
                        II 17350 cal/mol   „

3,5-XYLENOL $C_8H_{10}O$

ANDON, BIDDISCOMBE *et al.* (1960)

Saturated vapour pressure

t°	p mm	t°	p mm	
C. 9.57	0.0033	34.85	0.0586	
14.92	0.0061	39.94	0.0999	
20.35	0.0119	45.23	0.171	
24.95	0.0197	49.97	0.265	
30.42	0.0365	—	—	
L. 154.720	97.39	215.799	653.08	
166.472	148.21	218.298	696.84	
175.126	198.35	219.146	712.20	
182.389	250.46	219.584	720.26	
187.937	297.45	220.097	729.78	
192.743	343.64	220.692	740.84	
197.298	392.67	221.309	752.57	
201.925	448.10	221.709	760.28	
205.601	496.49	222.279	771.40	
209.151	547.11	222.724	780.12	
212.159	593.10	223.321	791.86	

Boiling point: 221.692 *dt/dp (10 mm):* 0.5190

Freezing point: 63.24

Heat of vaporization at 25°: 19800 cal/mol

Heat of combustion: 35424.7 cal/mol

o, m and *p*-ETHYLPHENOL $C_8H_{10}O$
See Addenda

α-QUINOL $C_6H_6O_2$

Saturated vapour pressure: NITTA, SEKI *et al.* (1951)

t°	p mm · 10³	t°	p mm · 10³	t°	p mm · 10³
58.9	1.13	64.1	1.70	72.3	3.86
58.9	1.16	67.7	2.63	76.1	5.20
59.0	1.17	72.3	3.87	—	—

β-QUINOL $C_6H_6O_2$

Saturated vapour pressure: (ibid.)

t°	p mm · 10³	t°	p mm · 10³	t°	p mm · 10³
61.2	1.48	75.2	6.02	77.4	7.80
64.4	2.14	75.2	5.89	77.4	7.58
68.2	3.19	75.3	6.11	—	—
71.8	4.29	—	—	—	—

Melting point: 16.4

QUINHYDRONE $C_{12}H_{10}O_4$

Saturated vapour pressure: (ibid.)

t°	p mm · 10³	t°	p mm · 10³	t°	p mm · 10³
44.4	3.26	50.7	5.83	56.4	11.2
47.9	4.68	53.8	9.32	60.4	15.3

Melting point: 168

B. PHENOL ETHERS

ANISOL C_7H_8O

Dielectric constant: PHILIPPE and PIETTE (1955)

t°	ε	t°	ε	
− 6.2	4.645	−39.6	2.874	
16.4	4.756	37.8	2.889	
38.6	5.036	35.7	4.997	
63.9	2.834	−25.8	4.868	
74.9	2.825	+ 3.75	4.554	
54.9	2.844	+13.95	4.480	
−45.0	2.861	—	—	

PHENETOL $C_8H_{10}O$

B. E. (1959)

Boiling point: 169.97 *dt/dp:* 0.52 (10 mm)

Freezing point: −30.2

Density

t°	d	
0	0.98371	
15	0.96985	
30	0.95601	

Viscosity

t°	$\eta \cdot 10^5$
15	1364
30	1040

Surface tension

t°	γ
15	33.45
20	32.88
30	31.64

Refractive index at 15° and *dn/dt*

He$_r$	H$_C$	Na$_D$	He$_y$	He$_{gr}$	H$_\beta$	He $_{viol}$	H$_\gamma$
1.50450	1.50506	1.50990	1.51000	1.51915	1.52141	1.52866	1.53164
0.00047	0.00047	—	0.00049	0.00050	0.00049	0.00051	0.00050

Dielectric constant

t°	ε	
20	4.216	PHILIPPE (not published)

DIPHENYL ETHER $\qquad$ $C_{12}H_{10}O$

Critical temperature: 494° ZHURAVLEV (1937)

Density at 30°: 1.0622 and *Orthobaric densities:* ZHURAVLEV (1937)

Melting point: 26.87 FURUKAWA, GINNINGS *et al.* (1951)
$\qquad$ 26.94° GLEBONSKI (1960)

Specific heat: FURUKAWA, GINNINGS *et al.* (1951)

		Solid			
$t°$	c_p	$t°$	c_p	$t°$	c_p
-255.16	3.563	-188.16	18.288	$-$ 73.16	34.199
253.16	4.316	183.16	18.926	68.16	35.006
251.16	5.060	178.16	19.550	63.16	35.821
249.16	5.805	173.16	20.160	58.16	36.651
247.16	6.532	168.16	20.769	53.16	37.490
245.16	7.242	163.16	21.388	48.16	38.338
243.16	7.935	158.16	22.024	43.16	39.20
241.16	8.575	153.16	22.662	38.16	40.07
239.16	9.196	148.16	23.310	33.16	40.95
237.16	9.787	143.16	23.962	28.16	41.84
235.16	10.343	138.16	24.627	23.16	42.55
233.16	10.860	133.16	25.305	18.16	43.66
231.16	11.341	128.16	25.996	13.16	44.58
229.16	11.792	123.16	26.701	8.16	45.51
227.16	12.220	118.16	27.409	$-$ 3.16	46.44
225.16	12.631	113.16	28.116	$+$ 1.84	47.37
223.16	13.033	108.16	28.833	6.84	48.30
218.16	13.960	103.16	29.564	11.84	50.19
213.16	14.799	98.16	30.304	16.84	51.16
208.16	15.568	93.16	31.065	21.84	51.76
203.16	16.278	88.16	31.845	25.00	52.12
198.16	16.962	83.16	32.612	$+$ 26.872	52.18
$-$ 193.16	17.631	$-$ 78.16	33.400	$-$	$-$

	Liquid			
$t°$	c_p	$t°$	c_p	
+ 26.872	64.17	166.84	79.19	
36.84	65.19	176.84	80.27	
46.84	66.26	186.84	81.34	
56.84	67.33	196.84	82.39	
66.84	68.42	206.84	83.45	
76.84	69.50	216.84	84.54	
86.84	70.59	226.84	85.56	
96.84	71.68	236.84	86.64	
106.84	72.75	246.84	87.72	
116.84	73.83	256.84	88.75	
126.84	74.89	266.84	89.82	
136.84	75.98	276.84	90.87	
146.84	77.14	286.84	91.92	
156.84	78.22	+296.84	92.97	

Heat of fusion: 4.115 cal/mol FURUKAWA, GINNINGS *et al.* (1951)

Heat of combustion (solid, 25°): 1462.53 kcal/mol FURUKAWA, GINNINGS *et al.* (1951)

Dielectric constant at 20°: 3.0922 MECKE and KLINGENBERG (1962)

C. KETONES

QUINONE $C_6H_4O_2$

NITTA, SEKI *et al.* (1951)

Saturated vapour pressure

t°	p mm	t°	p mm	
C. 11.7	0.038	58.7	2.50	
14.9	0.056	62.4	3.38	
17.4	0.073	66.6	4.55	
20.1	0.093	69.8	5.70	
21.0	0.102	73.8	7.51	
24.6	0.140	77.7	9.92	
27.7	0.192	81.9	12.95	
30.6	0.250	85.3	16.11	
31.0	0.264	91.4	22.74	
33.8	0.32	96.7	31.18	
36.9	0.41	98.4	34.52	
39.2	0.52	101.1	40.99	
42.9	0.73	104.4	48.02	
47.1	0.94	108.9	58.46	
49.8	1.20	112.9	75.38	
54.8	1.79	—	—	
L. 115.1	86.03	122.9	115.83	
118.9	99.74	123.5	118.52	
119.4	101.83	125.2	125.55	
120.9	107.38	127.1	133.67	
—	—	127.9	138.98	
—	—	128.4	141.03	

N.B. (p. 475): *Saturated vapour pressure:* The numbers of mm of COOLIDGE and COOLIDGE (1927) must be multiplied by 10^{-3}.

ACETOPHENONE C_8H_8O

FRIED and PICK (1961)
Boiling point: 201.8

Melting point: 19.7

Density at 20°: 1.0281

Refractive index: n_D at 20° = 1.5341

CAPROPHENONE $C_{13}H_{18}O$

See Addenda, pag. 448

BENZOPHENONE $C_{13}H_{10}O$

Freezing point: 48.060 MATHIEU (1953)
48.15 KOMANDIN and BONETSKAYA (1960)

Dielectric constant: (ibid.)

t°	ε	t°	ε	t°	ε
L. +147.0	9.20	− 3.0	14.00	−41.0	9.00
127.0	9.55	13.0	14.55	43.0	7.20
107.0	10.00	18.0	14.60	48.0	4.58
87.0	10.55	23.0	14.70	53.0	4.05
67.0	11.15	28.0	14.35	58.0	3.95
C. 47.0	11.83	33.0	13.63	63.0	3.88
27.0	12.62	35.0	13.10	−73.0	3.80
20.0	12.92	38.0	12.10	—	—
+ 7.0	13.50	−39.0	10.90	—	—

1,2-DIBENZOYLETHANE $C_{16}H_{14}O_2$

SPAGHT, THOMAS and PARKS (1932)

Melting point: 145.4

Heat of fusion: 39.1

Specific heat

t°	cal/gr	t°	cal/gr	t°	cal/gr	t°	cal/gr
30	0.303	80	0.354	130	0.405	170	0.512
40	0.313	90	0.364	140	—	180	0.515
50	0.323	100	0.374	150	0.506	190	0.518
60	0.333	110	0.384	160	0.509	—	—
70	0.344	120	0.395	—	—	—	—

D. ACIDS

BENZOIC ACID $C_7H_6O_2$

(See also Addenda, p. 449)

Melting point: 122.4 DAVIES and JONES (1954)
122.368 MATHIEU (1953)

Saturated vapour pressure: DAVIES and JONES (1954)

$t°$	p mm	$t°$	p mm	$t°$	p mm
70.48	0.0926	89.88	0.515	105.05	1.731
75.14	0.1450	95.35	0.817	109.85	2.558
80.43	0.2327	100.59	1.229	114.11	3.436
84.47	0.330	—	—	—	—

Specific heat: COLE, HUTCHENS *et al.* (1960)

$t°$	c_p	$t°$	c_p	$t°$	c_p
−262.38	0.630	−194.74	13.179	−73.09	24.57
261.40	0.792	189.82	13.721	67.17	25.17
260.36	0.977	184.67	14.248	61.22	25.78
259.21	1.208	179.41	14.734	55.59	26.36
258.02	1.469	174.07	15.202	49.96	26.93
256.77	1.750	168.69	15.683	44.40	27.51
255.38	2.080	163.33	16.174	38.63	28.15
253.88	2.462	158.19	16.631	32.72	28.74
252.16	2.900	153.68	17.081	27.34	29.35
250.25	3.404	147.93	17.535	21.53	29.93
248.09	3.982	142.82	18.005	15.67	30.63
245.45	4.649	139.98	18.266	10.90	31.12
242.81	5.348	134.54	18.762	8.81	31.37
239.86	6.074	129.17	19.231	5.16	31.78
236.45	6.873	123.95	19.705	−3.22	31.98
232.77	7.650	118.74	20.20	+ 0.71	32.46
228.84	8.424	113.14	20.69	6.66	33.12
224.51	9.219	107.54	21.26	12.72	33.75
219.28	10.074	101.89	21.79	13.78	30.94
214.53	10.773	96.30	22.31	18.78	34.34
209.30	11.492	90.61	22.86	24.04	35.00
204.06	12.131	84.84	23.43	27.49	35.50
−199.07	12.688	−78.98	23.99	30.12	35.65

Heat of sublimation: 21850 cal/mol DAVIES and JONES (1954)

SALICYLIC ACID $C_7H_6O_3$

DAVIES and JONES (1954)

Saturated vapour pressure

t°	p mm	t°	p mm	t°	p mm
95.20	0.232	109.96	0.778	125.13	2.415
100.49	0.365	115.01	1.150	134.96	4.87
105.18	0.531	119.98	1.653	—	—

Melting point: 158.6

Heat of sublimation: 22.74 kcal/mol

p-HYDROXYBENZOIC ACID $C_7H_6O_3$

DAVIES and JONES (1954)

Saturated vapour pressure

t°	p mm	t°	p mm	t°	p mm
125.32	0.0227	139.96	0.0798	154.95	0.2592
130.04	0.0344	145.36	0.1204	159.05	0.355
135.04	0.0521	150.08	0.1791	—	—

Heat of sublimation: 27.74 kcal/mol

o-METHOXYBENZOIC ACID $C_8H_8O_3$

DAVIES and JONES (1954)

Saturated vapour pressure

t°	p mm	t°	p mm
80.07	0.0272	90.28	0.0645
84.66	0.0409	95.28	0.0973

Melting point: 101.3

Heat of sublimation: 21.72 kcal/mol

ACETYLSALICYLIC ACID $C_9H_8O_4$

Dielectric constant: KOMANDIN and BONETSKAYA (1960)

$t°$	ε	$t°$	ε	$t°$	ε
143.0	6.40	55.0	6.50	15.0	3.90
120.0	6.43	50.0	6.48	+ 5.0	3.65
98.0	6.45	45.0	6.30	− 5.0	3.42
85.0	6.47	37.5	5.65	−15.0	3.25
65.0	6.48	34.0	5.35	−25.0	3.25
60.0	6.55	24.8	4.40	−34.0	3.25

E. ESTERS

ETHYL BENZOATE $C_9H_{10}O_2$

MUMFORD and PHILLIPS (1958)

Boiling point: 212.2

Density

$t°$	d
20	1.0468
25	1.0421

Viscosity

$t°$	$\eta \cdot 10^5$
20	2220
25	1990

Surface tension

$t°$	γ
20	35.4
25	34.75

Refractive index

$t°$	n_D	
20	1.5051	

METHYL SALICYLATE $C_8H_8O_3$

MATTHEWS, SUMNER and MOELWYN-HUGHES (1950)

Saturated vapour pressure

$t°$	p mm	$t°$	p mm	$t°$	p mm	$t°$	p mm	$t°$	p mm
+ 78.94	4.28	104.44	16.32	132.34	62.82	170.34	248.8	205.94	529.5
84.14	5.675	106.94	17.93	135.64	73.43	177.94	293.4	207.74	556.5
87.84	7.27	108.94	21.01	140.94	81.91	184.14	352.8	208.14	579.8
89.14	7.37	110.64	24.60	144.04	94.84	190.94	374.6	210.24	593.9
92.84	9.06	114.34	26.61	148.34	107.7	192.94	402.0	213.94	642.2
93.04	9.27	114.54	28.77	152.14	123.1	195.74	456.8	219.94	762.0
95.94	10.55	117.54	37.34	156.04	136.8	200.04	460.1	220.44	765.0
100.84	12.94	123.34	48.28	159.64	173.0	201.94	489.3	—	—
103.44	15.04	130.04	53.57	166.04	195.3	203.84	499.4	—	—

Refractive index: n_D at $20° = 1.52395$

METHYL *o*-METHOXYBENZOATE $C_9H_{10}O_3$

Dielectric constant: KOMANDIN and BONETSKAYA (1960)

$t°$	ε	$t°$	ε	$t°$	ε
100.0	6.10	−26.5	10.40	−56.0	9.30
87.0	6.60	37.0	10.80	58.5	8.00
67.5	7.20	33.5	10.90	60.0	6.80
58.0	7.50	43.0	11.00	63.0	5.30
47.0	7.80	46.0	11.05	65.5	4.50
29.5	8.40	49.5	11.00	67.0	4.10
+20.0	8.90	51.5	10.90	68.0	4.00
− 3.0	9.60	53.0	10.60	77.5	3.60
−13.2	9.90	−55.0	9.90	−78.0	3.50
−21.5	10.20	—	—	—	—

ETHYL PHENYLACETATE $C_{10}H_{10}O_2$

B. E. (1959)

Density

$t°$	d	
0	1.05035	
15	1.03636	
30	1.02240	

Viscosity

$t°$	$\eta \cdot 10^5$	
15	2952	
30	2137	

Surface tension

$t°$	γ	
16.70	35.81	
20	35.41	
30	34.19	

Refractive index at 15° and *dn/dt*

He_r	H_C	Na_D	He_y	He_g	II_β	He_{viol}
1.49501	1.49559	1.49972	1.49982	1.50751	1.50940	1.51536
0.00043	0.00043	—	0.00046	0.00048	0.00046	0.00047

Dielectric constant

$t°$	ε	
20	5.158	LAFONTAINE (1958)

DIPHENYL CARBONATE $C_{13}H_{10}O_3$

Specific heat: SINKE, HILDENBRAND *et al.* (1958)

$t°$	c_p	$t°$	c_p	$t°$	c_p	$t°$	c_p
Series I		Series II		Series III			
−257.54	2.34	−137.84	30.51	−259.16	1.84	−124.39	32.67
255.80	2.93	126.27	32.40	256.37	2.75	118.64	33.75
254.00	3.86	120.51	33.48	254.43	3.55	113.01	34.74
252.75	4.79	114.87	34.55	252.35	4.42	107.48	35.60
249.24	5.70	109.35	35.54	249.84	5.43	102.04	36.51
246.68	6.79	103.90	36.28	247.03	6.60	96.70	37.52
243.67	7.97	98.56	37.16	243.89	7.87	91.44	38.40
240.34	9.31	92.67	38.44	240.44	9.15	86.25	39.39
236.87	10.50	86.25	39.62	236.91	10.46	80.51	40.28
233.17	11.84	79.93	40.45	233.16	11.83	74.23	41.59
228.92	13.21	73.72	41.74	228.86	13.16	68,05	42.70
224.14	14.84	67.61	42.83	223.72	14.81	61.97	43.93
−219.03	16.45	61.60	43.97	218.61	16.63	55.98	45.11
		55.68	45.10	213.24	17.96	50.08	46.15
		49.85	46.06	207.78	19.21	44.26	47.47
		44.10	47.44	191.55	21.93	38.53	49.18
		38.44	48.64	185.94	22.84	27.31	50.85
		27.36	50.71	179.84	23.98	21.79	51.93
		21.90	51.64	174.04	24.99	16.34	53.27
		16.51	52.98	168.48	26.01	10.96	54.43
		11.20	54.22	163.14	26.67	5.64	55.65
		5.94	55.23	157.96	27.40	− 0.38	56.86
		− 0.75	56.52	152.94	28.19	+ 4.82	57.71
		+ 9.47	58.64	148.05	28.80	10.50	59.06
		14.48	60.13	143.27	29.62	16.58	61.04
		19.44	61.17	138.60	30.50	22.56	62.49
		24.34	62.51	134.02	31.16	28.48	63.92
		29.19	63.76	−129.53	31.77	+ 34.32	65.12
		33.98	65.49				
		38.70	66.68				
		+ 43.39	67.74				

5. OXYGENATED DERIVATIVES OF POLYMETHYLENES

CYCLOBUTANONE C_4H_6O

B. E. (1950)

Boiling point: 98.90 *dt/dp:* 0.47 (10 mm)

Density

t°	d
0	0.95428
15	0.93835
30	0.92231

Viscosity

t°	$\eta \cdot 10^5$
15	653
30	553

Surface tension

t°	γ
16.10	32.53
20	31.93
30	30.56

Refractive index at 15° and *dn/dt*

He_r	H_C	Na_D	He_y	He_g	H_β	He_{viol}	H_γ
1.42057	1.42084	1.42325	1.42335	1.42787	1.42901	1.43236	1.43379
0.00045	0.00043	—	0.00045	0.00047	0.00046	0.00047	0.00047

Dielectric constant: ARNDT, GÜNTHARD and GÄUMANN (1958)

t°	ε	t°	ε
−75	1.88	−16	16.17
67	1.96	0	15.47
60	2.12	+10	14.97
53	18.75	25	14.27
51.5	18.52	33	13.96
40	17.82	44	13.47
−27	17.00	55	12.96

CYCLOPENTANONE C_5H_8O

Dielectric constant: PHILIPPE and PIETTE (1955)

t°	ε	t°	ε
+20.00	13.48	−74.7	2.813
+ 1.80	14.08	—	—
−22.1	14.90	−54.6	2.851
34.5	15.33	51.8	2.867
50.0	15.88	45.9	15.74
51.9	15.99	−10.1	14.48
−64.5	2.825	+14.10	13.67

CYCLOHEXANOL $C_6H_{12}O$

Saturated vapour pressure: NOVAK, MALOUS and PICK (1960)

t°	p mm	t°	p mm	t°	p mm
93.73	53.83	112.70	136.90	136.22	340.2
97.02	69.08	116.86	164.20	142.41	423.4
99.71	78.20	120.35	189.5	148.72	521.2
102.52	89.08	125.54	231.5	155.71	645.4
104.83	98.70	130.95	281.6	160.70	744
108.82	115.30	—	—	—	—

Boiling point: 161.4 NOVAK, MALOUS and PICK (1960)

Density at 30°: 0.94156 NOVAK, MALOUS and PICK (1960)

Refractive index: n_D at 25° = 1.4645 NOVAK, MALOUS and PICK (1960)

Dielectric constant: PHILIPPE and PIETTE (1955)

t°	ε	t°	ε	
41.95	13.82	−41.1	2.72	
30.05	15.51	33.3	2.81	
26.40	16.05	20.1	3.31	
24.10	16.41	15.0	3.80	
23.40	15.61	11.8	5.74	
17.80	16.11	− 7.0	18.33	
8.10	16.90	+13.75	16.45	
7.50	16.96	21.25	15.85	
+ 0.55	17.61	24.20	15.85	
− 8.8	18.49	25.10	16.27	
10.2	18.60	30.30	15.46	
27.5	3.00	36.05	14.63	
34.6	2.79	+48.00	13.04	

CYCLOHEXANONE $C_6H_{10}O$

Dielectric constant: PHILIPPE and PIETTE (1955)

t°	ε	t°	ε	
+10.20	16.30	−64.8	3.03	
−10.1	17.48	50.3	3.70	
29.4	18.62	44.0	19.26	
33.2	18.84	31.5	18.60	
35.9	18.84	−19.7	18.05	
48.9	19.49	0.00	16.89	
55.8	3.38	+19.95	15.74	
−74.7	2.90	+24.45	15.48	

CAMPHOR $C_{10}H_{16}O$

Saturated vapour pressure: KUBOKAWA (1929)

$t°$	p mm	$t°$	p mm	$t°$	p mm
0.0	0.08	60.3	3.02		
13.0	0.19	65.2	4.20		
28.9	0.52	70.4	5.38		
35.6	0.79	75.2	6.88	(three series)	
43.9	1.29	80.3	8.95		
47.3	1.54	84.4	10.86		
49.5	1.78	90.2	13.54		
55.1	2.38				
0.0	0.07	92.2	14.3	149.9	152.0
15.6	0.21	100.2	19.7	154.9	179.5
24.2	0.39	104.9	24.6	160.4	212.0
34.9	0.75	110.1	31.1	164.2	241.8
42.0	1.17	115.6	38.9	170.2	290.7
46.9	1.52	120.7	47.3	175.2	344.1
50.0	1.81	125.8	60.6	179.6	396.6
56.0	2.53	130.5	73.3	184.8	456.3
61.0	3.27	135.2	87.6	189.9	520.3
64.8	4.02	140.6	106.9	192.7	557.5
70.7	5.25	145.8	132.1	193.6	570.5
76.2	6.78				
81.6	8.83				
87.0	12.09				
90.8	13.80				
99.6	19.1				
99.6	19.1				
103.9	23.1				
111.1	31.7				

6. HETEROCYCLIC OXYGEN COMPOUNDS

ETHYLENE OXIDE C_2H_4O

Dielectric constant: NICKERSON and McINTOSH (1957)

t°	ε	t°	ε	t°	ε
20.0	12.42	−10.0	14.50	−20.2	15.37
9.7	13.10	−14.8	14.85	−30.0	16.10
1.1	13.63	−15.2	14.88	−30.0	16.11
− 5.0	14.10	—	—	—	—

FURAN C_4H_4O

Critical temperature: 217.05° CHENG, McCOUBREY and PHILLIPS (1962)

Saturated vapour pressure: GUTHRIE, SCOTT et al. (1952)

t°	p mm	t°	p mm	t°	p mm
2.552	233.72	21.614	525.86	41.241	1074.6
7.267	289.13	26.469	633.99	46.232	1268.0
12.018	355.22	31.357	760.00	51.265	1489.1
16.797	433.56	36.279	906.06	56.329	1740.8
—	—	—	—	61.430	2026.0

Boiling point: 31.36 dt/dp: 0.37 (10 mm) B. E. (1959)
　　　　　　　31.33° (765 mm) CHENG, McCOUBREY and PHILLIPS (1962)

Freezing point: −85.62 GUTHRIE, SCOTT et al. (1952)

Transition point: −123.15 ibid.

Density

t°	d		t°	d	
0	0.96499	B.E. (1959)	10	0.95144	GUTHRIE, SCOTT
10.90	0.95053		15	0.94467	et al. (1952)
15	0.94485		20	0.93781	
20	0.93825				
25	0.93136				

Viscosity: B. E. (1959)

$t°$	$\eta \cdot 10^5$	
10.90	419	
20	380	
25	361	

Surface tension: B. E. (1959)

$t°$	γ	
16.40	24.57	
20	24.10	
25	23.38	

Refractive index at 15° and *dn/dt* B. E. (1959)

He_r	H_C	Na_D	He_y	He_g	H_β	He_{viol}	H_γ
1.42037	1.42099	1.42385	1.42395	1.43075	1.43240	1.43708	1.43951
0.00060	0.00060	—	0.00060	0.00062	0.00062	0.00060	0.00064

Idem at 20° GUTHRIE, SCOTT *et al.* (1952)

H_α	Na_D	Hg_{gr}	He_{bl}	H_β	He_{viol}
1.41822	1.42140	1.42418	1.42791	1.42954	1.43619

Dielectric constant: LAFONTAINE (1958)

$t°$	ε	
20	2.954	

Specific heat: GUTHRIE, SCOTT *et al.* (1952)

t°	c_p	t°	c_p	t°	c_p	t°	c_p
Crystals I				Crystals II		Liquid	
−261.44	0.919	−217.72	8.956	−119.89	17.169	−82.16	23.857
260.52	1.096	217.48	8.988	119.78	17.188	79.02	23.899
260.43	1.125	215.90	9.100	118.75	17.278	76.93	23.921
259.19	1.416	214.82	9.168	117.69	17.345	72.85	23.990
258.58	1.546	214.38	9.201	116.41	17.392	70.00	24.033
257.49	1.795	214.13	9.224	114.50	17.496	65.42	24.122
256.26	2.073	213.96	9.221	114.28	17.503	63.12	24.161
255.42	2.267	211.64	9.422	113.59	17.547	55.87	24.309
253.78	2.657	209.25	9.623	112.39	17.624	47.84	24.520
253.12	2.814	204.73	9.945	109.31	17.792	39.52	24.755
251.12	3.287	203.19	10.059	106.32	18.008	31.19	25.030
250.71	3.384	199.53	10.290	103.80	18.176	23.01	25.312
248.34	3.922	194.18	10.619	100.38	18.448	16.91	25.540
248.13	3.974	189.06	10.927	97.98	18.627	14.94	25.637
245.61	4.523	184.13	11.181	94.58	18.961	7.45	25.917
245.01	4.649	179.34	11.382	− 89.41	20.488	− 6.94	25.933
242.66	5.140	177.62	11.452			+ 0.95	26.284
241.84	5.314	169.66	11.789			2.26	26.319
239.79	5.723	160.65	12.192			9.13	26.630
238.66	5.939	153.72	12.545			12.20	26.778
235.28	6.552	152.00	12.604			17.59	27.038
231.40	7.194	147.61	12.851			21.61	27.229
227.06	7.824	147.05	12.857			+25.93	27.440
222.67	8.404	143.68	13.033				
219.63	8.765	143.44	13.038				
219.60	8.769	140.94	13.224				
219.14	8.809	140.58	13.219				
218.36	8.890	136.44	13.468				
−218.16	8.915	−130.98	13.849				

Heat of vaporization: GUTHRIE, SCOTT *et al.* (1952)

t°	cal/mol
+ 6.00	6810
20.00	6628
31.36	6474

Heat of melting: 908.8 cal/mol *ibid.*

Heat of transition: 489.2 cal/mol *ibid.*

Heat of combustion at 25°: 497.97 kcal/mol *ibid.*

FURFURALDEHYDE $C_5H_4O_3$

MATTHEWS, SUMNER and MOELWYN-HUGHES (1950)

Saturated vapour pressure

t°	p mm	t°	p mm	t°	p mm	t°	p mm	t°	p mm
+55.86	13.25	87.37	61.8	107.26	137.2	126.34	271.0	146.84	517.8
56.06	13.45	92.14	74.7	111.64	162.4	132.14	326.9	149.64	538.0
64.57	20.90	93.04	77.32	116.24	185.5	132.79	339.8	151.69	579.4
67.69	24.91	96.76	90.46	118.39	203.9	135.94	367.1	153.94	618.6
75.04	35.1	102.12	113.1	120.84	223.1	138.34	399.5	155.09	641.0
76.46	37.76	103.30	117.8	124.74	256.1	139.94	422.8	160.74	764.2
84.94	54.41	105.08	127.6	126.04	263.0	143.79	462.3	—	—

γ-BUTYROLACTONE $C_4H_6O_2$

McKINLEY and COPES (1950)

Saturated vapour pressure

t°	p mm	t°	p mm		
119	50.1	174	316.3		
132	79.4	189	501.2		
145	125.9	201	708.0		
159	199.6	—	—		

Freezing point: −43.53

Density at 25°: 1.1254

Refractive index: n_D^{25} 1.4348

DIOXAN $C_4H_8O_2$

Boiling point: 101.40 GRIFFITHS (1952)
101.38 HUET, PHILIPPE and BONO (1953)

Melting point: 11.78 GRUBB and OSTHOFF (1952)

Density

t°	d	
25	1.02808	GRIFFITHS (1952)
25	1.02797	HAMMOND and STOKES (1955)
14.60	1.0394	KETELAAR and VAN MEURS (1957)
23.30	1.0297	,,
31.35	1.0208	,,

Refractive index

t°	H$_\alpha$	Na$_D$	H$_\beta$	
21.2	1.4194	—	1.4268	HUET, PHILIPPE and BONO (1953)
25		1.4206		HAMMOND and STOKES (1955)
14.60		1.42456		KETELAAR and VAN MEURS (1957)
23.30		1.42048		,,
31.35		1.41672		,,

Specific magnetic susceptibility at 20°: $-0.595 \cdot 10^{-6}$ VON RAUTENFELD and STEURER (1942)

N.B. (p. 502): ROSENDAL should read HØJENDAHL.

8. MIXED OXYHALOGENATED DERIVATIVES

CARBONYL CHLORIDE or PHOSGENE $COCl_2$

GIAUQUE and OTT (1960)

Melting point: $-127.78°$

Specific heat (in gibbs/mol)

t°	c_p	t°	c_p	t°	c_p
Solid I		**Solid II**		**Liquid**	
−260.54	1.319	−140.32	14.87	−133.20	25.28
258.77	1.822	−137.19	15.13	−127.60	25.04
256.88	2.371	−131.06	M.P.II.	−120.68	24.84
254.96	3.472			−112.60	24.62
252.52	3.685				
249.54	4.885		**Vapour**		
246.13	5.440				
242.40	6.412	−258.15	7.949	−113.15	10.408
238.25	7.281	253.15	7.949	103.15	10.703
233.82	8.074	248.15	7.949	93.15	10.996
229.05	8.837	243.15	7.950	83.15	11.281
223.92	9.449	238.15	7.951	73.15	11.559
218.78	9.965	233.15	7.957	63.15	11.829
213.18	10.52	228.15	7.968	53.15	12.090
207.26	10.98	223.15	7.987	43.15	12.341
201.07	11.46	218.15	8.016	33.15	12.582
193.93	11.93	213.15	8.056	23.15	12.812
186.18	12.36	203.15	8.169	13.15	13.033
178.44	12.82	193.15	8.322	− 3.15	13.245
170.93	13.26	183.15	8.512	+ 6.85	13.447
163.33	13.73	173.15	8.733	7.56	13.460
155.67	14.17	163.15	8.979	16.85	13.639
149.51	14.61	153.15	9.245	25	13.791
144.64	14.87	143.15	9.526	26.85	13.824
133.64	15.26	133.15	9.816	76.85	14.631
133.74	16.08	127.78	9.973	126.85	15.284
−127.78	M.P.I.	123.15	10.110	+226.85	16.270

Heat of fusion : 1371.5 cal/mol

Heat of ftransition I: 1335.4 cal/mol at $-131.06°$
                    II: 1131   cal/mol at $-133.96°$

FORMYL FLUORIDE   CHOF

Vapour pressure: FISCHER and BUCHANAN (1964)

$t°$	p (mm)	$t°$	p (mm)	$t°$	p (mm)	$t°$	p (mm)
− 38.0	427.0	− 60.5	113.0	− 67.5	76.0	− 78.0	39.5
43.5	330.0	61.6	110.0	70.0	61.7	78.0	39.5
44.8	309.0	62.5	103.0	71.5	63.0	78.0	38.4
45.5	313.2	63.0	104.0	72.4	52.6	85.0	22.0
51.5	215.0	63.2	103.0	74.2	45.1	87.0	17.5
53.5	186.4	65.9	89.0	74.5	51.5	89.0	13.4
54.3	188.5	66.1	83.0	75.0	43.0	91.5	10.8
56.5	161.0	− 67.0	76.6	− 77.5	36.0	− 94.7	0.79
− 59.7	130.0						

CARBONYL CHLOROFLUORIDE   COFCl

Vapour pressure: FISCHER and BUCHANAN (1964)

$t°$	p (cm)	$t°$	p (cm)	$t°$	p (cm)	$t°$	p (cm)
− 62.4	290.4	− 72.0	163.8	− 87.0	57.8	− 102.6	13.2
63.0	278.3	74.0	144.6	90.0	44.0	105.8	9.9
64.7	256.0	75.5	130.6	− 97.4	22.5	− 108.9	7.4
− 67.5	214.1	− 77.7	104.2				

CAPROYL CHLORIDE $C_6H_{11}OCl$

SIMON (1929)

Boiling point: 152.60°   *Freezing point:* −87.3°

Density

$t°$	d	$t°$	d	$t°$	d
0	0.99541	15	0.98047	30	0.96540

Refractive index

$t°$	He $_r$	H_α	Na$_D$	He $_y$	He $_g$	H_β	He $_{viol}$	H_γ
15	1.42593	1.42615	1.42859	1.42877	1.43341	1.43467	1.43824	1.43981
25	1.42148	1.42181	1.42424	1.42435	1.42896	1.43024	1.43377	1.43505

MONOCHLOROACETYLCHLORIDE $C_2H_2Cl_2O$

TRICHLOROACETYLCHLORIDE C_2Cl_4O

See SERYAKOV, VAKS and SIDORINA (1960)

MONOFLUOROACETIC ACID   C$_2$H$_3$O$_2$F

Saturated vapour pressure: JASPER and MILLER (1955)

t°	p mm	t°	p mm	t°	p mm	t°	p mm	t°	p mm
20	4.00	55	5.59	90	34.96	120	131.5	150	409.8
25	4.10	60	7.32	95	44.26	125	160.8	155	487.7
30	4.20	65	9.69	100	55.68	130	195.7	160	587.2
35	4.30	70	12.71	105	69.60	135	237.1	165	682.5
40	4.39	75	16.55	110	86.51	140	285.7	170	903.1
45	4.49	80	21.38	115	106.90	145	343.1	—	—
50	4.59	85	27.44	—	—	—	—	—	—

Boiling point: 168.29° ibid.

Melting point: 35.3 ibid.

Density and *Surface tension:* JASPER and GRODZKA (1954)

t°	d	γ	t°	d	γ
36	1.3693	38.21	70	1.3238	34.43
40	1.3639	37.76	80	1.3105	33.32
50	1.3505	36.65	95	1.2905	31.64
60	1.3372	35.54	—	—	—

MONOCHLOROACETIC ACID   C$_2$H$_3$O$_2$Cl

GLASGOW Jr. and TIMMERMANS (1961)

Dielectric constant

t°	ε	t°	ε	t°	ε	t°	ε
Cooling		Heating		Cooling		Heating	
57.4	3.063	20.07	2.909	20.0	2.908	−38.0	2.802
55.0	3.050	41.0	2.974	14.6	2.895	22.0	2.814
50.6	3.021	58.7	3.142	1.0	2.857	12.0	2.830
45.2	2.987	60.8	3.184	−11.0	2.830	− 4.0	2.844
40.7	2.972	62.1	3.353	21.3	2.814	—	—
35.4	2.947	—	—	40.0	2.799	—	—
30.0	2.924	—	—	−60.8	2.778	—	—
25.0	2.917	—	—	—	—	—	—
20.0	2.904	—	—	—	—	—	—

Liquid		Solid		Solid		Solid	
Cooling		Heating		Cooling		Heating	
77.0	17.1	20.0	3.35	62.3	4.10	24.3	2.90
74.0	17.0	30.0	3.39	61.8	3.81	33.4	2.96
70.0	16.8	40.0	3.47	58.8	3.28	43.9	3.02
68.2	16.6	50.0	3.62	57.1	3.27	53.5	3.24
63.4	16.2	53.0	3.65	50.1	3.18	62.4	4.22
—	—	58.3	3.73	41.5	3.06	62.8	5.08
—	—	60.5	3.85	35.0	2.98	—	—
—	—	—	—	24.3	2.90		

MONOBROMOACETIC ACID $C_2H_3O_2Br$

GLASGOW Jr. and TIMMERMANS (1961)

Pressure for fusion and transitions

Cr III → L   Cr I → Cr II   Cr II → Cr III

$t°$	kg/cm²	$t°$	kg/cm²	$t°$	kg/cm²
54.8	335	15.2	563	15.2	1650
60.0	570	30.1	395	30.1	990
74.8	1370	45.1	200	45.1	500
89.8	2265	—	—	—	—

Specific heat

$t°$	c_p	$t°$	c_p	$t°$	c_p
−179.99	13.02	−115.01	17.11	−44.96	21.52
175.79	13.33	110.68	17.32	38.83	21.93
171.70	13.72	106.93	17.57	34.32	22.22
166.91	14.02	102.09	17.34	30.57	22.50
162.18	14.33	97.63	18.16	23.50	22.84
158.18	14.48	94.41	18.41	19.55	23.15
152.50	14.74	88.94	18.78	15.08	23.55
148.46	14.99	83.00	18.97	11.49	23.73
144.55	15.17	79.71	19.26	− 7.61	24.04
140.51	15.41	72.92	19.79	+ 0.88	24.83
136.16	15.64	72.72	19.80	4.04	25.12
131.39	16.08	69.24	19.98	7.47	25.49
126.88	16.32	60.10	20.51	12.67	26.11
122.87	16.63	51.87	21.11	28.22	29.79
−119.27	16.68	− 46.91	21.43	33.49	33.82
—	—	—	—	+37.19	39.30

DICHLOROACETIC ACID $C_2H_2O_2Cl_2$

GLASGOW Jr. and TIMMERMANS (1961)

Pressure for solid-liquid transition

$t°$	kg/cm²
15.2	100
30.1	695
45.0	1510–1605
59.4	2200

Dielectric constant

1. Cooling		2. Heating		3. Heating	
$t°$	ε	$t°$	ε	$t°$	ε
Liquid		**Solid**		**Solid to liquid**	
20.0	8.19	−124.0	2.31	9.8	2.90
15.5	8.19	105.0	2.32	10.3	2.96
13.5	8.19	75.0	2.33	10.65	3.01
11.5	8.19	65.0	2.33	11.6	3.20
7.0	8.19	60.0	2.34	12.55	3.42
0.0	8.19	52.0	2.38	13.1	4.20
		38.0	2.40	13.35	4.57
Solid		22.0	2.46	13.35	5.60
		− 15.0	2.48	—	—
+ 6.0	2.58	+ 3.0	2.60	—	—
− 3.0	2.56	+ 9.5	2.71	—	—
− 15.0	2.49	+ 10.4	2.95	—	—
− 30.0	2.43	—	—	—	—
− 45.0	2.38				
−124.0	2.31				

Specific heat

t°	c_p	t°	c_p
−179.56	14.38	−77.55	22.50
174.32	14.82	75.12	22.58
170.00	15.38	74.32	22.63
154.49	16.67	70.40	22.83
150.14	18.87	68.60	23.08
146.37	17.16	54.75	24.08
143.37	17.43	51.06	24.35
140.14	17.70	44.35	24.69
136.67	17.90	40.69	25.03
129.30	18.41	36.71	25.39
125.21	18.86	25.33	26.26
121.82	19.13	19.98	26.62
118.71	19.38	16.20	27.02
114.51	19.58	12.44	27.52
109.78	20.00	9.27	27.79
101.27	20.60	6.03	28.53
91.24	21.31	− 2.06	31.88
85.08	21.77	+ 4.06	34.15
− 81.11	22.07	+ 7.16	43.55

PENTACHLOROPHENOL C_6HOCl_5

HILDENBRAND, KRAMER and STULL (1958)

Melting point: 189.65

Specific heat

t°	c_p	t°	c_p	t°	c_p
−258.16	2.45	−193.16	19.78	−83.15	37.12
253.16	4.11	188.16	20.80	73.15	38.33
248.16	5.83	183.16	21.79	63.15	39.50
243.16	7.40	178.16	22.75	53.15	40.63
238.16	8.86	173.17	23.68	43.15	41.72
233.16	10.25	163.16	25.47	33.15	42.77
228.16	11.60	153.16	27.17	23.15	43.79
223.16	12.92	143.16	28.79	13.15	44.78
218.16	14.17	133.16	30.33	− 3.15	45.73
213.16	15.37	123.16	31.81	+ 6.85	46.66
208.16	16.53	113.15	33.23	16.85	47.56
203.16	17.65	103.16	34.59	25.00	48.27
−198.16	18.73	− 93.15	35.90	26.85	48.43

BENZOYL BROMIDE

Saturated vapour pressure

t°	p mm	t°	p mm	t°	p mm	
0	0.178	74.6	5.993	160.0	208.4	HARUICHI and YOSHIMOTO (1928)
6	0.211	80.0	7.910	166.0	248.5	,,
9.6	0.225	84.0	9.702	171.7	298.0	,,
15.8	0.252	90.0	12.98	181.2	405.0	,,
20.5	0.275	96.0	18.05	185.0	443.7	,,
29.8	0.444	100.0	21.1	188.0	492.7	,,
40.0	0.810	111.0	33.8	200.0	655.4	,,
50.6	1.458	120.0	47.6	—	—	,,
55.0	2.066	130.0	71.2	—	—	,,
59.8	2.800	140.5	104.5	—	—	,,
70.0	4.770	150.0	147.4	—	—	,,

Density, Viscosity and *Dielectric constant*

t°	d	$\eta \cdot 10^5$	ε	
10.0	1.5564	2334	22.54	GUTMANN and UTVARY (1958)
15.0	1.5516	2142	21.92	,,
20.0	1.5467	1956	21.33	,,
25.0	1.5416	1798	20.74	,,
30.0	1.5368	1652	20.17	,,
35.0	1.5319	1532	19.63	,,
40.0	1.5270	1432	19.09	,,

FLUORO ESTERS

See MACEY (1960)

CHLORO ESTERS

See MUMFORD and PHILLIPS (1950)

9. NITROGEN DERIVATIVES OF THE ALIPHATIC SERIES

A. AMINES

DIETHYLAMINE $\qquad$ C$_4$H$_{11}$N

Critical temperature: 223.3° COSTELLO and BOWDEN (1959)

Boiling point: 55.3° COSTELLO and BOWDEN (1959)

Saturated vapour pressure between 15° and 55°: $\log_{10} p \, (mm) =$
6.97237 — 1127.0/(t° + 220) COPP and EVERETT (1953)

Density

t°	d	t°	d	
−40	0.7687	60	0.6637	COSTELLO and BOWDEN (1959)
−20	0.7480	80	0.6414	,,
0	0.7272	100	0.6185	,,
20	0.7063	120	0.5936	,,
40	0.6849	140	0.5662	,,

METHYLDIETHYLAMINE $\qquad$ C$_5$H$_{13}$N

Saturated vapour pressure at 35.0°: 254.60 mm COPP (1955)
$\qquad\qquad\qquad$ at 47.8°: 400.75 mm *ibid.*

Boiling point: 65.95 *dt/dp:* 0.042 *ibid.*

Lower critical solution point in water: 49.42° (34% amine).

Heat of vaporization: 7.23 kcal/mol *ibid.*

DIMETHYLAMINE $\qquad$ C$_2$H$_7$N.

N.B. (p. 521): *Specific heat*, 0.7096 should read 0.37096.

TRIMETHYLAMINE $\qquad$ C$_3$H$_4$N

N.B. (p. 523): The *heat of vaporization* was measured at −23.16 instead of +23.16.

TRIETHYLAMINE $C_6H_{15}N$

Critical temperature: 258.9° COSTELLO and BOWDEN (1959)

Boiling temperature: 89.5°   COSTELLO and BOWDEN (1959)
                       89.55° COPP and EVERETT (1953)

Saturated vapour pressure: KRICHEVSKII, KHAZANOVA, SVETLOVA and PANINA (1960)

t°	p mm	t°	p mm	
13.58	36.7	32.20	94.9	
18.07	48.5	40.55	135.1	
23.50	62.8	60.25	292.5	
27.57	76.6	79.12	555.15	

$$\log_{10} p \, (\text{mm}) = 7.00853 - \frac{1307.8}{(t° + 272.3)} \text{ COPP and EVERETT (1953)}$$

Density

t°	d	t°	d	
−60	0.8005	+ 60	0.6903	COSTELLO and BOWDEN (1959)
−40	0.7829	80	0.6710	,,
−20	0.7650	100	0.6513	,,
0	0.7465	120	0.6310	,,
20	0.7277	140	0.6097	,,
40	0.7091	160	0.5864	,,
15.0	0.73275	25.0	0.72345	KRICHEVSKII, KHAZANOVA
17.5	0.73082	27.5	0.72110	SVETLOVA and PANINA (1960)
20.0	0.72807	30.0	0.71875	,,
22.5	0.72575	—	—	,,

Refractive index: KRICHEVSKII, KHAZANOVA, SVETLOVA and PANINA (1960)

t°	n_D	
16.0	1.4023	
18.0	1.4010	
20.0	1.4004	

n_D at 20° = 1.40025 KOHLER and ROTT (1954)

PROPYLAMINE C_3H_9N

COSTELLO and BOWDEN (1959)

Critical temperature: 223.8°

Boiling point: 48.5°

Density

t°	d	t°	d
−60	0.7970	+ 60	0.6752
−40	0.7768	80	0.6529
−20	0.7567	100	0.6296
0	0.7364	120	0.6047
+20	0.7163	140	0.5769
40	0.6960	—	—

Iso-PROPYLAMINE C_3H_9N

COSTELLO and BOWDEN (1959)

Critical temperature: 209.7°

Boiling point: 33.0°

Density

t°	d	t°	d
−60	0.7713	+20	0.6891
−40	0.7513	40	0.6665
−20	0.7312	60	0.6432
0	0.7103	80	0.6214
—	—	+100	0.5924

DIPROPYLAMINE $C_6H_{15}N$

COSTELLO and BOWDEN (1959)

Critical temperature: 277.0°

Boiling point: 109.0°

Density

t°	d	t°	d
−60	0.8130	+ 80	0.6849
−40	0.7948	100	0.6658
−20	0.7763	120	0.6458
0	0.7580	140	0.6253
+20	0.7398	160	0.6031
+40	0.7216	180	0.5799
+60	0.7032	—	—

DI-*iso*-PROPYLAMINE $C_6H_{15}N$

COSTELLO and BOWDEN (1959)

Critical temperature: 221.1°

Boiling point: 83.0°

Density

t°	d	t°	d	
−60	0.7918	+ 60	0.6769	
−40	0.7730	80	0.6571	
−20	0.7539	100	0.6366	
0	0.7345	120	0.6152	
+20	0.7153	140	0.5923	
+40	0.6964	+160	0.5671	

TRIPROPYLAMINE $C_9H_{21}N$

COSTELLO and BOWDEN (1959)

Critical temperature: 304.3°

Boiling point: 156.5°

Density

t°	d	t°	d	
−60	0.8189	+100	0.6917	
−40	0.8038	120	0.6744	
−20	0.7882	140	0.6570	
0	0.7724	160	0.6388	
+20	0.7564	180	0.6194	
40	0.7404	200	0.5990	
60	0.7245	+220	0.5765	
+80	0.7084	—	—	

BUTYLAMINE $C_4H_{11}N$

COSTELLO and BOWDEN (1959)
Critical temperature: 287.9°
Boiling point: 78.0° (758 mm)
Density

t°	d	t°	d	
−60	0.8144	+ 60	0.7067	
−40	0.7973	80	0.6870	
−20	0.7798	100	0.6671	
0	0.7620	120	0.6465	
+20	0.7440	140	0.6232	
+40	0.7253	160	0.5971	

Iso-BUTYLAMINE $C_4H_{11}N$

COSTELLO and BOWDEN (1959)
Critical temperature: 266.7°
Boiling point: 67.7° (758 mm)
Density

t°	d	t°	d	
−60	0.8042	+ 60	0.6942	
−40	0.7872	80	0.6743	
−20	0.7694	100	0.6535	
0	0.7513	120	0.6308	
+20	0.7330	140	0.6064	
+40	0.7136	+160	0.5805	

DIBUTYLAMINE $C_8H_{19}N$

COSTELLO and BOWDEN (1959)
Critical temperature: 322.6°
Boiling point: 159°
Density

t°	d	t°	d	
−40	0.8086	+120	0.6762	
−20	0.7921	140	0.6576	
0	0.7759	160	0.6390	
+20	0.7595	180	0.6191	
40	0.7431	200	0.5985	
60	0.7269	220	0.5764	
80	0.7099	240	0.5522	
+100	0.6932	+260	0.5271	

DI-*iso*-BUTYLAMINE $C_8H_{19}N$

COSTELLO and BOWDEN (1959)

Critical temperature: 281.3°

Boiling point: 139.1°

Density

t°	d	t°	d	
−60	0.8118	+100	0.6763	
−40	0.7949	120	0.6586	
−20	0.7782	140	0.6402	
0	0.7610	160	0.6215	
+20	0.7443	180	0.6009	
40	0.7273	200	0.5787	
60	0.7104	+220	0.5545	
+80	0.6938	—	—	

TRIBUTYLAMINE $C_{12}H_{27}N$

COSTELLO and BOWDEN (1959)

Critical temperature: 365.2°

Boiling point: 212.0°

Density

t°	d	t°	d	
−40	0.8237	+140	0.6861	
−20	0.8086	160	0.6699	
0	0.7935	180	0.6528	
+20	0.7784	200	0.6353	
40	0.7634	220	0.6171	
60	0.7482	240	0.5978	
80	0.7331	260	0.5774	
100	0.7178	+280	0.5559	
+120	0.7020	—	—	

AMYLAMINE $C_5H_{13}N$

The data of Costello and Bowden (1959) and Mumford and Phillips (1950) do not agree.

HEXYLAMINE $C_6H_{15}N$

Costello and Bowden (1959)

Critical temperature: 318.8°

Boiling point: 130.0°

Density

$t°$	d	$t°$	d	
−20	0.7970	+120	0.6784	
0	0.7810	140	0.6596	
+20	0.7649	160	0.6404	
40	0.7481	180	0.6200	
60	0.7310	200	0.5980	
80	0.7140	+220	0.5742	
+100	0.6964	—	—	

DODECYLAMINE $C_{12}H_{27}N$

Costello and Bowden (1959)

Critical temperature: 414.2°

Boiling point: 258.0°

Melting point: 26.8°

Density

$t°$	d	$t°$	d	
40	0.7841	180	0.6804	
60	0.7699	200	0.6648	
80	0.7554	220	0.6482	
100	0.7413	240	0.6322	
120	0.7265	260	0.6156	
140	0.7115	280	0.5985	
160	0.6960	300	0.5805	

HEXADECYLAMINE $C_{16}H_{35}N$

COSTELLO and BOWDEN (1959)

Critical temperature: 431.0°

Boiling point: 319.0°

Melting point: 45.0°

Density

t°	d	t°	d
60	0.7821	200	0.6851
80	0.7684	220	0.6710
100	0.7544	240	0.6560
120	0.7407	260	0.6405
140	0.7269	280	0.6249
160	0.7130	300	0.6075
180	0.6991	—	—

ETHYLENEDIAMINE $C_2H_8N_2$

HIEBER and WOERNER (1934)

Saturated vapour pressure

t°	p mm	t°	p mm
26.51	13.1	76.51	173.6
29.49	16.1	81.36	208.8
32.01	18.0	88.89	284.1
34.60	21.5	91.42	309.9
36.92	24.4	91.78	313.7
38.40	27.5	94.50	355.0
39.77	30.8	97.38	383.5
42.51	34.4	101.01	435.1
46.65	43.2	102.92	467.9
51.71	54.7	105.50	519.0
56.82	70.4	107.03	547.1
60.04	82.1	108.01	568.1
62.29	91.4	112.38	649.6
65.60	106.2	116.21	736.2
71.02	136.2	117.40	760.5
71.71	139.7	—	—

B. E. (1959)

Boiling point: 117.26 ; *dt/dp (10 mm):* 0.45

Density

$t°$	d	
0	0.91411	
15	0.90001	
30	0.88595	

Viscosity

$t°$	$\eta \cdot 10^5$	
15	1722	
30	1226	

Surface tension

$t°$	γ	
17.15	41.14	
20	40.77	
30	39.49	

Refractive index: $n^{15°}$ and *dn/dt*

He_r	H_α	Na_D	He_y	He_{gr}	H_β	He_{viol}	H_γ
1.45564	1.45603	1.45887	1.45897	1.46431	1.46555	1.46960	1.47010
0.00050	0.00050	—	0.00050	0.00052	0.00050	0.00050	—

Dielectric constant

$t°$	ε	
−31	3.25	LAFONTAINE (1958)

Heat of vaporization: at   0°: 16.04 cal/mol
at 20°: 11.20 cal/mol

Heat of melting: 26.23 cal/mol

As.-DIMETHYLHYDRAZINE $C_2H_8N_2$

ASTON, WOOD and ZOLKI (1953)

Saturated vapour pressure

$t°$	p mm	$t°$	p mm	
−35.41	3.51	− 2.07	36.65	
23.33	8.92	+ 5.06	55.62	
17.37	13.62	9.76	72.07	
13.13	18.20	15.21	96.39	
− 4.12	32.29	+19.93	122.40	

Freezing point: −57.209

Specific heat

$t°$	c_p	$t°$	c_p	$t°$	c_p
−260.16	C. 0.65	−188.16	11.055	−73.16	20.88
259.16	0.805	183.16	11.505	68.16	21.36
258.16	0.95	178.16	11.94	63.16	21.87
257.16	1.105	173.16	12.385	58.16	22.36
256.16	1.28	168.16	12.815	−57.209	22.46
255.16	1.46	163.16	13.255		
254.16	1.64	158.16	13.68	L. −57.209	36.25
253.16	1.82	153.16	14.12	53.16	36.43
252.16	2.00	148.16	14.555	48.16	36.65
251.16	2.18	143.16	14.99	43.16	36.86
250.16	2.36	138.16	15.42	38.16	37.08
249.16	2.535	133.16	15.84	33.16	37.26
248.16	2.72	128.16	16.255	28.16	37.44
243.16	3.74	123.16	16.675	23.16	37.60
238.16	4.71	118.16	17.10	18.16	37.76
233.16	5.56	113.16	17.515	13.16	37.90
228.16	6.345	108.16	17.93	8.16	38.07
223.16	7.09	103.16	18.33	− 3.16	38.23
218.16	7.76	98.16	18.735	+ 1.84	38.40
213.16	8.32	93.16	19.12	6.84	38.59
208.16	8.91	88.16	19.55	11.84	38.78
203.16	9.48	83.16	19.97	16.84	38.95
198.16	10.01	− 78.16	20.42	21.84	39.11
−193.16	10.54	—	—	+25.00	39.21

Heat of melting: 2407.4 cal/mol

TRIMETHYLHYDRAZINE $\quad\quad$ $C_3H_{10}N_2$

Specific heat: ASTON, ZOLKI and WOOD (1955)

$t°$	c_p	$t°$	c_p	$t°$	c_p	$t°$	c_p
−260.289	C. 0.78	−201.271	11.86	−161.872	16.91	−67.782	L. 43.34
258.457	1.08	207.925	10.92	155.676	17.71	61.694	43.63
256.176	1.44	211.341	10.38	149.668	18.33	56.363	43.845
252.899	2.18	205.556	11.26	143.848	18.99	52.363	43.93
250.602	2.70	201.258	11.87	138.200	19.66	46.977	44.055
247.843	3.32	196.373	12.59	132.710	20.24	40.535	44.13
244.729	3.11	191.699	13.30	127.389	20.77	34.148	44.16
248.903	3.11	189.358	13.64	121.135	21.36	24.329	44.33
247.147	3.50	181.439	14.65	114.987	21.91	16.038	44.45
244.817	4.02	176.295	15.26	−108.661	22.90	9.773	44.26
242.068	4.67	171.342	15.87			− 3.570	44.37
237.141	5.78	166.555	16.44			+ 2.577	44.42
233.351	6.54	161.916	16.93			8.678	44.425
229.259	7.27	156.988	17.54			14.730	44.44
223.932	8.28	−151.800	18.13			+20.721	44.45
219.357	9.08						
−214.229	9.91						

AZIDOALKANES

Density, *Viscosity* and *Refractive index*, see BROWN, CARY et al. (1957)

B. NITRILES

HYDROGEN CYANIDE   HCN

SINOZAKI, HARA and MITSUKURI (1926)

Saturated vapour pressure

t°	p mm	t°	p mm	t°	p mm
−16.42	120.05	+18.81	584.7	−86.07	0.132
13.24	140.78	21.74	654.4	78.64	0.376
13.09	142.32	24.59	730.6	73.40	0.745
12.04	149.80	27.62	816.2	66.72	1.562
11.04	157.58	30.59	911.1	66.05	1.673
10.31	163.16	33.92	1028.4	60.75	2.97
7.53	186.54	36.62	1128.2	55.64	4.97
4.20	219.81	40.09	1272.2	51.32	7.48
− 0.76	256.31	42.86	1393.2	46.16	11.78
+ 0.02	265.2	+46.23	1564.1	44.14	13.92
4.03	316.8			40.03	19.72
6.91	358.6			34.29	31.24
9.93	407.8			29.20	46.26
13.11	465.4			24.38	66.03
+15.82	519.4			19.14	96.26
				18.70	97.97
				14.33	131.29
				14.29	131.93
				13.98	134.29
				−13.60	137.45

t°	p mm	t°	p mm	
+ 0.04	263.8	−13.26	139.7	LANGE and BERGA (1950)
− 2.06	240.2	14.16	131.6	
− 5.96	201.7	15.26	122.8	
− 6.26	196.7	17.76	103.3	
− 8.96	173.4	20.86	84.3	
−11.76	151.8	−24.26	66.0	
−12.56	150.6	—	—	

Freezing point: −13.25 COATES and DAVIES (1950)

Triple point: −13.317 at 139.7 mm *ibid.*

Density, Viscosity and *Surface tension*

$t°$	d	$\eta \cdot 10^5$	γ	
25.00	0.67972	183.4	17.78	COATES and DAVIES (1950)
22.00	0.68414	188.5	18.12	,,
20.00	0.68708	—	18.33	,,
18.00	0.69001	195.5	18.56	,,
15.00	0.69438	201.4	18.89	,,
10.00	0.70167	211.4	19.45	,,
5.00	0.70893	222.8	20.02	,,
0.00	0.71618	235.5	20.62	,,
− 5.00	0.72341	249.2	21.20	,,
−10.00	0.73058	264.4	21.78	,,
−13.30	0.73521	275.6	22.16	,,

ACETONITRILE C_2H_3N

Boiling point: 81.57° BROWN and SMITH (1955)
81.54° LOUGUININE (1900)

Saturated vapour pressure at 45°: 208.35 mm
60°: 368.00 mm

Freezing point: −43.873 MATHIEU (1953)

Density: $d^{25°}$: 0.77656 *ibid.*

Refractive index $n_D^{25°}$: 1.34154 *ibid.*

Dielectric constant

$t°$	ε	$t°$	ε	
L.+ 20.00	37.45	C. −150.5	2.742	PHILIPPE and PIETTE (1955)
− 4.5	41.24	47.5	6.484	,,
29.0	45.05	46.0	9.600	,,
C. 49.5	5.162	L. 46.0	16.18	,,
77.0	2.948	46.0	21.39	,,
103.0	2.837	45.5	29.63	,,
132.0	2.772	45.0	43.24	,,
−158.0	2.731	45.0	48.00	,,
—	—	− 44.0	47.71	,,
L.+ 10	36.960	—	—	DEREPPE and VAN MEERSSCHE (1960)
25	34.584	—	—	,,
49	30.799	—	—	,,

Heat of vaporization: 170.08 cal/gr. LOUGUININE (1900)

PROPIONITRILE C_3H_5N

WEBER and KILPATRICK (1962)

Vapour pressure

t°	p mm	t°	p mm	
10.024	21.75	18.386	33.92	
15.187	28.65	23.810	44.49	
16.130	30.16			

Melting point: —92.78°   *Heat of fusion:* 1206.1 cal/mol

Heat of transition at —96.19°: 407.9 cal/mol

Heat of vaporization at 22.85°: 8632 cal/mol

Dielectric constant: DEREPPE and VAN MEERSSCHE (1960)

t°	ε
10	29.101
25	27.869
49	25.005

BUTYRONITRILE C_4H_7N

Dielectric constant: DEREPPE and VAN MEERSSCHE (1960)

t°	ε
10	24.976
25	23.276
49	20.970

N.B. (p. 531): *Boiling point:* HEINE should read HEIM

VALERONITRILE C_5H_9N

Freezing point: —96.23 WITSCHONKE (1954)

MUMFORD and PHILLIPS (1950)   DEREPPE and VAN MEERSSCHE (1960)

Density   *Surface tension*   *Dielectric constant*

t°	d	t°	γ	t°	ε
20	0.7993	20	27.6	10	21.166
25	0.7952	25	27.1	25	19.709
				49	17.587

Refractive index $n_D^{20°} = 1.3975$ MUMFORD and PHILLIPS (1950)

Dielectric constant

t°	ε	t°	ε	
L.+ 20.00	20.04	−152.0	2.613	PHILIPPE and PIETTE (1955)
− 1.0	22.65	133.0	2.650	,,
31.0	24.91	122.0	2.686	,,
60.5	27.58	110.0	2.975	,,
90.5	31.33	104.0	4.267	,,
C. 119.0	2.701	L. 96.5	10.29	,,
−161.0	2.603	96.0	28.70	,,
—	—	− 96.0	33.05	,,

CAPRONITRILE $C_6H_{11}N$

Boiling point: 163.95° SIMON (1929)
Freezing point: −79.4° ibid.
Density: (ibid.)

t°	d	
0	0.82157	
15	0.80939	
30	0.79710	

Refractive index: (ibid.)

t°	He_r	H_α	D	He_y	
15	1.40707	1.40736	1.40937	1.40954	
25	1.40298	1.40327	1.40529	1.40540	

t°	He_g	H_β	He_v	H_γ	
15	1.41358	1.41442	1.41772	1.41885	
25	1.40939	1.41034	1.41345	1.41465	

Dielectric constant: DEREPPE and VAN MEERSSCHE (1960)

t°	ε	
10	18.582	
25	17.263	
49	15.357	

		10°	25°	49°
HEPTANONITRILE	$C_7H_{13}N$	16.603	15.439	13.906
CAPRYLIC NITRILE	$C_8H_{15}N$	14.969	13.897	12.653
NONYLIC NITRILE	$C_9H_{17}N$	13.510	12.638	11.503
CAPRIC NITRILE	$C_{10}H_{19}N$	12.306	11.686	10.699
n-UNDECYLIC NITRILE	$C_{11}H_{21}N$	11.325	10.758	9.815
DODECYLIC NITRILE	$C_{12}H_{23}N$	10.501	10.014	9.174
n-TRIDECYLIC NITRILE	$C_{13}H_{25}N$	9.853	9.337	8.645

HEXADECYLNITRILE $C_{16}H_{31}N$

MUMFORD and PHILLIPS (1950)

Boiling point: 195° (8 mm) *Freezing point:* 31.7°

Refractive index: $n_D^{30°} = 1.4431$

Density, *Surface tension* and *Viscosity*

t°	d	γ	$\eta \cdot 10^4$	
30	0.8284	31.35	765	
35	0.8254	30.85	655	

ACRYLONITRILE C_3H_3N

Boiling point: 77.3° DAVIS and WIEDEMAN (1945)

Freezing point: —83.6° *ibid.*
    —83.5 GARNER, ADAMS and STUCHELL (1942)

Density and *Refractive index:* DAVIS and WIEDEMAN (1945)

t°	d	n_D	
20	0.8060	1.3911	
25	0.8004	1.3884	

Dielectric constant: $\varepsilon = 38$ *ibid.*

Specific heat: 0.50 cal/gr. *ibid.*

Heat of combustion: 7925 cal/gr. *ibid.*

SUCCINONITRILE $C_4H_4N_2$

See Addenda

C. OXIMES

DIAMYLKETOXIME $C_{11}H_{23}ON$

SIMON (1929)

Boiling point: 144.2° (12 mm)

Freezing point: —20.4°

Density and *Viscosity*

t°	d	$\eta \cdot 10^5$	
0	0.89012		
15	0.87945	34160	
30	0.86869	16760	

Refractive index

t°	He_r	H_α	Na_D	He_y	He_{gr}	H_β	He_{viol}	H_γ
15	1.45524	1.45544	1.45838	1.45847	1.46361	1.46482	1.46891	1.47107
25	1.45145	1.45156	1.45452	1.45462	1.45966	1.46089	1.46501	1.46701
dn/dt	0.000379	0.000388	0.000386	0.000385	0.000395	0.000393	0.000390	0.000406

METHYLAMYLKETOXIME $C_7H_{15}ON$

SIMON (1929)

Boiling point: 99.65° (12 mm)

Freezing point: +0.9°

Density and *Viscosity*

t°	d	$\eta \cdot 10^5$	
0	0.90677		
15	0.89494	15670	
30	0.88298	8071	

Refractive index

t°	He_r	H_α	Na_D	He_y	He_{gr}	H_β	He_{viol}	H_γ
15	1.44879	1.44913	1.45194	1.45204	1.45730	1.45846	1.46272	1.46447
25	1.44510	1.44545	1.44819	1.44829	1.45346	1.45462	1.45881	1.46036
dn/dt	0.000369	0.000368	0.000375	0.000375	0.000384	0.000394	0.000391	0.000411

10. NITROGEN DERIVATIVES OF THE CYCLIC SERIES

A. AROMATIC AMINES

ANILINE C_6H_7N

Critical temperature: 425.6° COSTELLO and BOWDEN (1959)

Boiling point: 184.7°   ,,   ,,
184.7° HORYNA (1959)
184.4° *dt/dp (10 mm):* 0.52 CRUTZEN, JOST and SIEG (1957)

Freezing point: −6.03 WITSCHONKE (1954)
−6.10 ROCK and SIEG (1955) and HORYNA (1959)

Density

$t°$	d	$t°$	d	
0	1.039	140	0.9162	COSTELLO and BOWDEN (1959)
20	1.022	160	0.8980	,,
40	1.006	180	0.8790	,,
60	0.9876	200	0.8600	,,
80	0.9700	220	0.8403	,,
100	0.9524	240	0.8204	,,
120	0.9344	260	0.8000	,,
20	1.02183	280	0.7786	CRUTZEN, JOST and SIEG (1957)

Refractive index

$t°$	n_D	
20	1.5860	HORYNA (1959)
20	1.58619	KORTÜM and FREIER (1954)
20	1.5862	ROCK and SIEG (1955) and WHEELER Jr. and JONES (1952)
20	1.5863	CRUTZEN, JOST and SIEG (1957)

N-METHYLANILINE C_7H_9N

COSTELLO and BOWDEN (1959)

Critical temperature: 428.6°

Density

t°	d	t°	d	
−20	1.019	+140	0.8871	
0	1.002	160	0.8694	
+ 20	0.9863	180	0.8509	
40	0.9700	200	0.8320	
60	0.9538	220	0.8123	
80	0.9375	240	0.7920	
100	0.9213	260	0.7712	
+120	0.9045	+280	0.7491	

N,N-DIMETHYLANILINE $C_8H_{11}N$

Critical temperature: 414.4° COSTELLO and BOWDEN (1959)

Boiling point: 194.15° *dt/dp (10 mm):* 0.53 CRUTZEN, JOST and SIEG (1957)
194.0° COSTELLO and BOWDEN (1959)

Melting point: 2.45° *ibid.*

Density: (ibid.)

t°	d	t°	d	
20	0.9577	160	0.8380	
40	0.9406	180	0.8197	
60	0.9241	200	0.8009	
80	0.9075	220	0.7810	
100	0.8905	240	0.7612	
120	0.8732	260	0.7410	
140	0.8559	280	0.7194	

Density at 20°: 0.95588 CRUTZEN, JOST and SIEG (1957)

Refractive index: $n_D^{20°} = 1.5584$ CRUTZEN, JOST and SIEG (1957)

N-ETHYLANILINE $C_8H_{11}N$

COSTELLO and BOWDEN (1959)

Critical temperature: 425.4°

Boiling point: 203.0

Density

$t°$	d	$t°$	d	
− 20	0.9951	+140	0.8598	
0	0.9784	160	0.8420	
+ 20	0.9618	180	0.8237	
40	0.9450	200	0.8048	
60	0.9281	220	0.7852	
80	0.9110	240	0.7650	
100	0.8942	260	0.7444	
+120	0.8772	+280	0.7226	

N,N-DIETHYLANILINE $C_{10}H_{15}N$

COSTELLO and BOWDEN (1959)

Critical temperature: 438.9°

Density

$t°$	d	$t°$	d	
− 20	0.9668	+160	0.8189	
0	0.9508	180	0.8005	
+ 20	0.9348	200	0.7822	
40	0.9189	220	0.7629	
60	0.9025	240	0.7431	
80	0.8862	260	0.7230	
100	0.8700	280	0.7015	
120	0.8533	+300	0.6802	
+140	0.8364	—	—	

DIPHENYLAMINE $C_{12}H_{11}N$

Critical temperature: 615.5° COSTELLO and BOWDEN (1959)

Boiling point: 302° *ibid.*

Melting point: 53.0 *ibid.*
53.2 KOVALENKO and TRIFONOV (1954)
52.94 WITSCHONKE (1954)

Density: COSTELLO and BOWDEN (1959)

t°	d	t°	d	
60	1.055	200	0.9411	
80	1.039	220	0.9242	
100	1.022	240	0.9076	
120	1.006	260	0.8901	
140	0.9903	280	0.8726	
160	0.9744	300	0.8548	
180	0.9580	—	—	

C. NITROGEN DERIVATIVES OF THE POLYMETHYLENES

CYCLOPENTANENITRILE C_6H_9N

Dielectric constant: PHILIPPE and PIETTE (1955)

t°	ε	t°	ε	
C.+ 20.00	22.68	−88.5	3.499	
− 3.0	24.51	80.0	6.014	
30.5	26.98	L. 76.5	14.03	
61.0	30.27	76.5	17.44	
62.0	30.36	76.5	19.80	
65.5	30.85	76.0	24.95	
72.5	31.83	76.0	29.59	
112.0	2.893	76.0	32.29	
−122.5	2.814	75.5	32.58	
—	—	74.5	32.40	
−105.0	2.917	−70.0	31.34	

CYCLOHEXYLAMINE $C_6H_{13}N$

Saturated vapour pressure: NOVAK, MATOUS and PUCK (1960)

t°	p mm	t°	p mm	t°	p mm
60.72	58.83	76.91	115.30	101.31	281.6
64.39	69.08	81.29	136.9	107.10	340.2
67.48	78.20	86.10	164.2	113.90	432.4
70.57	89.08	90.00	189.5	120.45	521.2
73.02	98.70	95.62	231.5	128.37	645.5

Boiling point: 134.75° *dt/dp (10 mm):* 0.50 B. E. (1959)
134.5° NOVAK, MATOUS and PUCK (1960)

Density

t°	d	
20	0.8672	NOVAK, MATOUS and PUCK (1960)
0	0.88485	B.E. (1959)
15	0.87128	,,
30	0.85777	,,

Viscosity: B. E. (1959)

t°	$\eta \cdot 10^5$
15	2517
20	1662

Surface tension: B. E. (1959)

t°	γ
15	32.12
20	31.51
30	30.29

Refractive index at 15° and *dn/dt* B.E. (1959)

He$_r$	H$_\alpha$	Na$_D$	Hc$_y$	He$_{gr}$	H$_\beta$	He viol	H$_\gamma$
1.45949	1.45988	1.46251	1.46261	1.46743	1.46861	1.47246	1.47373
dn/dt 0.00058	0.00058	—	0.00059	0.00060	0.00059	0.00060	0.00059

$n_D^{20°} = 1.4592$

Dielectric constant

t°	ε	
20	4.547	PHILIPPE (not published, see B.E. 1959)

ENDO- and EXO-2-CYANOBICYCLO [2.2.1]HEPTANE

Specific heat: see SEREGIN *et al.* (1962)

D. HETEROCYCLIC DERIVATIVES

PYRROLIDINE C_4H_8N

Saturated vapour pressure: HILDENBRAND, SINKE *et al.* (1959)

t°	p mm	t°	p mm	
20.68	49.96	85.12	727.30	
32.43	90.65	85.66	739.95	
48.62	189.10	86.62	763.30	
66.91	388.28	87.43	783.38	

Boiling point: 86.49 HILDENBRAND, SINKE *et al.* (1959)
    86.5 HELM, LANUM *et al.* (1958)

Melting point: —57.84° HILDENBRAND, SINKE *et al.* (1959)
    —57.85° HELM, LANUM *et al.* (1958)

Transition point: —66,01 HILDENBRAND, SINKE *et al.* (1959)

Density: HELM, LANUM *et al.* (1958)

t°	d	
20	0.85859	
25	0.85380	
30	0.84898	

Viscosity: HELM, LANUM *et al.* (1958)

t°	$\eta \cdot 10^5$	
20	756	
25	702	
30	655	

Surface tension: HELM, LANUM *et al.* (1958)

t°	γ	
20	29.65	
25	29.23	
30	28.80	

Refractive index: HELM, LANUM *et al.* (1958)

t°	He r	H$_C$	Na$_D$	Hg e	He v	H$_F$	Hg g
20	1.44009	1.44045	1.44283	1.44492	1.44763	1.44883	1.45363
25	1.43740	1.43777	1.44020	1.44226	1.44498	1.44614	1.45090
30	1.43477	1.43513	1.43753	1.43956	1.44224	1.44345	1.44816

Specific heat: McCULLOUGH, DOUSLIN *et al.* (1959)

t°	c_p	t°	c_p	t°	c_p	t°	c_p
	Crystals II				Crystals I		Liquid
−260.11	0.835	−192.12	12.226	−63.99	25.47	−54.81	35.880
259.97	0.852	188.74	12.505	63.52	26.78	52.79	35.977
258.70	1.092	186.68	12.664	63.14	27.06	50.64	36.077
258.27	1.166	183.40	12.898	62.92	27.46	50.22	36.114
257.34	1.372	177.89	13.257	62.74	27.65	47.07	36.261
256.80	1.472	172.19	13.611	62.34	29.65	45.29	36.336
255.98	1.645	166.66	13.956	61.98	30.45	44.18	36.377
255.38	1.782	160.74	14.321	61.79	31.52	41.11	36.493
254.41	2.002	154.43	14.711	−61.60	32.05	36.60	36.641
253.92	2.113	148.29	15.102			31.23	36.767
252.70	2.410	141.81	15.501			27.32	36.898
252.17	2.541	134.99	15.925			20.95	36.957
250.92	2.852	128.35	16.351			−10.26	37.065
250.06	3.076	121.85	16.784			+ 0.89	37.155
248.93	3.371	115.49	17.226			11.91	37.260
247.85	3.646	113.65	17.362			12.98	37.269
246.61	3.969	111.17	17.531			21.17	37.359
245.23	4.316	108.79	17.717			32.05	37.528
244.01	4.623	104.37	18.045			42.86	37.706
241.14	5.343	101.96	18.237			53.59	37.924
237.84	6.110	97.73	18.591			65.12	38.229
234.06	6.921	97.53	18.602			77.43	38.633
230.16	7.666	95.75	18.740				
225.78	8.419	90.91	19.185				
224.65	8.605	89.24	19.357				
220.64	9.211	84.45	19.848				
219.63	9.355	83.80	19.900				
218.10	9.563	82.90	20.006				
214.21	10.070	78.72	20.489				
213.56	10.150	78.16	20.578				
208.71	10.713	74.58	21.132				
208.49	10.759	73.39	21.293				
203.49	11.224	69.63	22.237				
203.26	11.251	− 68.92	22.346				
−197.81	11.728						

Heat of vaporization: 8990 cal/mol at 25° HILDENBRAND, SINKE *et al.* (1959)

Heat of melting: 2053 cal/mol at −57.84° *ibid.*

Heat of transition: 127 cal/mol at −66.01° *ibid.*

Heat of combustion: 9459.5 cal/gr *ibid.*

Specific heat: (ibid.)

t°	c_p	t°	c_p	t°	c_p	t°	c_p
		Series I			Series II		
−259.36	C. 1.008	−150.56	17.810	−257.39	C. 1.276	−103.46	17.993
257.48	1.284	100.86	18.139	254.94	1.894	98.79	18.362
255.49	1.789	96.25	18.601	252.22	2.546	94.19	18.724
253.47	2.266	91.14	18.937	249.34	3.256	89.66	19.114
251.04	2.878	85.56	19.591	246.34	3.939	85.20	19.680
248.30	3.502	80.14	20.659	243.52	4.689	80.86	20.632
245.85	4.132	74.88	20.938	240.42	5.454	76.60	20.861
243.53	4.713	69.66	21.987	236.86	6.293	72.40	21.441
237.75	6.100	65.25	24.36	232.68	7.222	68.30	22.449
234.05	6.951	65.08	24.41	228.19	8.032	L. 53.27	35.94
230.09	7.785	63.95	25.92	223.60	8.871	48.06	36.22
225.67	8.428	63.38	26.85	219.09	9.497	42.90	36.56
220.89	9.432	62.86	27.92	214.94	10.143	− 32.67	36.91
215.93	9.990	L. 54.43	35.93	209.80	10.647		
211.04	10.624	50.00	36.16	203.71	11.136		Vapour
206.46	11.002	44.89	36.32	198.01	11.753		
201.37	11.414	34.81	36.84	192.62	12.215	+126.85	27.59
194.94	11.970	29.79	36.86	187.47	12.678	226.85	34.59
187.98	12.573	24.78	36.82	177.74	13.336	326.85	40.47
181.38	13.086	19.79	36.99	173.06	13.620	426.85	45.34
175.05	13.408	14.81	36.96	168.50	13.882	526.85	49.46
168.92	13.826	9.84	37.04	164.05	14.149	626.85	52.94
162.98	14.150	− 4.89	37.08	159.67	14.392	726.85	55.92
157.20	14.500	+ 0.06	37.10	155.39	14.678		
151.57	14.854	4.99	37.15	151.19	14.898		
146.06	15.186	9.91	37.22	147.06	15.192		
140.67	15.508	14.81	37.33	142.99	15.416		
135.39	15.864	19.70	37.30	138.99	15.660		
130.20	16.171	24.58	37.41	135.05	15.983		
125.11	16.499	29.44	37.52	122.91	16.702		
120.10	16.794	34.29	37.68	117.94	16.968		
115.18	17.065	+ 39.12	37.75	113.03	17.176		
−110.33	17.480			−108.20	17.643		

PYRROLE C_4H_5N

HELM, LANUM *et al.* (1958)

Boiling point: 129.8°

Freezing point: −23.41°

Density

t°	d	
20	0.96985	
25	0.96565	
30	0.96133	

Viscosity

t°	$\eta \cdot 10^5$	
20	1352	
25	1233	
30	1129	

Surface tension

t°	γ	
20	37.61	
25	37.06	
30	36.51	

Refractive index

t°	He$_r$	H$_C$	Na$_D$	Hg$_e$	He$_v$	H$_F$	Hg$_g$
20	1.50503	1.50569	1.51015	1.51406	1.51923	1.52147	1.53075
25	1.50272	1.50333	1.50779	1.51164	1.51683	1.51904	1.52830
30	1.50038	1.50100	1.50543	1.50926	1.51440	1.51662	1.52588

PYRIDINE C$_5$H$_5$N

Critical temperature: 346.8° AMBROSE and GRANT (1957); AMBROSE *et al.* (1960)
346.85° CHENG, McCOUBREY and PHILLIPS (1962)

Saturated vapour pressure: HERINGTON and MARTIN (1953)

t°	p mm	t°	p mm
115.473	764.89	105.356	565.18
115.407	763.25	100.994	493.23
115.287	760.58	92.749	377.12
115.112	756.92	88.459	326.07
114.699	747.75	82.728	267.00
114.015	732.91	82.430	264.37
113.374	719.35	75.770	206.96
113.232	716.58	68.403	156.05
113.222	716.22	58.349	103.55
110.028	651.50	52.710	81.16
107.169	597.64	47.327	63.80

Second virial coefficient: see ANDON, COX *et al.* (1957) and HERINGTON and MARTIN (1953)

Boiling point: 115.2° HELM, LANUM *et al.* (1958)
115.256°*dt/dp (10 mm):* 0.4535 BIDDISCOMBE, COULSON *et al.* (1954)
115.4° ZIEBORAK and ZIEBORAK-ROCZNIKI (1955)
115.4° THOMPSON and UBBELOHDE (1950)

Freezing point: −41.71° BIDDISCOMBE, COULSON *et al.* (1954)
−41.67° HELM, LANUM *et al.* (1958)

Refractive index: HELM, LANUM *et al.* (1958)

t°	He$_r$	H$_C$	Na$_D$	Hg$_e$	He$_v$	H$_F$	Hg$_g$	
20	1.50481	1.50551	1.51016	1.51426	1.51971	1.52207	1.53219	HELM, LANUM *et al.*
25	1.50210	1.50278	1.50745	1.51147	1.51690	1.51927	1.52939	,, (1958)
30	1.49939	1.50000	1.50466	1.50873	1.51415	1.51650	1.52655	,,
20	—	1.50556	1.51020	1.51433	1.52221	—	—	BIDDISCOMBE, COULSON *et al.* (1954) and ANDON, COX and HERINGTON (1957)

Density, *Viscosity* and *Surface tension*

t°	d	$\eta \cdot 10^5$	γ	
15	—	—	36.86	BIDDISCOMBE, COULSON et al. (1954)
20	0.98310	—	36.25	
25	—	—	35.70	,,
30	0.97301	—	—	,,
20	0.98319	952	36.88	HELM, LANUM et al. (1958)
25	0.97824	884	36.33	,,
30	0.97319	815	35.78	,,

Specific heat: McCULLOUGH, DOUSLIN et al. (1957)

t°	c_p	t°	c_p	
101.04	23.79	177.04	28.43	
124.04	25.23	227.04	31.12	
147.04	26.65	—	—	

Heat of vaporization: 109.95 cal/gr. BIDDISCOMBE, COULSON et al. (1954)
　　　　　at 25°: 9656 cal/mol ANDON, COX et al. (1957)

Heat of fusion: 22.4 cal/gr. BIDDISCOMBE, COULSON et al. (1954)

Heat of combustion at 25°: 665.00 kcal/mol COX, CHALLONER and MEETHAM (1954)
　　　　　　　　　　　664.95 kcal/mol HUBBARD, FROW and WADDINGTON
　　　　　　　　　　　(1961)

a-PICOLINE or 2-METHYLPYRIDINE　　　　　C_6H_7N

(See also Addenda, p. 451)

Critical temperature: 348° AMBROSE and GRANT (1957); AMBROSE, COX and TOWNSEND (1960)

Saturated vapour pressure: HERINGTON and MARTIN (1953)

t°	p mm	t°	p mm	
130.037	773.28	114.552	491.90	
129.608	764.16	108.594	408.29	
129.290	757.45	101.283	321.82	
128.591	742.72	93.617	247.85	
127.828	726.70	88.566	207.02	
126.992	710.03	82.362	164.67	
125.664	683.61	76.836	133.20	
122.132	617.28	69.916	100.95	
117.647	540.20	64.363	79.96	

Second virial coefficient: ANDON, COX *et al.* (1957)

Boiling point: 129.4   HELM, LANUM *et al.* (1958)
           129.408 *dt/dp (10 mm)* 0.4695 HERINGTON and MARTIN (1957)
           129.44   HOPKE and SEARS (1951)

Freezing point: —66.71 HELM, LANUM *et al.* (1958)
           —66.81 BIDDISCOMBE, COULSON *et al.* (1954)

Density, Viscosity and *Surface tension*

$t°$	d	$\eta \cdot 10^5$	γ	
20	0.94440	805	33.18	HELM, LANUM *et al.* (1958)
25	0.93981	753	32.78	,,
30	0.93514	703	32.33	,,

Refractive index

$t°$	He_r	H_C	Na_D	Hg_e	He_v	H_F	Hg_g	
20	1.49590	1.49654	1.50102	1.50492	1.51008	1.51245	1.52211	HELM, LANUM *et al.*
25	1.49329	1.49394	1.49839	1.50230	1.50747	1.50978	1.51939	,, (1958)
30	1.49072	1.49135	1.49582	1.49967	1.50486	1.50714	1.51669	,,
20	—	1.49657	1.50101	1.50496	1.5125	—	—	BIDDISCOMBE, COULSON *et al.* (1954)

Magnetic susceptibility at 20°: —0.6478 · 10^{-6} FRENCH (1951)

Heat of vaporization: 9.0 kcal/mol HOPKE and SEARS (1951)
                    10.258 kcal/mol ANDON, COX *et al.* (1957)

Heat of fusion: 25.2 cal/gr. BIDDISCOMBE, COULSON *et al.* (1954)

Heat of combustion at 25°: 817.52 kcal/mol COX, CHALLONER and MEETHAM (1954)

β-PICOLINE or 3-METHYLPYRIDINE C_6H_7N

Critical temperature: 371.7° AMBROSE and GRANT (1957); AMBROSE, COX and TOWNSEND (1960)

Saturated vapour pressure: HERINGTON and MARTIN (1953)

t°	p mm	t°	p mm	
145.101	779.98	132.165	543.58	
144.659	770.50	129.368	501.21	
144.320	763.50	121.932	400.87	
143.993	757.02	115.583	328.50	
143.577	748.43	109.006	265.14	
143.293	742.69	103.922	223.12	
142.639	729.55	97.519	178.31	
142.132	719.67	92.059	146.10	
140.871	695.26	85.275	112.97	
137.714	637.09	81.282	96.54	

Second virial coefficient: ANDON, COX et al. (1957)

Boiling point: 144.143 *dt/dp (10 mm):* 0.4873 HERINGTON and MARTIN (1953)

Freezing point: −18.25 BIDDISCOMBE, COULSON et al. (1954)

Density

t°	d	
20	0.9566	ANDON, COX and HERINGTON (1957)
20	0.95658	BIDDISCOMBE, COULSON et al. (1954)
30	0.94736	,,

Refractive index

t°	H$_C$	Na$_D$	H$_e$	H$_F$	
20	1.50232	1.50682	1.51080	1.51845	BIDDISCOMBE, COULSON et al. (1954)
20	—	1.50682	1.51080	—	ANDON, COX and HERINGTON (1957)

Heat of vaporization at 25°: 10811 cal/mol ANDON, COX et al. (1957)

Heat of fusion: 26.5 cal/gr BIDDISCOMBE and COULSON (1954)

Heat of combustion at 25°: 819.74 kcal/mol COX, CHALLONER and MEETHAM (1954)

γ-PICOLINE or 4-METHYLPYRIDINE C_6H_7N

Critical temperature: 372.5° AMBROSE and GRANT (1957);
AMBROSE, COX and TOWNSEND (1960)

Saturated vapour pressure: HERINGTON and MARTIN (1953)

t°	p mm	t°	p mm	
145.462	762.00	123.021	400.06	
145.378	760.59	116.506	326.35	
145.034	753.54	109.660	261.10	
144.745	747.41	104.738	221.17	
144.246	737.41	98.323	176.65	
143.604	724.87	94.654	154.69	
142.127	696.22	88.166	121.35	
140.126	658.81	82.830	98.60	
137.174	606.70	79.600	86.65	
135.281	574.92	76.906	77.62	
129.837	490.98	—	—	

Boiling point: 145.356 *dt/dp (10 mm):* 0.4887 HERINGTON and MARTIN (1953)

Second virial coefficient: ANDON, COX et al. (1957)

Freezing point: +3.58 BIDDISCOMBE, COULSON et al. (1954)

Density at 20°: 0.9548 *ibid.*
         30°: 0.9456 *ibid.*

Refractive index

t°	H_C	Na_D	H_e	H_F	
20	1.50144	1.50584	1.50975	1.51720	BIDDISCOMBE, COULSON et al. (1954)
20	—	1.50584	1.50975	—	ANDON, COX and HERINGTON (1957)

Heat of fusion: 29.7 cal/gr. BIDDISCOMBE, COULSON et al. (1954)

Heat of vaporization at 25°: 10061 cal/gr *ibid.*
                           10834 cal/mol ANDON, COX et al. (1957)

Heat of combustion at 25°: 816.99 kcal/mol COX, CHALLONER and MEETHAM (1954)

LUTIDINE-2,3 or 2,3-DIMETHYLPYRIDINE C_7H_9N

Critical temperature: 382.30: Ambrose, Cox and Townsend (1960)

Saturated vapour pressure: Coulson, Cox *et al.* (1959)

t°	p mm	t°	p mm	t°	p mm	t°	p mm
162.412	785.29	159.586	729.20	148.764	543.20	122.909	248.37
162.077	778.48	159.141	720.70	145.829	499.93	116.337	199.57
161.672	770.32	158.603	710.48	141.757	444.45	107.822	148.25
161.199	760.85	157.940	698.06	137.704	394.32	99.543	109.38
160.668	750.29	155.326	650.82	133.429	346.46	—	—
160.125	739.67	152.203	597.63	128.606	298.22	—	—

Critical solution point in water: **lower;** at 16.5°: 74% H_2O Cox (1954)
upper; at 192.6°: 61.5% H_2O

Freezing point: −15.27 Coulson, Cox *et al.* (1959)

LUTIDINE-2,4 or 2,4-DIMETHYLPYRIDINE C_7H_9N

Critical temperature: 374° Ambrose and Grant (1957);
Ambrose, Cox and Townsend (1960)

Saturated vapour pressure: Coulson, Cox *et al.* (1959)

t°	p mm	t°	p mm	t°	p mm	t°	p mm
159.825	788.89	156.690	726.23	147.860	570.78	118.836	235.84
159.092	773.86	156.107	715.08	147.450	564.25	113.387	196.25
158.333	758.50	155.900	711.07	145.909	540.28	103.767	139.86
157.801	748.00	155.739	708.01	140.601	463.91	90.305	83.93
157.712	746.21	155.232	698.46	134.371	385.60	86.054	70.68
157.202	736.16	152.789	653.85	130.192	339.32	76.246	46.78
156.693	726.30	150.386	612.21	124.673	285.18	—	—

Freezing point: −64.00 Coulson, Cox *et al.* (1959)

Critical solution point in water: **lower;** at 23.4°: 74.5% H_2O Cox (1954)

upper; at 188.7°: 63% H_2O

Density, Viscosity and *Dielectric constant:* RAMPOLLA and SMYTH (1958)

$t°$	d	$\eta \cdot 10^5$	ε	
20	0.9296	887	9.60	
40	0.9120	676	8.88	
60	0.8945	538	8.21	

LUTIDINE-2,5 or 2,5-DIMETHYLPYRIDINE C_7H_9N

Critical temperature: 371.0° AMBROSE, COX and TOWNSEND (1960)

Saturated vapour pressure: HERINGTON and MARTIN (1953)

$t°$	p mm	$t°$	p mm	
157.299	765.90	134.062	398.50	
155.815	736.48	131.669	370.70	
155.273	725.98	130.857	361.59	
155.155	723.48	126.322	314.18	
152.371	671.33	123.279	285.27	
150.972	646.67	119.232	250.27	
148.991	612.38	114.862	216.41	
147.417	586.11	111.895	195.55	
145.250	551.57	109.268	178.59	
142.806	514.77	101.938	137.45	
141.497	495.78	97.185	115.25	
138.935	460.49	90.342	88.60	
136.358	426.72	86.101	74.79	
—	—	85.098	71.76	

Boiling point: 157.008 *dt/dp (10 mm):* 0.4991 COULSON, COX et al. (1959)

Freezing point: —15.61 *ibid.*

Critical solution point in water: **lower;** at 13.1°: 73% H_2O Cox (1954)
upper; at 206.9°: 62% H_2O

Heat of combustion at 25°: 970.02 kcal/mol COX, CHALLONER and MEETHAM (1954)

LUTIDINE-2,6 or 2,6-DIMETHYLPYRIDINE C_7H_9N

Critical temperature: 350.6° AMBROSE and GRANT (1957);
AMBROSE, COX and TOWNSEND (1960)

Second virial coefficient: ANDON, COX et al. (1957)

Saturated vapour pressure: HERINGTON and MARTIN (1953)

t°	p mm	t°	p mm
144.300	765.22	125.637	447.22
143.917	757.30	122.877	410.92
142.850	735.65	120.305	379.30
141.532	709.02	116.979	341.36
139.909	678.16	113.949	309.25
138.750	656.24	112.351	293.55
136.638	618.10	108.211	255.69
135.162	592.55	105.723	234.75
133.468	564.22	100.326	194.32
131.655	535.01	95.180	161.30
129.190	497.55	83.938	105.01
127.495	473.01	79.290	87.06

Boiling point: 144.045° *dt/dp (10 mm):* 0.4818 COULSON, COX et al. (1959)
and BIDDISCOMBE, COULSON et al. (1954)

144.6° LIPLAVK and BOLITER (1951)

143.4° (740 mm) BROWN, JOHNSON and PODALL (1954)

Melting point: −6.07 BROWN, JOHNSON and PODALL (1954)

−6.16 BIDDISCOMBE, COULSON et al. (1954) and COULSON, COX et al. (1959)

−6.3 CATHCART and REYNOLDS (1951)

−5.9 COULSON and JONES (1946)

Critical solution point in water: **lower;** at 34.0°: 70% H_2O
upper; at 230.7°: 59% H_2O

Density: 20° 0.92257 BIDDISCOMBE, COULSON et al. (1954)

25° 0.9183 BROWN, JOHNSON and PODALL (1954)

30° 0.91355 BIDDISCOMBE, COULSON et al. (1954)

Refractive index

t°	H_C	Na_D	H_e	H_F	
20	1.49334	1.49767	1.50153	1.50895	BIDDISCOMBE, COULSON et al. (1954)
20	—	1.4971	—	—	BROWN, JOHNSON and PODALL
25	—	1.4953	—	—	„ (1954)

Heat of vaporization at 25°: 88.16 cal/gr. BIDDISCOMBE, COULSON *et al.* (1954)

11009 cal/mol ANDON, COX *et al.* (1957)

Heat of fusion: 22.4 cal/gr. BIDDISCOMBE, COULSON *et al.* (1954)

Heat of combustion at 25°: 968.20 kcal/mol COX, CHALLONER and MEETHAM (1954)

LUTIDINE-3,4 or 3,4-DIMETHYLPYRIDINE C_7H_9N

Critical temperature: 410.56° AMBROSE, COX and TOWNSEND (1960)

Saturated vapour pressure: COULSON, COX *et al.* (1959)

t°	p mm	t°	p mm	t°	p mm	t°	p mm
180.349	783.49	177.931	737.34	169.891	599.13	145.423	300.32
179.860	773.99	177.384	727.20	166.617	549.14	139.127	247.51
179.401	765.09	177.035	720.78	163.196	500.53	132.352	199.36
179.274	762.64	176.327	707.89	159.324	449.74	123.572	148.61
178.933	756.18	175.761	697.77	155.228	400.62	112.101	98.86
178.487	747.75	173.104	651.65	150.485	349.24	—	—

Boiling point: 179.132 *dt/dp* (10 mm) 0.5238 COULSON, COX *et al.* (1959)

Melting point: −11.12° COULSON, COX *et al.* (1959)

Critical solution point in water: **lower;** at −3.6°: 75.5 % H_2O COX (1954)

upper; at 162.5°: 64 % H_2O COX (1954)

LUTIDINE-3,5 or 3,5-DIMETHYLPYRIDINE C_7H_9N

Critical temperature: 394.10° AMBROSE, COX and TOWNSEND (1960)

Saturated vapour pressure: COULSON, COX *et al.* (1959)

t°	p mm	t°	p mm	t°	p mm	t°	p mm
172.729	776.02	169.790	719.67	154.971	483.05	132.720	248.60
172.307	767.76	169.344	711.39	152.456	449.97	125.975	199.77
171.961	761.03	168.620	698.15	148.007	395.94	118.063	152.75
171.265	747.62	165.941	650.87	143.329	344.88	109.544	112.80
170.862	739.87	162.850	599.51	138.193	295.09	98.423	73.97
170.306	729.32	159.412	546.21	—	—	—	—

Freezing point: −6.54 COULSON, COX *et al.* (1959)

PIPERIDINE $C_5H_{11}N$

Critical temperature: 320.85° CHENG, McCOUBREY and PHILLIPS (1962)

QUINOLINE C_9H_7N

MALANOWSKI (1961)

Saturated vapour pressure: (not quite pure)

t°	p mm	t°	p mm
237.94	765.23	227.98	615.44
237.75	762.18	224.46	568.48
237.25	753.81	219.75	510.00
236.90	748.13	216.53	427.7
235.65	728.56	212.64	430.6
235.27	722.23	208.42	388.4
234.80	714.98	240.02	348.1
234.28	707.01	199.18	307.9
233.29	692.05	199.21	307.9
232.92	686.54	192.95	261.3
232.23	676.32	187.51	225.4
231.59	666.58	178.15	173.1
230.26	647.57	165.37	117.9
229.43	635.44	164.67	115.5

Boiling temperature: 237.63°

Refractive index $n_D^{20°}$: 1.6273

Iso-QUINOLINE C_9H_7N

Saturated vapour pressure: MALANOWSKI (1960) (not quite pure)

t°	p mm	t°	p mm
243.70	767.22	218.66	430.0
243.52	765.14	216.70	411.2
243.29	761.13	215.79	401.9
242.74	751.92	212.57	371.0
242.07	741.18	211.07	357.2
241.19	726.41	209.15	340.2
240.47	713.92	207.14	322.7
239.42	699.11	204.82	303.7
238.14	679.43	203.49	293.5
236.99	661.96	201.69	279.9
235.53	640.94	201.71	279.9
234.09	620.47	199.25	262.1
232.95	604.36	196.61	243.8
230.62	573.40	193.14	221.6
225.77	512.00	189.32	198.9
230.04	565.08	184.95	175.6
226.99	526.6	182.43	168.0
224.30	494.5	177.21	139.4
221.93	466.8	174.03	126.6
220.50	451.3	166.78	100.6

Boiling point: 243.24°

Refractive index $n_D^{30°}$: 1.62077

2-, 4-, 6- and 8-METHYLQUINOLINES $C_{10}H_9N$

See Rampolla and Smyth (1958)

QUINALDINE or 2-METHYLQUINOLINE $C_{10}H_9N$

Saturated vapour pressure: Malanowski (1961)

t°	p mm	t°	p mm	t°	p mm
247.86	762.18	234.92	561.48	213.13	321.1
247.34	753.10	233.52	542.57	211.55	307.6
246.92	745.99	231.93	522.2	209.48	290.6
246.21	733.50	230.90	508.9	207.31	273.9
245.29	717.82	229.20	487.7	207.35	273.8
244.52	705.73	227.68	469.4	204.90	256.1
243.57	689.54	226.27	453.0	202.95	241.8
242.52	674.17	224.69	435.3	200.64	226.3
241.58	658.34	222.93	415.8	197.98	209.8
240.22	637.65	221.54	401.1	195.11	192.6
239.06	620.24	219.75	383.2	191.41	172.4
237.11	605.93	218.28	368.2	186.35	148.0
236.34	589.92	216.63	352.9	178.30	114.2
235.96	576.20	215.02	337.8	—	—

Boiling point: 247.75°

Refractive index: at 20°: n_D 1.6128
at 30°: n_D 1.60771

LEPIDINE or 4-METHYLQUINOLINE $C_{10}H_9N$

Malanowski (1961)

Saturated vapour pressure

t°	p mm	t°	p mm	t°	p mm
265.82	763.21	252.89	570.83	230.21	315.6
265.41	756.43	251.70	547.49	224.56	270.9
264.96	748.13	248.93	511.60	221.00	245.0
261.44	690.04	245.50	469.7	216.66	216.6
259.56	660.51	242.47	435.5	210.48	180.7
257.25	625.77	237.92	387.6	202.46	141.7
255.94	606.16	232.80	338.3	118.58	125.4

Boiling temperature: 265.63°

Refractive index at 20°: $n_D = 1.6204$

7-METHYLQUINOLINE $C_{10}H_9N$

Saturated vapour pressure: MALANOWSKI (1961)

t°	p mm	t°	p mm	
258.00	765.28	235.06	440.3	
257.74	760.87	232.05	407.4	
256.96	746.79	228.44	370.8	
256.08	731.66	226.25	349.7	
254.95	713.64	223.28	322.7	
254.07	698.62	220.06	295.6	
252.99	681.59	216.30	266.2	
252.98	681.59	213.54	246.6	
251.95	664.64	210.68	227.5	
250.50	642.12	208.59	214.2	
248.85	617.45	205.32	194.5	
247.08	592.34	210.19	172.1	
245.51	570.19	198.57	159.1	
243.78	546.87	195.30	143.6	
241.95	522.4	190.95	125.2	
239.89	496.6	184.38	101.2	
238.03	473.8	—	—	

Boiling temperature: 257.71°

Refractive index at 20°: n_D: 1.6169

8-METHYLQUINOLINE $C_{10}H_9N$

Saturated vapour pressure: MALANOWSKI (1961)

t°	p mm	t°	p mm	
248.15	764.12	223.75	422.3	
247.71	756.93	222.22	406.4	
247.32	750.81	220.32	386.6	
246.10	729.03	218.12	364.4	
243.91	692.81	215.87	343.3	
241.95	661.72	213.15	319.0	
240.61	640.71	210.86	298.7	
239.36	622.08	207.79	273.5	
237.97	602.11	205.49	258.2	
236.73	584.22	202.74	238.8	
235.13	560.85	200.31	222.6	
233.69	542.15	197.97	207.9	
232.15	522.4	192.61	177.1	
230.54	501.9	184.32	137.1	
229.23	485.6	179.83	118.8	
227.33	462.9	178.95	115.6	
225.60	443.1			

Boiling temperature: 247.90°

Refractive index at 20°: n_D: 1.6167

TRIETHYLENEDIAMINE or
1,4-DIAZABICYCLO [2:2:2] OCTANE $\qquad$ $C_6H_{12}N_2$

(See also Addenda, p. 454)

WADA, KISHIDA *et al.* (1960)

Melting point: 161.1 $\qquad$ *Transition point:* 79.8

Specific heat

$t°$	c_p	$t°$	c_p	$t°$	c_p
Series I		Series II		Series III	
−170.15	14.39	−196.05	12.25	−237.43	6.307
161.13	15.04	189.81	12.81	233.65	7.184
150.00	15.71	182.90	13.39	229.56	8.015
145.20	16.44	175.44	13.97	224.98	8.836
136.09	17.23	−167.79	14.58	219.76	9.636
127.23	18.01			214.08	10.38
118.94	18.75			207.77	11.12
110.59	19.53			200.77	11.80
101.78	20.38			−193.34	12.48
92.57	21.28				
83.57	22.21				
− 74.43	23.18				

$t°$	c_p	$t°$	c_p	$t°$	c_p	$t°$	c_p
Series IV				Series V		Series VI	
−268.24	0.014	−256.67	1.144	−74.50	23.17	−21.47	29.55
267.24	0.027	255.10	1.500	65.60	24.14	−12.64	30.81
266.00	0.055	253.31	1.947	56.35	25.20	− 3.77	31.99
264.87	0.099	251.29	2.495	46.91	26.33	+ 5.62	33.34
263.81	0.161	249.03	3.136	37.82	27.45	15.10	34.93
262.79	0.238	246.39	3.895	28.99	28.59	24.14	36.43
261.69	0.340	243.90	4.604	−20.20	29.76	33.33	37.99
260.49	0.481	241.28	5.330			42.70	39.73
259.29	0.657	−258.25	6.119			52.09	41.66
−258.04	0.871					61.45	43.91
						+70.72	46.66

Heat of fusion: 1450 cal/mol

Transition heat: 2300 cal/mol

HEXAMETHYLENETETRAMINE or UROTROPINE $C_6H_{12}N_4$

Specific heat: CHANG and WESTRUM (1960)

$t°$	c_p	$t°$	c_p	$t°$	c_p	$t°$	c_p
		Series I				Series III	
−221.61	9.894	98.36	19.92	+44.75	39.32	−268.11	0.027
217.61	10.19	89.23	20.96	54.03	40.69	266.90	0.069
211.30	10.62	80.12	22.04	63.75	42.14	266.17	0.110
204.41	11.01	71.31	23.10	+73.21	43.54	265.65	0.167
197.43	11.39	69.65	24.18			265.11	0.220
190.54	11.81	64.91	24.89	Series II		264.48	0.326
183.41	12.25	55.08	25.16			263.52	0.490
175.78	12.72	45.72	26.37	−241.28	7.301	262.30	0.780
167.59	13.29	36.86	27.56	238.95	7.764	260.99	1.155
159.54	13.91	28.00	28.79	235.75	8.309	259.60	1.610
158.43	14.00	19.05	30.03	231.89	8.845	258.10	2.134
151.90	14.54	9.94	31.31	227.50	9.349	256.51	2.728
149.57	14.74	− 0.76	32.57	222.87	9.790	254.83	3.338
141.18	15.50	+ 8.40	33.96	−217.69	10.19	253.04	3.982
133.06	16.28	17.44	35.28			250.99	4.691
124.86	17.08	26.56	36.63			248.55	5.461
116.27	17.96	35.78	38.00			245.66	6.269
107.35	18.92					242.47	7.041
						−239.15	7.728

11. OXYGEN-NITROGEN DERIVATIVES

A. ALIPHATIC NITRO DERIVATIVES

NITROMETHANE CH_3NO_2

Saturated vapour pressure

McCULLOUGH, SCOTT *et al.* (1954)   BROWN and SMITH (1955)

t°	p mm	t°	p mm	t°	p mm	t°	p mm
55.711	149.41	101.186	760.00	101.36	767.09	74.31	309.37
61.298	187.57	106.994	906.06	101.04	759.63	64.33	211.86
66.919	233.72	112.826	1074.6	100.30	742.34	60.55	182.25
72.557	289.13	118.681	1268.0	95.85	645.36	55.00	144.83
78.231	355.22	124.564	1489.1	89.34	522.24	49.88	116.38
83.925	433.56	130.473	1740.8	83.96	435.50	—	—
89.655	525.86	136.404	2026.0	—	—	—	—
95.408	633.99	—	—	—	—	—	—

Boiling point: 101.186 McCULLOUGH, SCOTT *et al.* (1954)
101.07 BROWN and SMITH (1955)

Density at 25°: 1.1307 BROWN and SMITH (1955)

Dielectric constant: PHILIPPE and PIETTE (1955)

t°	ε	t°	ε	
C. +20.00	38.57	−59.0	3.827	
− 4.0	42.83	49.0	4.063	
25.0	46.64	41.5	4.077	
50.0	3.946	37.5	4.165	
104.5	3.515	32.0	4.447	
156.5	3.359	31.0	5.323	
121.0	3.475	30.0	6.764	
107.5	3.536	29.0	8.87	
93.0	3.591	L. 29.0	15.41	
77.0	3.680	28.5	22.10	
−69.0	3.740	−28.5	35.53	

TETRANITROMETHANE CO_8N_4

Saturated vapour pressure

t°	p mm	t°	p mm	
40	26.5	80	164	EDWARDS (1952)
50	43.3	90	239	,,
60	68.0	100	339	,,
70	108.0	—	—	,,
0	1.9	30	14.9	NICHOLSON (1949)
13.8	5.7	40	25.8	,,
20	8.4	—	—	,,

Dielectric constant: PHILIPPE and PIETTE (1955)

t°	ε	t°	ε
+ 20.00	2.317	− 101.5	2.148
− 12.0	2.209	100.0	2.160
55.5	2.182	85.0	2.169
90.5	2.165	− 51.5	2.183
124.0	2.139	+ 25.00	2.295
− 113.5	2.143	+ 29.80	2.304

2,2-DINITROPROPANE $\qquad$ $C_3H_6O_4N_2$

CROWE and SMYTH (1950)

Melting point: 52.9

Transition points: −5.0 and −7.0

Dielectric constant

Cooling

t°	ε	t°	ε	t°	ε
L. 56.2	35.7	**C.I** 48.2	41.1	− 6.8	28.75
53.3	36.3	39.3	37.9	**C.II** 6.9	14.80
53.2	38.9	20.6	34.3	7.3	4.56
53.0	40.7	10.6	32.6	7.6	3.02
52.8	41.4	1.7	32.0	13.8	2.65
51.9	42.4	− 5.2	31.8	− 15.7	2.62
		− 8.3	31.7	−	−

Warming

t°	ε	t°	ε	t°	ε
C. −33.5	2.43	− 5.1	11.18	51.9	42.6
23.6	2.43	5.1	18.50	**L.** 52.6	40.6
10.7	2.60	− 5.0	29.70	52.8	39.5
5.7	2.65	+ 2.9	31.30	53.0	37.7
5.3	2.80	12.8	33.70	53.2	35.9
5.2	3.23	24.5	36.3	55.2	35.7
− 5.1	7.80	39.3	39.5	58.2	35.3

METHYL NITRATE CH_3O_3N · · · · ·

GRAY and SMITH (1953)

Boiling point: 64.6

Melting point: —82.96

Refractive index: $n_D^{18°} = 1.37605$

Specific heat

$t°$	c_p	$t°$	c_p	$t°$	c_p
C.—259.21	0.985	—235.71	6.82	—135.16	18.4
258.71	1.05	234.86	6.82	121.96	19.1
258.09	1.18	228.56	7.45	120.26	19.5
257.39	1.34	227.86	8.30	98.66	21.4
256.56	1.53	227.06	8.30	93.66	22.8
255.22	1.85	220.26	8.94	92.16	23.0
254.05	2.22	213.06	9.40	L. 79.46	31.17
253.00	2.35	210.46	10.2	73.16	32.17
251.59	2.62	208.56	10.4	68.76	32.60
250.24	2.86	206.76	10.6	66.16	32.92
248.56	3.25	180.16	14.3	56.66	33.5
247.00	3.72	178.16	14.3	43.16	35.0
244.34	4.25	172.56	15.0	29.16	35.9
240.11	5.03	170.46	14.8	— 7.86	36.8
238.81	5.83	168.26	15.1	+ 3.84	37.5
237.86	6.96	151.66	16.6	+22.34	37.3
—236.76	6.91	—149.66	16.6		

Heat of melting: 1970 cal/mol

NITROGLYCEROL, etc., see KEMP, GOLDHAGEN and ZIHLMAN (1957)
ALKYL NITRATES, see FAIRBROTHER, SKINNER and EVANS (1957)

B. ALIPHATIC AMIDES

FORMAMIDE CH_3ON

LEADER (1951)

Freezing point: 2.51

Density, Viscosity and *Dielectric constant*

$t°$	d	$\eta \cdot 10^5$	ε	$t°$	ε
3	1.1474	654	118.3	15.0	113.5
5	1.1458	618	117.5	25.0	109.5
20	1.1332	385	111.5	30.0	107.5
40	1.1161	237	103.5	35.0	105.6

N-METHYLACETAMIDE C_3H_7ON

and all other N-ALKYLAMIDES, see DAWSON, SEARS and GRAVES (1955);
VAUGHN and SEARS (1958)

CAPROAMIDE $C_5H_{11}ON$

Melting point: 101.0° SIMON (1929)

α-GLYCINE $C_2H_5O_2N$

Saturated vapour pressure: TAKAGI, HIKARA and SEKI (1959)

$t°$	$p \, mm \cdot 10^3$	$t°$	$p \, mm \cdot 10^3$	
138.9	1.344	145.9	2.459	
140.6	1.557	147.3	2.877	
142.0	1.789	149.2	3.289	
143.4	1.978	150.6	3.899	
144.7	2.350	152.6	4.362	

Specific heat: HUTCHENS, COLE and STOUT (1960)

$t°$	c_p	$t°$	c_p	$t°$	c_p
−263.15	0.061	−183.15	9.449	−53.15	18.52
258.15	0.231	173.15	10.34	43.15	19.14
253.15	0.572	163.15	11.16	33.15	19.80
248.15	1.067	153.15	11.95	23.15	20.46
243.15	1.682	143.15	12.69	13.15	21.14
238.15	2.374	133.15	13.40	− 3.15	21.81
233.15	3.108	123.15	14.08	0.00	22.02
228.15	3.853	113.15	14.74	+ 6.85	22.48
223.15	4.600	103.15	15.39	16.85	23.16
218.15	5.321	93.15	16.02	25.00	23.71
213.15	6.012	83.15	16.65	26.85	23.84
203.15	7.287	73.15	17.28	36.85	24.53
−193.15	8.427	− 63.15	17.90	+37.00	24.54

TYROSINE, PROLINE, TRYPTOPHAN, see Addenda, pp. 459–461

l-ALANINE $C_3H_7O_2N$

Specific heat: HUTCHENS, COLE and STOUT (1960)

$t°$	c_p	$t°$	c_p	$t°$	c_p
−263.15	0.118	−183.15	11.44	−53.15	23.00
258.15	0.400	173.15	12.56	43.15	23.80
253.15	0.920	163.15	13.61	33.15	24.60
248.15	1.607	153.15	14.60	23.15	25.41
243.15	2.412	143.15	15.56	13.15	26.22
238.15	3.286	133.15	16.49	− 3.15	27.02
233.15	4.151	123.15	17.38	0.00	27.27
228.15	4.997	113.15	18.24	+ 6.85	27.82
223.15	5.832	103.15	19.08	16.85	28.60
218.15	6.640	93.15	19.89	25.00	29.22
213.15	7.414	83.15	20.68	26.85	29.36
203.15	8.850	73.15	21.46	36.85	30.11
−193.15	10.19	−63.15	22.23	+37.00	30.12

PHENYLALANINE see Addenda, p. 458

C. MISCELLANEOUS DERIVATIVES

MORPHOLINE C_4H_9ON

B. E. (1959)

Boiling point: 128.94° dt/dp (10 mm) 0.45

Density

$t°$	d
0	1.01918
15	1.00495
30	0.99074

Viscosity

$t°$	$\eta \cdot 10^5$
15	2534
30	1792

Surface tension

$t°$	γ
15	38.27
20	37.63
30	36.24

Refractivedex: in at 15° and *dn/dt*

He$_r$	H$_\alpha$	Na$_D$	He$_y$	He$_{gr}$	H$_\beta$	He$_{viol}$	H$_\gamma$
1.45430	1.45468	1.45733	1.45743	1.46236	1.46351	1.46736	1.46877
0.00047	0.00049	—	0.00046	0.00047	0.00049	0.00049	0.00049

Dielectric constant

t°	ε	
20	7.46	PHILIPPE (not published)

ETHANOLAMINE   C$_2$H$_7$ON

MATTHEWS, SUMNER and MOELWYN-HUGHES (1950)

Saturated vapour pressure:

t°	p mm	t°	p mm	t°	p mm
65.4	6.7	92.2	32.4	125.0	145.9
65.5	7.1	93.2	34.8	126.9	159.4
69.5	8.7	94.6	37.5	128.8	171.4
70.8	9.4	96.4	40.8	132.0	193.3
71.0	9.8	98.7	45.0	133.3	205.5
72.1	10.8	99.5	47.8	136.0	227.2
73.3	11.2	101.7	53.6	137.9	242.0
75.4	13.2	104.1	59.6	141.5	280.0
76.9	14.0	105.0	63.3	144.6	316.8
78.4	15.4	105.5	64.2	147.1	340.7
81.1	17.4	107.5	70.6	150.8	406.5
84.0	20.9	108.9	76.0	154.7	445.3
85.0	21.7	112.1	84.8	158.5	518
86.4	24.6	114.2	93.4	161.4	554
86.8	24.9	117.3	105.1	167.0	652
90.0	28.6	121.0	122.9	170.9	751

Saturated vapour pressure: 73° (10 mm) *ibid.*

Boiling point: 170.95 *dt/dp* (10 mm) 0.46 B.E. (1959)

Freezing point: 9.3 MATTHEWS, SUMNER and MOELWYN-HUGHES (1950)

Density: B.E. (1959)

t°	d	
0	1.03135	
15	1.01949	
30	1.00763	

Viscosity: B. E. (1959)

t^v	$\eta \cdot 10^5$
15	30855
30	14417

Surface tension: B. E. (1959)

$t°$	γ
15.80	49.39
20	48.89
30	47.74

Refractive index at 15° and *dn/dt* B.E. (1959)

He_r	H_α	Na_D	He_y	He_{gr}	H_β	He_{viol}	H_γ
1.45295	1.45331	1.45588	1.45598	1.46080	1.46189	1.46541	1.46673
0.00036	0.00035	—	0.00036	0.00036	0.00036	0.00035	0.00035

Dielectric constant: LAFONTAINE (1958)

$t°$	ε
−10	3.475
−15	3.368

N.B. (p. 588): Suppress REITMEIER, SIVERTZ and TARTAR (1940)

Heat of combustion at 25°: −3616 DOW CHEMICAL COMPANY (1956)

Heat of vaporization at −273.1°: 22.010 cal/mol MATTHEWS, SUMNER and
MOELWYN-HUGHES (1950)

OXIMES and their esters, see VOGEL, CRESSWELL *et al.* (1952)

KETOXIMES $C_7H_{14}NOH$ and $C_{11}H_{22}NOH$, see p. 347

ETHYL CYANOACETATE $C_5H_7O_2N$

B.E. (1959)

Boiling temperature: 94.80° (11 mm)

Density

$t°$	d
0	1.08192
15	1.06652
30	1.05106

Viscosity

t°	$\eta \cdot 10^5$	
15	3256	
30	2148	

Surface tension

t°	γ	
15.48	36.96	
20	36.48	
30	35.42	

Refractive index at 15° and *dn/dt*

He_r	H_α	Na_D	He_y	He_gr	H_β	He viol	H_γ
1.41660	1.41704	1.4191	1.41920	1.42325	1.42437	1.42733	1.42883
0.00038	0.00039	—	0.00038	0.00039	0.00040	0.00039	0.00044

Dielectric constant: LAFONTAINE (1958)

t°	ε	
−10	31.62	
−15	32.14	

D. AROMATIC NITRO DERIVATIVES

NITROBENZENE $C_6H_5NO_2$

Saturated vapour pressure: BROWN (1952)

t°	p mm	t°	p mm	
134.10	82.23	185.70	405.18	
139.75	100.30	188.90	441.33	
145.17	120.64	192.98	490.74	
149.73	140.20	196.63	538.87	
154.61	164.01	200.41	592.53	
159.77	192.80	203.88	645.62	
164.45	222.33	206.62	690.23	
168.72	252.39	209.49	739.54	
172.96	285.04	210.626	759.98	
178.48	333.44	210.629	760.04	
182.07	367.64	—	—	

Boiling point: 210.66 BROWN (1952)

Freezing point: 5.72 WITSCHONKE (1954)
            5.716 MATHIEU (1953)

Density at 25° 1.19833 BROWN (1952)

Refractive index $n_D^{25°}$: 1.5499 BROWN (1952)

Dielectric constant: PHILIPPE and PIETTE (1955)

t°	ε	t°	ε	
L.+10.80	37.33	− 27.0	2.829	
4.50	38.34	10.2	3.087	
C. 3.00	3.398	− 3.2	3.220	
0.15	3.297	+ 4.95	3.583	
−18.2	2.960	5.35	4.019	
37.5	2.702	**L.** 6.75	37.99	
−54.0	2.610	15.45	36.52	
		+25.05	34.85	

ε 26.1°: 34.369 PYLE (1931)

Ortho-NITROTOLUENE $C_7H_7O_2N$

Freezing point: I: −3.55 BONAUGURI and BERNARDI (1958)
            II: −9.25

Dielectric constant: PHILIPPE and PIETTE (1955)

t°	ε	t°	ε	
+17.70	27.27	−54.9	2.732	
5.80	28.82	25.7	3.030	
− 1.7	29.68	12.0	3.396	
3.9	29.79	9.9	3.469	
7.3	3.567	4.5	3.680	
18.2	3.193	− 3.51	3.761	
35.3	2.889	+12.15	28.01	
−73.9	2.694	+22.75	26.54	

2,4,6-TRINITROTOLUENE $C_7H_5O_6N_3$

Saturated vapour pressure: EDWARDS (1950)

$t°$	p cm	$t°$	p cm	$t°$	p cm
53.0	$2.64.10^{-5}$	78.3	$6.22.10^{-4}$	110.6	$8.26.10^{-3}$
60.1	$5.43.10^{-5}$	79.8	$6.55.10^{-4}$	110.5	$7.96.10^{-3}$
60.8	$6.32.10^{-5}$	80.1	$6.37.10^{-4}$	131.1	$3.48.10^{-2}$
61.5	$6.86.10^{-5}$	80.2	$7.16.10^{-4}$	131.5	$3.45.10^{-2}$
61.0	$6.22.10^{-5}$	82.4	$7.96.10^{-4}$	141.4	$6.21.10^{-2}$
72.1	$3.11.10^{-4}$	86.9	$1.19.10^{-3}$	142.0	$6.58.10^{-2}$
72.1	$3.14.10^{-4}$	86.9	$1.13.10^{-3}$	142.5	$6.17.10^{-2}$
72.3	$3.11.10^{-4}$	99.0	$3.37.10^{-3}$		
78.5	$6.44.10^{-4}$	99.5	$3.92.10^{-3}$		
78.5	$5.88.10^{-4}$	99.5	$4.07.10^{-3}$		

Heat of melting: 5600 cal/mol EDWARDS (1950)

ETHYL AZOXYBENZOATE $C_{18}H_{14}O_5N_2$

Melting point: 113.7 SPAGHT, BENSON and PARKS (1932)

Clearing point: 122.5 SPAGHT, BENSON and PARKS (1932)

Specific heat: SPAGHT, BENSON and PARKS (1932)

$t°$	c_p	$t°$	c_p	$t°$	c_p
crystals		anisotropic liquid		isotropic liquid	
30	0.315	116.2	0.471	130	0.472
40	0.326			140	0.475
50	0.337			150	0.478
60	0.348				
70	0.358				
80	0.369				
90	0.380				
100	0.391				
110	0.401				

Heat of fusion: 14.3 cal/gr. SPAGHT, BENSON and PARKS (1932)

Heat of clearing: 3.8 cal/gr. SPAGHT, BENSON and PARKS (1932)

ALKOXYBENZALAZINES: see SHAW and BROWN (1959)

SALIPYRINE $C_{18}H_{18}O_4N_2$

Dielectric constant: KOMANDIN and BONETSKAYA (1960)

$t°$	ε	$t°$	ε	$t°$	ε
20.0	5.90	-8.0	3.50	-33.5	3.33
15.0	5.00	-18.0	3.50	-37.0	3.30
11.5	4.50	-23.0	3.45	-38.5	3.30
5.0	3.90	-28.0	3.36	-39.5	3.30
0.0	3.70				

12. MIXED HALOGEN-NITROGEN DERIVATIVES

TRIFLUOROACETONITRILE C_2NF_3

PACE and BOBKA (1961)

Saturated vapour pressure

$t°$	p mm	$t°$	p mm
−131.388	3.007	−86.186	251.82
121.595	13.134	79.875	377.23
111.568	34.052	74.992	505.65
101.162	84.117	71.740	607.81
− 94.245	143.730	−67.604	766.55

Boiling point: −67.69°

Melting point: −144.43°

Specific heat

$t°$	c_p	$t°$	c_p	$t°$	c_p	$t°$	c_p
−260.58	1.490	−214.81	11.49	−188.95	14.33	−139.95	28.75
257.62	2.480	210.66	12.10	187.29	14.47	136.38	28.60
257.14	2.667	210.54	12.01	187.22	14.48	135.00	28.57
253.98	3.660	208.62	12.30	186.45	14.55	130.08	28.61
252.75	4.043	206.49	12.52	185.21	14.64	128.61	28.51
250.16	4.878	205.87	12.63	182.62	14.91	121.80	28.50
247.94	5.455	203.76	12.88	181.84	14.91	117.21	28.50
245.11	6.228	202.94	12.88	181.19	15.03	115.04	28.41
242.61	6.819	201.11	13.04	176.36	15.45	110.87	28.36
239.73	7.518	198.87	13.36	176.19	15.57	108.09	28.38
237.25	8.040	198.65	13.32	171.37	15.97	103.85	28.28
234.92	8.524	196.45	13.54	171.10	15.94	100.98	28.33
229.94	9.483	194.36	13.77	166.43	16.37	96.65	28.33
225.06	10.21	192.41	13.96	165.89	16.39	93.92	28.34
219.41	10.91	191.98	14.03	161.41	16.89	89.53	28.29
218.31	11.04	191.82	14.06	−141.21	28.70	82.48	28.28
−215.28	11.46	−189.88	14.23			− 76.18	28.25

Heat of fusion: 1187.7 cal/mol

TRICHLOROACETONITRILE C_2NCl_3

Davies and Jenkin (1954)

Boiling point: 85.7

Saturated vapour pressure

$t°$	p mm	$t°$	p mm	
16.80	49.0	50.15	222.0	
17.30	51.0	56.00	273.5	
20.00	58.0	61.65	340.5	
23.40	68.5	65.40	388.0	
26.55	80.0	66.90	458.5	
31.00	98.5	73.65	521.0	
35.05	118.5	76.65	572.5	
40.40	147.5	79.75	635.5	
47.00	192.5	83.40	709.5	

Density

$t°$	d	$t°$	d	
25.00	1.4403	35.0	1.4223	

Refractive index

$t°$	n_D	$t°$	n_D	
20	1.4409	27.0	1.4375	

Dispersion: $n_D - n_C = 0.00248$

$n_F - n_D = 0.00620$

$n_G - n_D = 0.00116$

Dielectric constant at 19°: 7.85

Heat of vaporization: 8160 cal/mol

TETRAMETHYLAMMONIUM HYDROGEN DICHLORIDE $C_4H_{13}NCl_2$

Specific heat: CHANG and WESTRUM (1962)

$t°K$	c_p	$t°K$	c_p	$t°K$	c_p
Series I		16.35	2.250	Series VI	
128.72	28.30	18.04	2.897	116.25	26.49
		19.99	3.692	124.69	27.75
Series II		21.94	4.521	132.84	28.89
		24.46	5.613	140.91	29.99
154.31	31.77	27.39	6.869	149.24	31.11
162.91	32.87	30.57	8.183		
171.73	33.94	33.84	9.470	Series VII	
180.52	34.98	37.40	10.81		
189.18	36.02	41.34	12.03	228.99	40.65
197.83	37.04	45.67	13.36	237.57	41.64
206.71	38.08	50.49	14.67	245.99	42.69
215.75	39.12	55.94	15.98	254.64	43.64
224.84	40.20	61.95	17.32	263.66	44.78
		68.40	18.61	272.80	45.90
				282.00	47.01
Series III		Series IV		291.10	48.18
5.82	0.069			299.96	49.27
6.41	0.100	70.35	18.93	308.81	50.45
7.19	0.148	77.01	20.14	317.62	51.65
8.08	0.232			326.67	52.97
8.95	0.331	Series V		335.81	54.64
9.87	0.465			344.86	56.29
10.94	0.664	73.59	19.50		
12.18	0.940	80.38	20.78		
13.49	1.300	87.52	22.11		
14.86	1.728	95.09	23.27		
		103.13	24.53		
		111.45	25.83		

CHLORHYDRATES of ARGININE, HISTIDINE and LYSINE, see Addenda, pp. 455–457.

2-CHLORO-2-NITROPROPANE $C_3H_6O_2NCl$

CROWE and SMYTH (1950)

Freezing point: -21.5

Transition points: -57.4 and -59.3

Dielectric constant

Cooling

$t°$	ε	$t°$	ε	$t°$	ε
-14.0	25.40	-27.3	30.70	-59.2	27.00
19.3	26.52	30.7	30.60	59.3	23.85
21.5	30.02	33.9	30.35	59.3	11.50
21.7	30.70	38.6	29.92	59.5	4.30
22.8	31.90	40.4	29.85	59.6	4.10
23.3	31.80	46.9	29.67	61.6	3.65
23.7	31.42	50.1	29.64	64.1	3.25
24.1	31.00	53.0	29.65	69.7	2.94
-25.1	30.70	-58.7	29.67	-70.9	2.90

Warming immediately

$t°$	ε	$t°$	ε	$t°$	ε
III -70.4	2.82	I -54.2	27.90	-22.2	30.38
64.5	3.00	50.4	28.70	21.7	29.85
59.0	4.25	46.5	29.38	21.5	29.40
58.0	6.40	40.8	30.23	21.3	29.00
57.4	15.42	33.0	31.20	21.1	28.47
II 57.3	22.90	29.1	31.55	20.9	27.90
57.2	27.11	25.3	31.38	-18.6	26.88
-57.1	27.30	-23.3	30.88	—	—

Warming after 24 hr: below transition point

$t°$	ε	$t°$	ε	$t°$	ε
III -62.8	2.93	-54.2	24.33	-21.9	29.91
60.9	3.22	47.5	26.25	21.8	29.55
59.0	4.03	41.8	27.93	21.6	29.34
58.0	5.74	35.9	29.50	21.5	29.10
II 57.6	10.75	32.0	30.35	21.4	28.86
57.4	20.55	26.2	31.10	21.3	28.62
57.3	23.35	23.3	30.35	21.1	27.97
-56.1	23.85	-22.4	30.30	21.0	27.35
				-19.6	26.60

Heat of fusion: 320 cal/mol

Heat of transition: 2280 cal/mol

o-CHLORONITROBENZENE	$C_6H_4O_2NCl$
m-CHLORODINITROBENZENE	$C_6H_3O_4N_2Cl$
1,4-DICHLORO-2-NITROBENZENE	$C_6H_3O_2NCl_2$
1-CHLORO-4-BROMO-2-NITROBENZENE	$C_6H_3O_2NClBr$

See JOSHI and DAS TULI (1951)

PICRYL CHLORIDE $C_6H_2O_6N_3Cl$

Melting point: 80.5 NITTA, SEKI *et al.* (1951)

Saturated vapour pressure: NITTA, SEKI *et al.* (1951)

t°	p mm
68.1	1.02
69.9	1.29
72.8	1.63
74.1	1.99
79.7	3.26

BENZOTRIFLUORIDES: see KARDON and SAYLOR (1953)

13. SULPHUR DERIVATIVES

CARBON DISULPHIDE   CS₂

Vapour pressure: WADDINGTON, SMITH, WILLIAMSON and SCOTT (1962)

t°	p mm	t°	p mm	
3.588	149.41	46.225	760.00	
8.772	187.57	51.744	906.06	
13.999	233.72	57.295	1074.6	
19.269	289.13	62.885	1268.0	
24.582	355.22	68.531	1489.1	
29.927	433.56	74.210	1740.8	
35.318	525.86	79.927	2026.0	
40.751	633.99	—	—	

Saturated vapour pressure at 20°: 297.50 mm HUET, PHILIPPE and BONO (1953)

N.B. (p. 611): *Saturated vapour pressure:* correct SAMESHIMA (1925) instead of (1935)

Boiling point: 46.23 HUET, PHILIPPE and BONO (1953)
46.25 DE BROUCKERE and GILLET (1935)

Melting point: −111.954 HUET, PHILIPPE and BONO (1953)
−111.908 MATHIEU (1953)

Critical solution point with CH₃OH: 35.0 DE BROUCKERE and GILLET (1935)

Density at 0°: 1.2929 HUET, PHILIPPE and BONO (1953)

Compression: STEVENSON (1957)

Dielectric constant: PHILIPPE and PIETTE (1955)

t°	ε	t°	ε	
+ 20.00	2.634	−140.0	3.007	
− 14.5	2.712	160.0	2.992	
40.0	2.759	148.0	3.003	
82.5	2.874	125.0	3.005	
−107.0	2.937	− 29.5	2.745	

Heat of combustion: at 25°: 402.69 kcal/mol GOOD, LACINA and McCULLOUGH (1961)

CARBON OXYSULPHIDE COS

Transition under high pressure: STEVENSON (1957)

Density: PARTINGTON and NEVILLE (1951)

t°	d	t°	d	t°	d
−99.5	1.274	− 30.3	1.131	+ 36.2	0.936
88.2	1.251	23.3	1.113	44.1	0.907
80.0	1.238	16.0	1.097	51.7	0.878
72.3	1.220	9.7	1.083	59.8	0.841
65.5	1.208	− 1.7	1.052	66.3	0.804
58.3	1.196	+ 3.6	1.040	75.1	0.762
52.9	1.188	7.9	1.023	85.4	0.691
46.2	1.168	16.3	1.004	93.5	0.606
39.1	1.155	21.6	0.981	99.8	0.523
− 34.3	1.142	+ 29.8	0.956	+100.9	0.499

Surface tension: PARTINGTON and NEVILLE (1951)

t°	γ	t°	γ
−97.5	27.05	−19.3	15.88
87.6	26.31	− 6.1	13.00
76.0	25.73	+ 2.2	11.43
69.5	24.06	11.3	9.80
56.5	22.84	18.7	8.28
49.5	21.20	29.0	6.93
40.4	20.03	+40.1	5.41
−29.1	17.31	—	—

ETHYLENE SULPHIDE or THIACYCLOPROPANE C_2H_4S

Saturated vapour pressure: GUTHRIE, SCOTT and WADDINGTON (1952)

t°	p mm	t°	p mm
18.29	187.58	54.93	760.00
23.41	233.72	60.31	906.06
28.58	289.13	65.72	1074.6
33.78	355.22	71.12	1268.0
39.01	433.56	76.66	1489.1
44.29	525.86	82.18	1740.8
49.59	633.99	87.73	2026.0

METHANETHIOL or METHYL MERCAPTAN   CH₄S

Heat of combustion at 25°: 363.04 kcal/mol GOOD, LACINA and McCULLOUGH (1961)

ETHANETHIOL or ETHYLMERCAPTAN   C₂H₆S

Saturated vapour pressure: McCULLOUGH, SCOTT *et al.* (1952)

t°	p mm	t°	p mm	
0.405	187.57	35.000	760.00	
5.236	233.72	40.092	906.06	
10.111	289.13	45.221	1074.6	
15.017	355.22	50.390	1268.0	
19.954	433.56	55.604	1489.1	
24.933	525.86	60.838	1740.8	
29.944	633.99	66.115	2026.0	

Boiling point: 32.9° (704.1 mm) MATHIAS and DE CARVALHO FILHO (1958)
　　　　　　　35.0 HAINES, HELM *et al.* (1954)

Freezing point: −147.89 HAINES, HELM *et al.* (1954)
　　　　　　　　−147.90 McCULLOUGH, SCOTT *et al.* (1952)
　　　　　　　　−147.926 GLASGOW Jr., KROUSKOP and ROSSINI (1951)

Density: 25°: 0.83316 McCULLOUGH, SCOTT *et al.* (1952)
　　　　　20°: 0.83914 HAINES, HELM *et al.* (1954)
　　　　　25°: 0.83316　　　　　,,

Viscosity: 20°: 293·10⁻⁵　　　　,,
　　　　　25°: 279·10⁻⁵　　　　,,

Surface tension: 20°: 23.5 HAINES, HELM *et al.* (1954)
　　　　　　　　25°: 22.8　　　　,,

Refractive index

t°	He$_r$	H$_\alpha$	Na$_D$	Hg$_{gr}$	He$_v$	H$_\beta$	Hg$_g$	
20	1.42763	1.42810	1.43105	1.43356	1.43695	1.43836	1.44228	HAINES, HELM *et al.* (1954)
25	1.42442	1.42486	1.42779	1.43027	1.43363	1.43505	1.44085	,,
25	—	—	1.42779	—	—	—	—	McCULLOUGH, SCOTT *et al.* (1952)
25	—	—	—	—	—	—	1.44067	MATHIAS and FILHO (1958)

Dielectric constant at 25°: 6.667 MATHIAS and DE CARVALHO FILHO (1958)

Specific heat: McCULLOUGH, SCOTT *et al.* (1952)

$t°$	c_p	$t°$	c_p	$t°$	c_p
Crystals				Liquid	
−258.78	1.019	−214.46	9.471	−143.11	27.298
257.63	1.244	210.30	9.983	138.04	27.218
256.32	1.527	208.95	10.149	135.73	27.194
254.64	1.901	204.38	10.663	134.19	27.149
252.62	2.373	203.46	10.759	127.12	27.069
251.21	2.731	198.51	11.299	125.60	27.045
250.23	2.963	197.73	11.384	119.12	26.967
248.74	3.318	191.67	12.068	115.49	26.925
247.58	3.601	187.38	12.519	105.39	26.825
245.79	4.023	185.07	12.776	95.31	26.746
242.65	4.747	182.62	13.010	85.33	26.696
239.58	5.425	177.99	13.470	75.29	26.679
235.59	6.220	176.86	13.573	65.30	26.662
230.28	7.169	171.29	14.104	57.10	26.727
225.04	8.019	170.85	14.155	47.20	26.794
221.96	8.465	165.92	14.609	37.34	26.902
219.94	8.763	160.36	15.138	27.54	27.029
219.53	8.822	−154.62	15.727	17.81	27.191
−216.30	9.239	—	—	− 8.16	27.372
				+ 1.41	27.559
				10.91	27.783
				20.32	28.033
				25.90	28.198
				30.10	28.316
				33.14	28.398
				40.24	28.622
				+ 42.10	28.685

Heat of combustion: 8326.10 cal/gr McCULLOUGH, HUBBARD *et al.* (1957)

PROPANETHIOL-1 or n-PROPYL MERCAPTAN C_3H_8S

Boiling point: 65.3° (701.5 mm) MATHIAS and DE CARVALHO FILHO (1958)

Density at 25°: 0.83598 MATHIAS (1950)

Refractive index at 25°: *(ibid.)*

He_r	H_α	Na_D	He_y	Hg_c	He_{gr}	H_β	He_{bl}	He_v	Hg_g	H_γ
1.43188	1.43227	1.43511	1.43515	1.43749	1.44072	1.44204	1.44349	1.44621	1.44767	1.44784

Dielectric constant at 25°: 5.720 *ibid.*

Heat of combustion at 25°: 673.19 kcal/mol HUBBARD and WADDINGTON (1954)

PROPANETHIOL-2 or *Iso*-PROPYL MERCAPTAN C_3H_8S

Saturated vapour pressure: McCULLOUGH, FINKE, SCOTT *et al.* (1954)

$t°$	p mm	t^u	p mm	
10.697	149.41	52.558	760.00	
15.770	187.57	57.985	906.06	
20.899	233.72	63.461	1074.6	
26.071	289.13	68.979	1268.0	
31.282	355.22	74.540	1489.1	
36.536	433.56	80.143	1740.8	
41.833	525.86	85.795	2026.0	
47.175	633.99	—	—	

Boiling point: 49.8 (696.2 mm) MATHIAS and DE CARVALHO FILHO (1958)

Freezing point: —130.5205 McCULLOUGH, FINKE, SCOTT *et al.* (1954)

Density at 25°: 0.80895 MATHIAS (1950)

Refractive index at 25°: *(ibid.)*

He$_r$	H$_\alpha$	Na$_D$	He$_y$	Hg$_c$	He$_{gr}$	H$_\beta$	He$_{bl}$	He$_v$	Hg$_g$	Hγ
1.41836	1.41878	1.42154	1.42160	1.42387	1.42705	1.42839	1.42974	1.43246	1.43387	1.43419

Dielectric constant at 25°: 5.952 MATHIAS and DE CARVALHO FILHO (1958)

Specific heat: McCULLOUGH, FINKE, SCOTT *et al.* (1954)

t°	c$_p$	t°	c$_p$	t°	c$_p$	t°	c$_p$
Crystals I		**Crystals I**		**Crystals I**		**Liquid**	
−260.27	0.986	−218.51	9.841	−164.33	17.138	−123.90	31.401
260.09	1.034	217.85	9.931	162.89	17.539	116.34	31.476
258.91	1.309	217.68	9.946	162.42	17.618	107.99	31.554
258.54	1.409	212.72	10.571			99.77	31.635
257.43	1.689	211.93	10.678	**Crystals II**		95.90	31.672
256.90	1.834	206.96	11.292			91.59	31.725
255.44	2.240	206.56	11.333			86.13	31.790
255.12	2.329	203.06	11.740	159.10	19.196	76.03	31.924
253.05	2.929	200.09	12.104	157.31	19.497	65.73	32.076
252.85	2.986	198.78	12.266	156.37	19.656	55.65	32.263
250.66	3.618	193.42	12.942	154.69	19.933	45.65	32.461
250.24	3.742	193.32	12.959	154.47	19.965	35.73	32.705
248.13	4.338	187.62	13.728	153.90	20.027	25.41	32.986
247.66	4.469	186.62	13.860	150.97	20.631	24.18	33.014
245.33	5.097	181.69	14.513	147.90	21.293	15.19	33.282
244.93	5.191	179.88	14.751	147.73	21.336	14.71	33.293
242.10	5.902	176.45	15.222	145.09	21.869	− 4.37	33.634
239.02	6.589	173.09	15.709	141.07	23.138	+ 6.79	34.052
235.59	7.263	172.26	15.831	140.01	23.434	17.82	34.469
231.93	7.916	168.21	16.471	−134.76	25.777	28.70	34.895
227.79	8.560	165.02	16.994			39.11	35.333
−223.09	9.237	−164.62	17.083			+ 48.47	35.764

Heat of melting: 1371 cal/mol McCULLOUGH, FINKE, SCOTT *et al.* (1954)

Heat of transition at —160.65°: 12.63 cal/mol *ibid.*

Heat of combustion at 25°: 671.76 kcal/mol HUBBARD and WADDINGTON (1954)

BUTANETHIOL-1 or *n*-BUTYL MERCAPTAN $C_4H_{10}S$

Boiling point: 95.7 (703 mm) Mathias and De Carvalho Filho (1958)
98.45 Scott, Finke *et al.* (1957)

Triple point: −115.69 Scott, Finke *et al.* (1957)

Density at 25°: 0.83679 Mathias (1950)

Refractive index at 25°: Mathias (1950)

He_r	H_α	Na_D	He_y	Hg_c	He_{gr}	H_β	He_{bl}	He_v	Hg_g	H_γ
1.43698	1.43739	1.44014	1.44021	1.44248	1.44562	1.44691	1.44832	1.45098	1.45237	1.45259

Dielectric constant at 25°: 5.073 Mathias and De Carvalho Filho (1958)

Specific heat: Scott, Finke *et al.* (1957)

Crystals							
$t°$	c_p	$t°$	c_p	$t°$	c_p	$t°$	c_p
−260.25	0.802	−250.03	3.237	−216.97	11.037	−175.27	17.475
260.08	0.839	248.13	3.758	213.97	11.602	170.12	18.095
258.95	1.059	249.70	3.872	209.29	12.467	163.66	18.872
258.49	1.154	245.55	4.454	204.15	13.319	156.86	19.667
257.53	1.347	245.32	4.516	198.59	14.216	149.32	20.531
256.82	1.511	242.65	5.237	192.80	15.090	141.57	21.425
255.95	1.715	239.50	6.066	187.86	15.818	137.22	21.916
255.02	1.940	235.90	6.944	187.12	15.942	134.19	22.283
254.21	2.140	231.78	7.919	182.87	16.511	129.95	22.803
252.89	2.481	227.30	8.912	181.29	16.732	127.14	23.155
252.25	2.645	222.36	9.969	−176.79	17.275	−122.93	23.751
250.55	3.093	−218.09	10.814				

Liquid						Vapour	
−112.93	39.09	−72.83	38.49	− 9.18	39.71	+ 87.04	32.35
106.63	38.90	63.23	38.52	+ 1.10	40.10	109.04	33.82
101.88	38.78	53.19	38.60	11.28	40.56	144.04	36.08
98.89	38.74	42.72	38.76	21.35	41.01	180.04	38.29
96.08	38.70	39.53	38.84	31.32	41.47	+227.40	41.03
91.16	38.61	30.03	39.07	+41.17	41.95		
−82.47	38.53	−19.56	39.37	—	—		

BUTANETHIOL-2 or *Sec.*-BUTYL MERCAPTAN $C_4H_{10}S$

Saturated vapour pressure in function of the boiling point of water: see
McCULLOUGH, FINKE *et al.* (1958)
Boiling point: 37.4° (134 mm) MATHIAS (1950)
             35.5° (130 mm) MATHIAS and DE CARVALHO FILHO (1958)
Freezing point: −140.14 McCULLOUGH, FINKE *et al.* (1958)
Density at 25°: 0.82456 MATHIAS (1950)
Refractive index at 25°: *ibid.*

He_r	H_α	Na_D	He_y	Hg_c	He_{gr}	H_β	He_{bl}	He_v	Hg_g	H_γ
1.43075	1.43111	1.43385	1.43391	1.43617	1.43929	1.44059	1.44196	1.44460	1.44608	1.44619

Dielectric constant at 25°: 5.466 MATHIAS and DE CARVALHO FILHO (1958)

Specific heat: McCULLOUGH, FINKE *et al.* (1958)

$t°$	c_p	$t°$	c_p	$t°$	c_p	$t°$	c_p
−260.72	1.191	−213.85	11.614	−219.92	10.93	−115.13	37.866
260.33	1.291	208.72	12.398	215.21	11.71	104.95	37.803
259.69	1.454	203.53	13.127	209.61	12.67	94.81	37.784
259.02	1.613	198.25	13.842	204.01	13.61	91.66	37.788
258.38	1.805	193.24	14.552	198.45	14.60	84.70	37.805
257.88	1.945	190.04	15.009	196.03	15.10	81.89	37.817
256.92	2.213	188.15	15.273	192.90	15.73	72.19	37.895
256.13	2.433	185.74	15.598	188.80	16.68	63.75	37.974
255.23	2.695	184.37	15.793	171.53	38.618	62.05	38.019
253.56	3.189	182.95	15.983	167.00	38.545	53.94	38.130
253.33	3.261	180.69	16.274	162.06	38.469	51.50	38.169
251.34	3.845	178.96	16.493	157.14	38.396	41.04	38.428
250.63	4.053	177.77	16.658	155.38	38.371	30.67	38.704
249.19	4.476	175.40	16.947	152.80	38.347	24.86	38.880
247.44	4.960	173.34	17.201	151.42	38.314	18.06	39.110
246.95	5.111	172.58	17.314	150.78	38.318	15.22	39.213
244.69	5.715	167.57	17.917	146.33	38.246	5.67	39.571
244.44	5.776	167.52	17.913	145.68	38.246	− 3.31	39.670
241.40	6.568	162.32	18.540	144.30	38.226	+ 3.80	39.980
238.31	7.286	162.29	18.546	140.60	38.162	8.97	40.198
234.83	8.003	158.87	18.953	137.66	38.165	18.85	40.638
230.49	8.837	157.61	19.120	135.58	38.098	24.29	40.869
225.43	9.751	156.84	19.210	133.00	38.072	28.17	41.076
225.29	9.780	153.63	19.627	−125.34	37.970	+ 33.71	41.367
220.18	10.642	153.06	19.684				
219.78	10.702	149.44	20.122			**Vapour**	
218.92	10.851	−146.71	20.564			+ 73.04	31.83
−214.12	11.574					95.04	33.29
						130.04	35.56
						+180.04	38.68

2-METHYLPROPANETHIOL-1 or *Iso*-BUTYL MERCAPTAN C$_4$H$_{10}$S

Saturated vapour pressure in function of the boiling point of water: see SCOTT, McCULLOUGH *et al.* (1958)

Boiling point: 41.2° (142 mm) MATHIAS (1950)
                40.2° (132 mm) MATHIAS and DE CARVALHO FILHO (1958)

Freezing point: −144.85 SCOTT, McCULLOUGH *et al.* (1958)

Density at 25°: 0.82880 MATHIAS (1950)

Refractive index at 25°: MATHIAS (1950)

He$_r$	H$_\alpha$	Na$_D$	He$_y$	Hg$_e$	He$_{gr}$	H$_\beta$	He$_{bl}$	He$_v$	Hg$_g$	H$_\gamma$
1.43272	1.43314	1.43582	1.43589	1.43814	1.44125	1.44256	1.44389	1.44655	1.44791	1.44815

Dielectric constant at 25°: 4.961 MATHIAS and DE CARVALHO FILHO (1958)

Specific heat: SCOTT, McCULLOUGH *et al.* (1958)

t°	c$_p$	t°	c$_p$	t°	c$_p$	t°	c$_p$
Crystals							
−260.75	1.185	−244.97	5.695	−185.42	16.293	−217.15	11.37
260.30	1.294	241.72	6.579	180.48	17.027	211.25	12.40
259.70	1.459	238.32	7.390	179.42	17.178	204.92	13.45
258.97	1.643	234.77	8.158	174.76	17.876	198.00	14.68
258.35	1.816	230.92	8.921	173.68	18.018	190.44	16.32
257.60	2.011	226.68	9.687	172.83	18.138	187.94	16.94
256.68	2.283	222.13	10.482	169.48	18.644	182.42	21.10
256.07	2.452	219.49	10.915	168.87	18.776	176.73	37.34
254.82	2.824	217.32	11.266	166.84	19.059	168.64	37.44
254.33	2.960	215.48	11.564	166.13	19.127	157.55	37.45
252.92	3.383	210.47	12.387	163.40	19.558	−146.60	37.50
252.48	3.511	205.04	13.219	160.32	20.008		
250.91	3.978	199.20	14.076	159.73	20.082		
250.28	4.157	193.33	14.996	157.02	20.508		
248.74	4.616	190.76	15.430	154.33	20.892		
247.79	4.900	−187.82	15.944	−149.86	21.569		
−246.48	5.268						

(Continued)

$t°$	c_p	$t°$	c_p	$t°$	c_p	$t°$	c_p
Vapour		Liquid					
+ 78.04	32.04	−135.74	37.49	−68.77	37.85	+17.57	40.72
100.04	33.49	125.22	37.50	58.62	38.02	21.70	40.93
140.04	36.12	114.51	37.50	48.55	38.26	28.77	41.27
180.04	38.64	103.87	37.54	38.06	38.53	32.77	41.48
+227.04	41.33	93.87	37.61	27.17	38.88	43.71	42.07
		82.78	37.70	16.40	39.26	54.50	42.62
		79.01	37.71	− 5.26	39.70	65.15	43.23
		− 72.34	37.82	+ 6.62	40.21	+75.64	43.81

2-METHYLPROPANETHIOL-2 or

Tert.-BUTYL MERCAPTAN $C_4H_{10}S$

Saturated vapour pressure: McCULLOUGH, SCOTT *et al.* (1953)

$t°$	p mm	$t°$	p mm	
20.496	149.41	64.217	760.00	
25.785	187.57	69.908	906.06	
31.127	233.72	75.654	1074.6	
36.519	289.13	81.449	1268.0	
41.959	355.22	87.294	1489.1	
47.446	433.56	93.188	1740.8	
52.983	525.86	99.138	2026.0	
58.573	633.99	—	—	

Boiling point: 61.60° (700.8 mm) MATHIAS (1950)

         61.6°   (699.4 mm) MATHIAS and DE CARVALHO FILHO (1958)

         64.2° HAINES, HELM *et al.* (1954)

Freezing point: +1.26 McCULLOUGH, SCOTT *et al.* (1953)

         +1.11 HAINES, HELM *et al.* (1954)

Transition points: −121.56, −116.16, −73.76 McCULLOUGH, SCOTT *et al.* (1953)

Density at 25°: 0.79426 MATHIAS (1950)

Density, *Viscosity* and *Surface tension:* HAINES, HELM *et al.* (1954)

t°	d	$\eta \cdot 10^5$	γ	
20	0.80020	638	20.8	
25	0.79472	588	20.2	
30	0.78929	544	19.6	

Refractive index: (*ibid.*)

t°	He_r	H_C	Na_D	Hg_e	He_v	H_F	Hg_g
20	1.41992	1.42046	1.42320	1.42550	1.42852	1.42991	1.43534
25	1.41699	1.41739	1.42007	1.42230	1.42545	1.42677	1.43214
30	1.41392	1.41431	1.41697	1.41930	1.42231	1.42362	1.43894

Refractive index at 25°: MATHIAS (1950)

He_r	H_α	Na_D	He_y	Hg_e	He_{gr}	H_β	He_{bl}	He_v	Hg_g	H_γ
1.41678	1.41714	1.41984	1.41991	1.42216	1.42526	1.42654	1.42791	1.43057	1.43193	1.43216

Dielectric constant at 25°: 5.341 MATHIAS and DE CARVALHO FILHO (1958)

Specific heat: McCULLOUGH, SCOTT *et al.* (1953)

t°	c_p	t°	c_p	t°	c_p	t°	c_p
				Series I			
Crystals I		**Crystals II**		**Crystals IV**		**Liquid**	
−218.23	10.300	−117.08	33.764	−69.98	33.386	+10.79	41.146
213.26	10.940			65.06	33.566	12.62	41.255
208.18	11.607	**Crystals III**		62.14	33.669	21.99	41.693
202.56	12.318			60.29	33.715		
196.86	13.074	−116.50	32.417	54.70	33.967		
191.13	13.890	110.02	32.669	52.16	34.031		
189.66	14.105	109.42	32.808	49.07	34.188		
185.35	14.735	103.51	33.091	42.47	34.429		
184.39	14.861	101.75	33.215	41.21	34.456		
179.20	15.578	101.69	33.194	38.02	34.603		
178.14	15.717	92.64	33.617	30.40	34.913		
172.22	16.570	91.53	33.669	29.32	35.016		
171.59	16.653	81.96	34.140	27.11	35.124		
164.95	17.644	−80.35	34.225	20.79	35.382		
157.79	18.744			12.37	35.816		
150.86	19.878			− 4.57	36.401		
143.25	21.242						
135.75	22.837						
−128.42	24.913						

				Series II			
$t°$	c_p	$t°$	c_p	$t°$	c_p	$t°$	c_p
Crystals I				Crystals II		Crystals IV	
−260.81	1.060	−204.43	12.069	−119.74	33.878	−65.52	33.594
259.45	1.413	200.07	12.626	119.04	33.851	48.69	34.206
257.71	1.865	198.96	12.757	118.24	33.720	31.97	34.894
256.97	2.078	193.40	13.548	117.93	33.828	23.24	35.301
255.44	2.541	191.69	13.805	117.60	33.705	14.61	35.727
253.85	3.050	188.15	14.314	−116.72	33.828	9.57	35.971
252.86	3.369	183.42	15.000			−2.21	37.542
249.63	4.329	182.16	15.163	Crystals III			
249.62	4.346	175.47	16.099			Liquid	
247.06	4.942	175.35	16.131	−116.13	32.341		
244.42	5.706	174.79	16.193	111.44	32.603	+ 7.75	41.019
242.52	6.152	168.54	17.111	109.05	32.845	8.11	41.015
237.14	7.346	165.41	17.535	108.95	32.831	13.77	41.282
232.38	8.234	161.22	18.217	106.09	33.077	15.62	41.370
230.60	8.616	153.59	19.435	104.18	33.085	23.06	41.760
225.78	9.261	146.09	20.718	99.16	33.325	29.08	42.039
224.15	9.503	138.97	22.110	96.29	33.407	38.13	42.494
218.41	10.260	136.99	22.540	− 87.20	33.930	47.08	42.939
214.10	10.802	133.12	23.476			+55.93	43.375
213.67	10.813	129.38	24.555				
209.34	11.443	125.78	25.827				
−207.77	11.656	−123.07	27.058				

Heat of melting: 593.2 cal/mol   at + 1.26   McCullough, Scott *et al.* (1953)

Heat of transition: 972.0 cal/mol at −121.56   ,,

   154.9 cal/mol at −116.16   ,,

   232.0 cal/mol at − 73.76   ,,

PENTANETHIOL-1 or AMYL MERCAPTAN $C_5H_{12}S$

Saturated vapour pressure: Finke, Scott *et al.* (1952)

$t°$	p mm	$t°$	p mm	
76.470	149.41	126.638	760.00	
82.569	187.57	133.131	906.06	
88.721	233.72	139.671	1074.6	
94.918	289.13	146.255	1268.0	
101.167	355.22	152.896	1489.1	
107.457	433.56	159.580	1740.8	
113.802	525.86	166.314	2026.0	
120.193	633.99	—	—	

Boiling point: 126.5 HAINES, HELM *et al.* (1954)

                122.9 (697.5 mm) MATHIAS and DE CARVALHO FILHO (1958)

Freezing point: −75.70 HAINES, HELM *et al.* (1954); FINKE, SCOTT *et al.* (1952)

Density, Viscosity and *Surface tension*

t°	d	$\eta \cdot 10^5$	γ	
20	0.84209	639	26.8	HAINES, HELM *et al.* (1954)
25	0.83763	601	26.3	,,
30	0.83317	568	25.7	,,

Refractive index

t°	He$_r$	H$_\alpha$	Na$_D$	Hg$_e$	He$_v$	H$_\beta$	Hg$_g$	
25°	1.44078	—	1.44395	1.44391	1.44928	1.45194	1.45457	MATHIAS and DE CARVALHO FILHO (1958)
20	1.44374	1.44420	1.44692	1.44922	1.45224	1.45360	1.45902	HAINES, HELM *et al.*
25	1.44121	1.44170	1.44439	1.44666	1.44974	1.45104	1.45639	,, (1954)
30	1.43872	1.43912	1.44180	1.44410	1.44707	1.44841	1.45371	,,

Dielectric constant at 25°: 4.672 MATHIAS and DE CARVALHO FILHO (1958)

Specific heat: FINKE, SCOTT *et al.* (1952)

t°	c_p	t°	c_p	t°	c_p	t°	c_p
−260.32	0.788	−213.11	12.975	−151.40	22.589	−46.87	45.081
258.78	1.095	210.08	13.558	149.17	22.871	43.78	45.193
257.18	1.440	206.40	14.271	145.34	23.334	41.96	45.272
256.53	1.587	204.07	14.752	136.94	24.358	36.78	45.413
255.19	1.918	199.47	15.547	133.71	24.751	35.39	45.415
252.68	2.584	196.95	15.994	124.94	25.841	31.25	45.572
251.50	2.920	192.31	16.814	121.71	26.229	24.05	45.794
249.76	3.408	189.12	17.363	109.73	27.754	20.66	45.933
248.53	3.762	186.93	17.674	97.78	29.398	12.85	46.214
246.48	4.352	184.80	18.049	86.51	31.957	10.17	46.337
245.53	4.618	181.29	18.555	L. 72.82	44.675	− 1.81	46.716
243.03	5.346	180.44	18.707	70.46	44.734	+ 0.71	46.834
242.28	5.567	176.84	19.234	67.15	44.739	9.08	47.286
238.83	6.579	173.34	19.689	64.49	44.775	11.95	47.404
234.94	7.637	170.53	20.117	61.46	44.886	19.81	47.906
230.55	8.818	168.65	20.349	58.48	44.838	23.05	48.076
225.23	10.150	164.56	20.892	57.94	44.875	28.73	48.396
219.03	11.642	160.38	21.454	53.12	45.031	37.37	48.905
218.08	11.871	160.10	21.479	− 50.84	45.025	47.84	49.518
−215.21	12.541	−155.45	22.070				

Heat of melting: 4190 cal/mol *ibid.*

HEXANETHIOL-1 or HEXYL MERCAPTAN $C_6H_{14}S$

Boiling point: 149.7° (698.6 mm) MATHIAS and DE CARVALHO FILHO (1958)
Refractive index at 25° *(ibid.)*

He_r	H_α	Na_D	He_v	H_β	Hg_g
1.44403	1.44711	1.44716	1.45342	1.45500	1.45765

Dielectric constant at 25°: 4.344 *ibid.*

HEPTANETHIOL-1 or HEPTYL MERCAPTAN $C_7H_{16}S$

Boiling point: 174.5° (696.2 mm) MATHIAS and DE CARVALHO FILHO (1958)
Refractive index at 25° *(ibid.)*

1.44649	1.44953	1.44959	1.45478	1.45734	1.45988

Dielectric constant at 25°: 4.109 *ibid.*

DIMETHYL SULPHIDE or 2-THIAPROPANE C_2H_6S

Saturated vapour pressure: McCULLOUGH, HUBBARD *et al.* (1957)

$t°$	p mm	
2.69	189.7	
18.87	381.0	
37.34	761.8	

Boiling point: 37.3 McALLAN, CULLUM *et al.* (1951)
Melting point: —98.25 *ibid.*
Density (ibid.)

$t°$	d	
20	0.8483	
25	0.8424	

Refractive index (ibid.)

$t°$	H_α	Na_D	Hg_e	H_β	Hg_g
20	1.4322	1.4353	1.4378	1.4427	1.4485
25	1.4289	1.4319	1.4345	1.4393	1.4452

Specific heat: McCULLOUGH, HUBBARD *et al.* (1957)

Vapour

t°	c_p	
45.04	18.38	
82.04	19.64	
127.04	21.15	
177.04	22.74	
227.04	24.24	

METHYL ETHYL SULPHIDE or 2-THIABUTANE C_3H_8S

Saturated vapour pressure: SCOTT, FINKE *et al.* (1951)

t°	p mm	t°	p mm	
23.435	149.41	61.104	633.99	
28.695	187.57	72.241	906.06	
33.997	233.72	77.870	1074.6	
39.339	289.13	83.551	1268.0	
44.717	355.22	89.265	1489.1	
50.136	433.56	95.020	1740.8	
55.600	525.86	100.825	2026.0	

Boiling point: 66.7 HAINES, HELM *et al.* (1954)
66.655 SCOTT, FINKE *et al.* (1951)
66.6 McALLAN, CULLUM *et al.* (1951)

Melting point: −105.91 McALLAN, CULLUM *et al.* (1951) and HAINES, HELM *et al.*
(1954)
−105.93 SCOTT, FINKE *et al.* (1951)

Density

t°	d	
20	0.8422	McALLAN, CULLUM *et al.* (1951)
25	0.8369	,,
20	0.84221	HAINES, HELM *et al.* (1954)
25	0.83679	,,
30	0.83145	,,

Viscosity and *Surface tension:* Haines, Helm *et al.* (1954)

$t°$	$\eta \cdot 10^5$	γ	
20	373	24.9	
25	354	24.2	
30	337	23.4	

Refractive index

$t°$	He_r	H_α	Na_D	Hg_e	He_v	H_β	Hg_g	
20	1.43703	1.43747	1.44035	1.44278	1.44616	1.44759	1.45334	Haines, Helm *et al.* (1954)
25	1.43410	1.43450	1.43737	1.43984	1.44302	1.44455	1.45028	,,
30	1.43115	1.43153	1.43437	1.43678	1.44005	1.44146	1.44715	,,
20	—	1.4374	1.4403	1.4428	—	1.4475	1.4532	Mc Allan, Cullum *et al.*
25	—	1.4343	1.4372	1.4397	—	1.4444	1.4500	,, (1951)

Specific heat: Scott, Finke *et al.* (1951)

Vapour

$t°$	c_p	
93.04	26.17	
129.04	27.91	
176.00	30.11	
214.05	31.85	

t°	c_p	t°	c_p	t°	c_p
C. −259.01	0.832	−193.76	13.823	−118.38	20.880
257.98	1.041	191.04	14.184	115.06	21.142
256.18	1.419	186.88	14.671	111.68	21.430
255.37	1.599	186.59	14.733	L. 125.95	32.569
253.75	1.989	186.45	14.740	119.68	32.445
252.40	2.347	182.54	15.179	110.86	32.318
251.22	2.652	180.85	15.344	101.25	32.219
248.72	3.325	177.45	15.696	96.64	32.184
248.33	3.438	174.00	16.040	94.69	32.206
244.98	4.337	168.59	15.581	86.68	32.157
244.41	4.476	167.43	16.676	85.60	32.186
240.39	5.534	160.60	17.320	76.75	32.181
236.48	6.507	159.67	17.409	73.68	32.184
232.43	7.441	153.49	17.963	63.30	32.270
228.10	8.348	150.63	18.216	52.66	32.397
223.30	9.324	146.61	18.555	41.31	32.564
217.97	10.275	141.95	18.961	29.75	32.809
217.07	10.433	139.55	19.156	23.93	32.983
210.96	11.443	133.13	19.696	18.30	33.104
206.79	12.079	132.31	19.750	13.03	33.274
205.36	12.288	126.42	20.230	− 6.81	33.436
202.47	12.665	126.06	20.316	+ 5.26	33.834
199.64	13.056	124.17	20.417	16.21	34.124
198.58	13.193	−121.12	20.641	+ 24.45	34.545
−194.83	13.685				

Heat of combustion at 25°: 675.17 kcal/mol HUBBARD and WADDINGTON (1954)

DI-*n*-BUTYL SULPHIDE $C_8H_{18}S$

DI-*iso*-BUTYL SULPHIDE $C_8H_{18}S$

DI-*iso*-AMYL SULPHIDE $C_{10}H_{20}S$

see MUMFORD and PHILLIPS (1950)

METHYL *iso*-PROPYL SULPHIDE or 3-METHYL-2-THIABUTANE $C_4H_{10}S$

Saturated vapour pressure: McCULLOUGH, FINKE *et al.* (1955)

t°	p mm	
44.90	190.0	
63.47	380.0	
84.82	760.0	

Melting point: −101.52 *ibid.*

Specific heat: (ibid.)

t°	c_p	t°	c_p	t°	c_p
Crystals		Crystals		Liquid	
−260.62	0.985	−217.93	11.193	−95.97	37.76
260.00	1.139	213.46	11.980	89.72	37.76
259.41	1.272	208.18	12.885	86.89	37.79
258.54	1.490	202.88	13.710	82.44	37.80
258.08	1.598	197.51	14.511	73.12	37.89
256.95	1.897	192.08	15.354	62.83	38.04
256.59	1.991	186.58	16.185	52.61	38.24
255.26	2.363	180.69	16.976	43.87	38.46
254.95	2.439	174.40	17.781	38.44	38.61
253.38	2.872	167.95	18.596	33.31	38.77
253.06	2.973	160.74	19.503	27.27	38.97
251.25	3.493	153.23	20.406	22.35	39.12
250.87	3.605	146.01	21.261	16.22	39.36
248.94	4.159	138.56	22.124	− 5.28	39.80
248.55	4.249	131.41	22.939	+ 5.52	40.27
246.51	4.850	130.88	23.030	16.20	40.77
246.17	4.952	126.83	23.628	26.75	41.27
243.73	5.614	123.47	23.919	30.16	41.48
240.52	6.474	120.75	24.258	40.47	42.01
237.15	7.282	115.85	24.870	50.65	42.56
233.20	8.182	115.63	24.889	60.71	43.12
228.62	9.149	114.61	25.045	+70.63	43.73
223.56	10.199	109.25	25.850		
−218.69	11.056	−108.64	25.976		

Heat of fusion: 2236 cal/mol *ibid.*

METHYL *tert.*-BUTYL SULPHIDE or
3,3-DIMETHYL-2-THIABUTANE $C_5H_{12}S$

Vapour pressure: SCOTT, GOOD, TODD, MESSERLY, BERG, HOSSENLOPP, LACINA, OSBORN and McCULLOUGH (1962)

t°	p mm	t°	p mm	t°	p mm
33.713	71.87	56.709	187.57	98.892	760.00
36.543	81.64	62.586	233.72	105.128	906.06
39.388	92.52	68.507	289.13	111.420	1074.6
42.242	104.63	74.478	355.22	117.761	1268.0
45.107	118.06	80.507	433.56	124.156	1489.1
47.990	132.95	86.585	525.86	130.595	1740.8
50.890	149.41	92.706	633.99	137.088	2026.0

Melting point: −82.31°

Heat of combustion at 25°: 986.42 kcal/mol

Heat of vaporization and *Vapour heat capacity* see authors

METHYL n-PROPYL SULPHIDE or 2-THIAPENTANE $C_4H_{10}S$

Boiling point: 95.6 McALLAN, CULLUM et al. (1951)

Melting point: —112.98 *ibid.*
            —112.99 SCOTT, FINKE et al. (1957)

Density and *Refractive index:* McALLAN, CULLUM et al. (1951)

$t°$	d	H_x	Na_D	Hg_e	H_β	Hg_g
20	0.8424	1.4413	1.4442	1.4466	1.4512	1.4566
25	0.8375	1.4387	1.4415	1.4440	1.4485	1.4540

Specific heat: SCOTT, FINKE et al. (1957)

Crystals

$t°$	c_p	$t°$	c_p	$t°$	c_p	$t°$	c_p
—260.59	0.837	—250.52	3.190	—218.16	11.186	—167.03	19.187
260.29	0.893	250.21	3.273	217.14	11.395	163.39	19.621
259.30	1.096	248.11	3.829	213.24	12.194	160.73	19.920
258.62	1.232	247.85	3.897	207.91	13.230	157.23	20.322
257.89	1.390	246.65	4.490	202.58	14.153	150.78	21.027
256.69	1.670	245.31	4.579	197.23	15.037	144.04	21.754
256.33	1.749	242.44	5.361	191.65	15.934	137.05	22.481
254.61	2.151	239.30	6.192	186.75	16.673	134.09	22.778
254.59	2.161	235.72	7.095	185.72	16.839	129.81	23.239
252.73	2.626	231.63	8.115	181.45	17.415	125.24	23.773
—252.48	2.686	227.27	9.159	175.94	18.109	—122.79	24.070
		—222.46	10.257	—169.78	18.875		

Liquid

$t°$	c_p	$t°$	c_p	$t°$	c_p	$t°$	c_p
—105.71	37.75	— 72.27	37.91	—24.88	38.98	+25.50	41.05
102.36	37.76	61.58	38.03	14.60	39.34	31.78	41.36
100.26	37.75	50.97	38.26	— 4.41	39.73	35.69	41.55
96.37	37.76	45.74	38.38	+ 5.66	40.16	42.27	41.88
92.37	37.76	—35.26	38.67	15.63	40.60	+52.62	42.42
— 82.53	37.81						

DIETHYL SULPHIDE or 3-THIAPENTANE $C_4H_{10}S$

Saturated vapour pressure: SCOTT, FINKE, HUBBARD *et al.* (1952)

$t°$	p mm	$t°$	p mm	$t°$	p mm
45.920	149.41	74.452	433.56	104.098	1074.6
51.536	187.57	80.286	525.86	110.165	1268.0
57.204	233.72	86.169	633.99	116.279	1489.1
62.905	289.13	92.100	760.00	122.433	1740.8
68.659	355.22	98.073	906.06	—	—

Boiling point: 92.1 HAINES, HELM *et al.* (1954) and MUMFORD and PHILLIPS (1950)

Melting point: —103.96 SCOTT, FINKE, HUBBARD *et al.* (1952)
                 —103.93 HAINES, HELM *et al.* (1954)

Density

$t°$	d	
20	0.83623	HAINES, HELM *et al.* (1954)
25	0.83120	,,
30	0.82625	,,
20	0.8367	MUMFORD and PHILLIPS (1950)
25	0.8316	,,

Viscosity

$t°$	$\eta \cdot 10^5$	
20	440	HAINES, HELM *et al.* (1954)
25	417	,,
30	396	,,
20	446	MUMFORD and PHILLIPS (1950)
25	422	,,

Surface tension

$t°$	γ	
20	25.2	HAINES, HELM *et al.* (1954)
25	24.5	,,
30	23.9	,,
20	25.3	MUMFORD and PHILLIPS (1950)
25	24.7	,,

Refractive index

t°	He_r	H_α	Na_D	Hg_e	He_v	H_β	Hg_g	
20	1.43971	1.44015	1.44298	1.44539	1.44858	1.44998	1.45568	HAINES, HELM *et al.*
25	1.43695	1.43736	1.44017	1.44256	1.44577	1.44716	1.45280	,, (1954)
30	1.43408	1.43453	1.43734	1.43972	1.44290	1.44428	1.44988	,,

$n_D^{20°} = 1.4425$ MUMFORD and PHILLIPS (1950)

Specific heat: SCOTT, FINKE, HUBBARD *et al.* (1952)

Crystals

t°	c_p	t°	c_p	t°	c_p	t°	c_p
−257.18	1.292	−244.24	4.252	−210.27	11.633	−176.32	17.002
256.53	1.430	242.29	4.734	204.98	12.590	170.07	17.820
255.46	1.645	238.75	5.572	201.66	13.142	163.58	18.624
254.93	1.756	235.15	6.419	199.67	13.476	156.90	19.435
252.99	2.184	230.99	7.355	195.50	14.156	150.47	20.190
252.60	2.273	226.17	8.414	194.31	14.374	144.24	20.897
250.07	2.865	221.19	9.476	189.22	15.178	138.20	21.570
250.06	2.869	219.03	9.931	188.90	15.234	125.19	22.996
247.29	3.516	215.54	10.615	183.43	16.062	119.17	23.660
246.23	3.771	−213.14	11.081	−182.84	16.132	−113.75	24.262

Liquid

t°	c_p	t°	c_p	t°	c_p	t°	c_p
−91.20	37.50	−56.04	37.95	−22.57	38.89	13.55	40.41
86.92	37.52	52.65	38.01	15.97	39.14	16.20	40.53
83.42	37.54	45.88	38.18	12.73	39.26	22.61	40.85
76.56	37.62	42.54	38.26	6.19	39.53	32.83	41.36
73.10	37.65	35.83	38.45	− 2.98	39.67	+48.93	41.95
66.26	37.75	32.51	38.56	+ 3.50	39.94	—	—
−62.84	37.80	−25.85	38.78	6.66	40.08	—	—

Melting heat: 2845.0 cal/mol *ibid.*

METHYL *n*-BUTYL SULPHIDE or 2-THIAHEXANE $C_5H_{12}S$

McCULLOUGH, FINKE *et al.* (1961)

Saturated vapour pressure

t°	p mm	t°	p mm	t°	p mm
73.752	149.41	104.442	433.56	136.317	1074.6
79.798	187.57	110.725	525.86	142.839	1268.0
85.888	233.72	117.048	633.99	149.403	1489.1
92.025	289.13	123.423	760.00	156.019	1740.8
98.211	355.22	129.847	906.06	162.676	2026.0

Triple point: —97.85

Specific heat

t°	c_p	t°	c_p	t°	c_p	t°	c_p
		Crystals				**Liquid**	
−261.55	0.669	−245.79	4.972	−186.49	19.214	−86.25	43.881
261.24	0.742	244.77	5.285	185.42	19.392	86.04	43.907
260.07	0.956	243.02	5.832	181.92	19.914	83.21	43.919
259.75	1.030	239.72	6.860	176.79	20.655	80.58	43.954
258.75	1.245	236.03	7.984	171.00	21.477	79.54	43.966
258.21	1.375	232.17	9.103	164.90	22.253	74.50	44.032
257.44	1.560	227.97	10.276	158.99	22.991	64.46	44.196
256.36	1.829	223.32	11.503	152.79	23.760	54.49	44.424
255.92	1.947	218.26	12.791	146.31	24.510	44.60	44.713
254.32	2.391	216.71	13.177	140.01	25.211	34.80	45.068
254.13	2.438	211.73	14.359	133.86	25.871	25.08	45.442
252.38	2.950	206.30	15.530	127.85	26.525	15.45	45.877
252.12	3.016	201.23	16.522	121.97	27.155	− 5.92	46.328
250.41	3.550	196.01	17.507	115.69	27.773	+ 3.52	46.817
249.97	3.667	190.57	18.506	110.43	28.387	13.27	47.356
248.25	4.220	−190.13	18.581	−107.37	28.742	23.34	47.929
−247.65	4.394	—	—	—	—	26.26	48.099
						36.19	48.691
						46.00	49.328
						55.69	49.970
						65.27	50.609
						74.74	51.261
						+84.86	51.975

Heat of fusion: 2976 cal/mol

Heat of combustion: 9472.27 cal/gr

ETHYL *n*-PROPYL SULPHIDE or 3-THIAHEXANE $C_5H_{12}S$

McCULLOUGH, FINKE *et al.* (1961)

Triple point: −117.05

Specific heat

$t°$	c_p	$t°$	c_p	$t°$	c_p
	Crystals		·	Liquid	
−261.48	0.822	−206.87	15.177	−107.56	43.105
261.44	0.829	202.61	15.978	101.57	43.103
259.68	1.189	201.32	16.217	101.37	43.091
259.66	1.205	196.58	17.069	91.27	43.142
257.87	1.608	190.46	18.155	81.23	43.237
257.87	1.614	184.22	19.162	76.07	43.307
256.04	2.092	178.23	20.018	71.26	43.400
256.04	2.096	177.36	20.135	65.92	43.490
254.06	2.643	172.18	20.852	55.85	43.750
254.04	2.648	172.11	20.849	45.85	44.043
251.92	3.272	166.19	21.643	35.93	44.381
251.90	3.281	165.82	21.685	26.09	44.764
249.59	3.989	159.95	22.451	15.87	45.212
249.50	4.019	159.62	22.481	− 5.26	45.741
246.98	4.811	153.90	23.191	+ 5.21	46.298
246.80	4.869	153.61	23.216	15.11	46.848
243.98	5.744	148.02	23.882	15.56	46.881
243.84	5.797	147.77	23.896	25.24	47.445
240.66	6.786	141.94	24.567	35.25	48.039
237.06	7.867	141.83	24.593	45.14	48.654
232.98	9.023	135.57	25.289	54.93	49.266
228.63	10.181	135.33	25.314	64.57	49.835
223.82	11.406	134.44	25.416	74.09	50.469
219.62	12.411	131.81	25.693	83.52	51.067
218.50	12.666	129.79	25.908	+ 92.87	51.675
214.30	13.620	129.41	25.955		
212.84	13.938	−124.55	26.458		
−208.53	14.848	—	—		

Heat of fusion: 2529 cal/mol

Heat of combustion: 9468.12 cal/gr

DI-*n*-PROPYL SULPHIDE or 4-THIAHEPTANE   C₆H₁₄S

Specific heat: McCULLOUGH, FINKE *et al.* (1961)

t°	c_p	t°	c_p	t°	c_p	t°	c_p
			Crystals				Liquid
−260.52	1.381	−243.01	7.002	−171.28	23.019	−99.41	48.713
260.36	1.413	239.70	8.092	167.55	23.629	92.80	48.769
258.86	1.842	235.94	9.196	160.98	24.668	88.29	48.804
258.81	1.857	231.76	10.394	156.64	25.331	84.71	48.852
257.28	2.300	227.28	11.617	154.07	25.747	81.19	48.890
257.01	2.380	222.30	12.923	146.91	26.890	75.67	49.006
255.64	2.809	217.89	14.020	143.28	27.454	65.68	49.218
255.23	2.930	216.77	14.292	140.38	27.893	55.77	49.505
253.99	3.333	212.73	15.202	140.00	27.992	45.94	49.846
253.22	3.588	207.14	16.430	137.02	28.468	35.71	50.267
252.31	3.883	201.17	17.631	134.94	28.814	25.09	50.771
250.94	4.342	194.99	18.846	130.48	29.603	15.62	51.288
250.34	4.534	188.50	20.114	128.00	30.026	14.60	51.338
248.54	5.141	185.47	20.679	124.15	30.758	− 7.13	51.747
248.04	5.313	181.46	21.360	120.84	31.398	+ 2.68	52.377
245.94	6.021	179.08	21.751	113.96	32.977	9.92	52.846
−245.84	6.042	−174.34	22.527	−107.81	35.551	20.86	53.598
						31.66	54.359
						+41.87	55.065

DI-*n*-BUTYL SULPHIDE or 5-THIANONANE   C₈H₁₈S

Specific heat: McCULLOUGH, FINKE *et al.* (1961)

t°	c_p	t°	c_p	t°	c_p	t°	c_p
			Crystals				Liquid
−261.44	0.977	−243.75	6.863	−162.14	29.767	−68.09	61.689
261.18	1.048	240.70	8.029	155.21	31.021	61.55	61.894
260.34	1.240	237.45	9.261	148.52	32.206	52.91	62.243
260.16	1.289	233.93	10.562	142.04	33.277	42.47	62.767
259.04	1.584	230.02	11.955	135.31	34.373	31.68	63.397
258.91	1.626	225.73	13.442	128.32	35.457	21.01	64.099
257.64	1.989	220.98	15.068	122.99	36.267	−10.04	64.915
257.52	2.022	218.34	15.937	121.52	36.535	+ 1.24	65.817
256.00	2.489	215.79	16.772	117.00	37.216	12.36	66.809
255.76	2.568	211.96	17.986	110.60	38.202	13.19	66.875
254.23	3.066	206.22	19.687	104.33	39.153	23.03	67.777
253.62	3.277	200.41	21.266	97.69	40.187	33.20	68.738
252.26	3.737	194.04	22.936	94.49	40.653	43.24	69.721
251.52	4.002	187.62	24.561	94.18	40.710	53.15	70.707
250.00	4.553	181.56	25.920	90.70	41.293	62.94	71.706
249.39	4.777	175.38	27.193	88.52	41.633	72.00	72.679
247.73	5.394	174.70	27.322	88.17	41.696	+82.37	73.785
246.75	5.760	−168.82	28.500	− 82.28	42.572	—	—
−245.04	6.384	—	—	—	—	—	—

DI-*iso*-PROPYL SULPHIDE
or 2,4-DIMETHYL-3-THIAPENTANE $C_6H_{14}S$

McALLAN, CULLUM *et al.* (1951)
Boiling point: 119.8
Freezing point: −78.08
Density and *Refractive index*

t°	d	H_α	Na_D	Hg_e	H_β	Hg_g
20	0.8146	1.4360	1.4388	1.4411	1.4455	1.4509
25	0.8104	1.4335	1.4362	1.4385	1.4429	1.4482

ETHYL *tert.*-BUTYL SULPHIDE
or 2,2-DIMETHYL-3-THIAPENTANE $C_6H_{14}S$

McALLAN, CULLUM *et al.* (1951)
Boiling point: 120.4
Freezing point: −88.95
Density and *Refractive index*

t°	d	H_α	Na_D	Hg_e	H_β	Hg_g
20	0.8206	1.4390	1.4417	1.4440	1.4485	1.4538
25	0.8161	1.4362	1.4390	1.4413	1.4457	1.4510

DI-*n*-AMYL SULPHIDE or 6-THIAUNDECANE $C_{10}H_{22}S$
SIMON (1929)
Boiling point: 230.1°   *Freezing point:* −51.3°
Density

t°	d
0	0.85538
15	0.84394
30	0.83243

Refractive index

t°	He_r	H_α	Na_D	He_y	He_{gr}	H_β	He_v	H_γ
15°	1.45543	1.45573	1.45847	1.45867	1.46381	1.46502	1.46922	1.47069
25°	1.45136	1.45170	1.45442	1.45462	1.45979	1.46093	1.46512	1.46674

DIMETHYL DISULPHIDE or 2,3-DITHIABUTANE $C_2H_6S_2$

Saturated vapour pressure: SCOTT, FINKE *et al.* (1950)

t°	p mm	t°	p mm	t°	p mm	t°	p mm
0.00	6.77	40	59.85	61.411	149.41	97.393	525.86
15	16.75	45	75.11	67.301	187.57	103.540	633.99
20	22.06	50	93.40	73.234	233.72	109.739	760.00
25	28.73	55	115.21	79.201	289.13	115.984	906.06
30	37.03	60	141.19	85.218	355.22	122.273	1074.6
35	47.31			91.283	433.56	128.611	1268.0

Boiling point: 109.6 HAINES, HELM *et al.* (1954)
109.739 SCOTT, FINKE *et al.* (1950)
110 McALLAN, CULLUM *et al.* (1951)

Melting point: −84.69 McALLAN, CULLUM *et al.* (1951)
−84.72 HAINES, HELM *et al.* (1954)
−84.73 SCOTT, FINKE *et al.* (1950)

Density

t°	d	
20	1.06250	HAINES, HELM *et al.* (1954)
25	1.05690	,,
30	1.05138	,,
20	1.0623	McALLAN, CULLUM *et al.* (1951)
25	1.0570	,,

Viscosity and *Surface tension:* HAINES, HELM *et al.* (1954)

t°	$\eta \cdot 10^5$	γ	
20	619	33.6	
25	585	32.8	
30	555	32.2	

Refractive index: (a) MCALLAN, CULLUM *et al.* (1951)
      (b) HAINES, HELM *et al.* (1954)

t°		He_r	H_α	Na_D	Hg_e	He_v	H_β	Hg_g
(a)	20	—	1.5215	1.5259	1.5295	—	1.5367	1.5457
	25	—	1.5183	1.5227	1.5263	—	1.5334	1.5423
(b)	20	1.52103	1.52163	1.52592	1.52970	1.53473	1.53683	1.54577
	25	1.51803	1.51871	1.52298	1.52669	1.53174	1.53387	1.54270
	30	1.51512	1.51575	1.51998	1.52366	1.52860	1.53075	1.53958

Specific heat: SCOTT, FINKE *et al.* (1950)

t°	c_p	t°	c_p	t°	c_p	t°	c_p
C.−260.08	1.076	−217.21	10.953	−141.88	19.890	−48.90	34.091
259.03	1.290	212.30	11.805	140.59	20.019	43.59	34.080
257.30	1.673	206.93	12.677	133.60	20.595	33.32	34.141
257.02	1.741	201.53	13.455	132.42	20.700	23.09	34.204
254.86	2.279	196.10	14.228	124.80	21.327	12.89	34.294
254.67	2.331	190.60	14.980	123.89	21.412	2.78	34.432
252.60	2.880	187.36	15.396	115.62	22.086	− 1.08	34.449
252.17	3.000	185.18	15.677	115.03	22.119	+ 7.30	34.583
250.39	3.482	180.94	16.135	106.60	22.810	10.81	34.656
249.24	3.785	179.77	16.276	105.86	22.887	17.31	34.780
247.69	4.192	174.56	16.821	98.95	23.451	22.61	34.899
245.84	4.675	173.86	16.878	91.99	24.116	27.25	34.973
244.59	5.009	169.09	17.373	L. 81.17	34.331	27.48	34.958
242.30	5.594	166.48	17.627	76.89	34.235	37.67	35.189
238.88	6.463	162.94	17.978	74.06	34.221	48.28	35.468
235.38	7.262	158.31	18.414	69.25	34.176	58.80	35.762
231.02	8.211	156.01	18.640	64.22	34.127	69.24	36.065
225.78	9.296	149.94	19.187	59.06	34.115	+79.11	36.366
−220.52	10.333	−148.38	19.333	−53.89	34.091	—	—

Heat of fusion: 2197.1 cal/mol *ibid.*

DIETHYL DISULPHIDE or 3,4-DITHIAHEXANE $C_4H_{10}S_2$

Saturated vapour pressure: SCOTT, FINKE, MCCULLOUGH *et al.* (1952)

t°	p mm	t°	p mm	
0.00	0.73	75.00	55.23	
15.00	2.24	80.00	68.02	
20.00	3.11	100.567	149.41	
25.00	4.24	107.079	187.57	
30.00	5.75	113.627	233.72	
35.00	7.67	120.230	289.13	
40.00	10.16	126.884	355.22	
45.00	13.32	133.579	433.56	
50.00	17.32	140.336	525.86	
55.00	22.23	147.136	633.99	
60.00	28.26	153.986	760.00	
65.00	35.59	160.884	906.06	
70.00	44.55			

Boiling point: 152.6 HAINES, HELM *et al.* (1954)
          153.98 SCOTT, FINKE, MCCULLOUGH *et al.* (1952)

Melting point: —101.52 HAINES, HELM *et al.* (1954)
          —101.54 SCOTT, FINKE, MCCULLOUGH *et al.* (1952)

Density, Viscosity and *Surface tension*

t°	d	$\eta \cdot 10^5$	γ	
20	0.99311	860	31.3	HAINES, HELM *et al.* (1954)
25	0.98818	805	30.7	,,
30	0.98332	757	30.2	,,

Refractive index: HAINES, HELM *et al.* (1954)

t°	He_r	H_α	Na_D	Hg_e	He_v	H_β	Hg_g
20	1.50299	1.50354	1.50731	1.51055	1.51491	1.51680	1.52453
25	1.50035	1.50097	1.50470	1.50793	1.51230	1.51411	1.52179
30	1.49771	1.49826	1.50198	1.50524	1.50947	1.51140	1.51899

Heat of melting: 2247.6 cal/mol SCOTT, FINKE, MCCULLOUGH *et al.* (1952)

Specific heat: SCOTT, FINKE, McCULLOUGH *et al.* (1952)

t°	c_p	t°	c_p	t°	c_p
C. −260.53	1.397	−218.24	13.509	L.−104.99	45.844
260.16	1.501	215.77	14.033	101.29	45.834
259.44	1.711	211.08	14.985	97.51	45.815
259.13	1.800	206.01	15.947	92.81	45.834
258.14	2.109	203.44	16.386	92.79	45.832
257.91	2.183	200.87	16.833	88.97	45.836
256.76	2.535	197.78	17.355	85.34	45.842
256.10	2.741	196.00	17.679	79.41	45.887
255.07	3.091	191.94	18.353	69.89	45.963
253.98	3.453	191.05	18.508	59.89	46.126
253.16	3.748	189.52	18.754	49.43	46.304
251.60	4.282	186.40	19.273	48.92	46.311
251.17	4.424	185.38	19.426	39.11	46.508
248.89	5.204	184.07	19.608	28.87	46.796
248.56	5.312	180.67	20.089	18.72	47.112
246.22	6.090	176.29	20.685	8.66	47.432
245.14	6.448	174.33	20.969	− 3.40	47.625
243.38	7.010	167.27	21.931	+ 1.31	47.786
241.69	7.540	157.85	23.218	6.53	48.000
238.24	8.591	148.34	24.481	11.19	48.170
234.77	9.547	138.77	25.740	16.38	48.401
231.08	10.520	129.62	26.974	+ 26.14	48.819
227.03	11.523	120.82	28.238		
222.71	12.541	−110.85	30.440		
−219.85	13.170	—	——		

DI-*n*-PROPYL DISULPHIDE or 4,5-DITHIA-OCTANE $C_6H_{14}S_2$

Boiling point: 195 McALLAN, CULLUM *et al.* (1951)

Melting point: —85.59 *ibid.*

Density: (ibid.)

t°	d	
20	0.9596	
25	0.9549	

Refractive index: (ibid.)

t°	H_α	Na_D	Hg_e	H_β	Hg_g
20	1.4945	1.4980	1.5010	1.5066	1.5135
25	1.4920	1.4954	1.4984	1.5040	1.5103

CYCLOPENTANETHIOL $C_5H_{10}S$

Berg, Scott *et al.* (1961)

Specific heat:

$t°$	c_p	$t°$	c_p	$t°$	c_p	$t°$	c_p
Stable crystals				Metastable crystals			
−261.31	0.845	−192.88	14.557	−260.60	1.031	−165.45	18.281
261.17	0.871	192.57	14.599	260.39	1.081	159.61	19.033
260.01	1.115	188.61	15.125	259.41	1.322	153.52	19.872
259.72	1.174	187.28	15.290	259.23	1.359	151.17	20.173
258.66	1.440	186.74	15.365	257.96	1.695	147.41	20.784
258.19	1.551	183.58	15.828	257.82	1.731	146.22	20.935
257.28	1.793	181.60	16.069	256.39	2.138	140.84	21.751
256.48	2.010	180.83	16.154	256.28	2.169	−135.92	22.705
255.75	2.204	178.00	16.513	254.65	2.653		
254.61	2.524	176.17	16.739	254.55	2.676	Liquid	
254.02	2.693	172.64	17.202	252.89	3.184		
252.75	3.063	170.44	17.499	252.81	3.202		
252.21	3.217	166.98	17.962	250.96	3.770	−110.66	35.625
250.84	3.637	161.04	18.810	250.88	3.793	106.96	35.529
250.33	3.774	160.02	18.945	248.69	4.470	106.43	35.517
248.66	4.278	154.87	19.761	248.57	4.513	102.53	35.479
248.02	4.468	154.33	19.818	246.08	5.246	100.28	35.437
246.11	5.021	148.70	20.716	245.79	5.328	92.66	35.387
245.19	5.278	148.62	20.734	242.78	6.173	86.19	35.365
243.23	5.816	145.61	21.267	239.35	7.073	84.59	35.389
240.03	6.660	143.02	21.713	235.44	8.033	77.06	35.421
236.55	7.516	142.89	21.722	231.44	8.906	66.91	35.540
232.83	8.344	142.44	21.801	226.97	9.787	56.30	35.755
228.69	9.177	141.92	21.906	221.75	10.770	45.77	36.041
224.05	10.021	140.74	22.123	219.48	11.150	35.35	36.390
219.37	10.826	140.44	22.177	214.89	11.900	25.03	36.815
219.03	10.883	137.38	22.738	209.49	12.741	14.84	37.271
218.43	10.989	137.18	22.753	203.50	13.572	− 4.29	37.805
214.60	11.590	137.12	22.789	197.21	14.396	+ 6.62	38.415
213.92	11.693	136.90	22.841	190.82	15.211	17.36	39.020
209.31	12.376	135.44	23.108	188.50	15.526	27.95	39.682
208.89	12.446	135.13	23.202	184.76	16.012	29.47	39.780
203.92	13.115	132.06	23.770	183.36	16.173	39.80	40.444
203.74	13.142	131.19	23.972	179.34	16.636	50.44	41.168
198.41	13.835	−129.73	24.265	178.09	16.778	61.37	41.901
−198.34	13.841	—	—	173.94	17.269	72.23	42.682
				172.16	17.474	82.92	43.444
				−165.93	18.238	+ 93.34	44.195

CYCLOHEXANETHIOL $C_6H_{12}S$

MATHIAS, DE CARVALHO FILHO and CECCHINI (1961)

Boiling point: 78.0° (57 mm)   *Density* at 25°: 0.94393

Refractive index

$t°$	He_r	Na_D	Hg_e	He_{bl}	H_β	Hg_g
25	1.48746	1.49099	1.49105	1.49711	1.50008	1.50311

Dielectric constant at 25°: 5.420

BENZENETHIOL C_6H_6S

MATHIAS, DE CARVALHO FILHO and CECCHINI (1961)

Boiling point: 165.4° (698.4 mm)   *Density* at 25°: 1.07264

Refractive index

$t°$	He_r	Na_D	Hg_e	He_{bl}	H_β	Hg_g
25	1.57959	1.58696	1.58718	1.60042	1.60733	1.61430

Dielectric constant at 25°: 4.382

α-TOLUENETHIOL C_7H_8S

MATHIAS, DE CARVALHO FILHO and CECCHINI (1961)

Boiling point: 195.9° (699.9 mm)   *Density* at 25°: 1.05088

Refractive index

$t°$	He_r	Na_D	Hg_e	He_{bl}	H_β	Hg_g
25	1.59653	1.56720	1.57357	1.75372	1.58500	1.59079

Dielectric constant at 25°: 4.705

TRIMETHYLENESULPHIDE or THIACYCLOBUTANE C_3H_6S

Saturated vapour pressure: SCOTT, FINKE *et al.* (1953)

$t°$	p mm	$t°$	p mm	
48.357	149.41	88.998	633.99	
54.044	187.57	100.977	906.06	
59.771	233.72	107.027	1074.6	
65.534	289.13	113.118	1268.0	
71.341	355.22	119.249	1489.1	
77.187	433.56	125.421	1740.8	
83.073	525.86	131.639	2026.0	

Boiling point: 95.0 HAINES, HELM *et al.* (1954)

               94.968 SCOTT, FINKE *et al.* (1953)

Freezing point: −73.26 SCOTT, FINKE *et al.* (1953)

               −73.25 HAINES, HELM *et al.* (1954)

Transition point: −96.46 SCOTT, FINKE *et al.* (1953)

Density, *Viscosity* and *Surface tension*

$t°$	d	$\eta \cdot 10^5$	γ	
20	1.02000	638	36.3	HAINES, HELM *et al.* (1954)
25	1.01472	607	35.6	,,
30	1.00957	576	35.0	,,

Refractive index: HAINES, HELM *et al.* (1954)

$t°$	He $_r$	H_α	Na$_D$	Hg$_e$	He$_{bl}$	H_β	Hg$_g$
20	1.50603	1.50660	1.51020	1.51330	1.51737	1.51922	1.52648
25	1.50318	1.50379	1.50738	1.51050	1.51453	1.51635	1.52362
30	1.50035	1.50093	1.50448	1.50755	1.51154	1.51337	1.52059

Specific heat: SCOTT, FINKE *et al.* (1953)

$t°$	c_p	$t°$	c_p	
Crystals		**Liquid**		
−106.38	17.607	−71.18	24.490	
101.96	18.132	66.72	24.510	
101.53	18.181	61.84	24.572	
92.96	18.886	61.07	24.564	
90.73	19.223	51.83	24.689	
88.03	19.662	41.91	24.876	
85.17	20.101	32.08	25.113	
84.46	20.227	22.35	25.374	
79.01	21.081	12.73	25.667	
− 78.46	21.146	− 3.23	25.981	
		+ 6.15	26.327	
		12.00	26.546	
		21.23	26.906	
		30.30	27.280	
		39.28	27.661	
		+48.13	28.037	

Heat of melting: 1971 cal/mol *ibid.*

Heat of transition: 159.8 cal/mol *ibid.*

THIACYCLOPENTANE C_4H_8S

Saturated vapour pressure: HAINES, HELM *et al.* (1954)

$t°$	p mm	$t°$	p mm	$t°$	p mm
71.182	149.41	102.056	433.56	134.046	1074.6
77.278	187.57	108.365	525.86	140.574	1268.0
83.405	233.72	114.716	633.99	147.163	1489.1
89.580	289.13	121.114	760.00	153.775	1740.8
95.803	355.22	127.558	906.06	160.451	2026.0

Boiling point: 120.9 HAINES, HELM *et al.* (1954)

Freezing point: —96.18 HUBBARD, FINKE *et al.* (1952)
　　　　　　　　—96.16 HAINES, HELM *et al.* (1954)

Density, Viscosity and *Surface tension*

$t°$	d	$\eta \cdot 10^5$	γ	
20	0.99869	1042	35.8	HAINES, HELM *et al.* (1954)
25	0.99379	971	35.0	
30	0.98928	914	34.6	

Refractive index: HAINES, HELM *et al.* (1954)

$t°$	He $_r$	H_α	Na_D	Hg_0	He_{bl}	H_β	Hg_g
20	1.50101	1.50154	1.50483	1.50764	1.51132	1.51295	1.51945
25	1.49840	1.49891	1.50217	1.50495	1.50864	1.51021	1.51676
30	1.49583	1.49634	1.49962	1.50237	1.50600	1.50761	1.51408

Specific heat: HUBBARD, FINKE *et al.* (1952)

Crystals

$t°$	c_p	$t°$	c_p	$t°$	c_p
—260.04	0.962	—235.95	6.877	—187.31	12.909
259.05	1.186	230.75	7.874	185.04	13.092
257.73	1.479	225.53	8.745	181.01	13.384
257.11	1.625	220.25	9.515	174.07	13.878
256.08	1.883	218.78	9.713	166.98	14.390
254.11	2.390	213.57	10.375	159.73	14.915
253.59	2.532	208.72	10.935	156.50	15.135
251.94	2.959	203.76	11.435	152.73	15.435
249.82	3.527	200.25	11.752	150.65	15.582
249.48	3.628	198.32	11.925	144.44	16.057
246.51	4.388	196.02	12.137	137.92	16.583
245.38	4.694	—192.78	12.427	—137.33	16.625
—240.66	5.850	—	—	—	—

(Continued)

t°	c_p	t°	c_p	t°	c_p	t°	c_p
Crystals		Liquid					
−131.40	17.141	−92.99	28.80	−54.22	29.73	− 1.13	32.05
131.09	17.163	88.31	28.89	44.66	30.06	+ 9.04	32.62
124.47	17.770	84.34	28.93	35.23	30.47	19.96	33.22
124.23	17.786	83.11	28.96	25.92	30.86	29.33	33.74
116.86	18.523	82.79	28.98	16.35	31.30	30.27	33.82
109.75	19.335	78.57	29.07	12.40	31.50	39.71	34.34
103.72	20.174	71.20	29.24	6.73	31.76	50.92	35.02
− 99.20	21.799	−63.07	29.45	− 6.54	31.80	+60.24	35.54

Heat of melting: 1757.2 cal/mol *ibid.*

THIACYCLOHEXANE $C_5H_{10}S$

Saturated vapour pressure: McCULLOUGH, FINKE *et al.* (1954)

t°	p mm	
78.28	100.0	
95.75	190.0	
117.15	380.0	
131.10	570.0	

Boiling point: 141.75 McCULLOUGH, FINKE *et al.* (1954)
93° (82 mm) JEFFERY, PARKER and VOGEL (1961)

Melting point: 19.0447 McCULLOUGH, FINKE *et al.* (1954)

Transition points: I −33.14 *ibid.*
II −71.76 *ibid.*

Density   *Surface tension* JEFFERY, PARKER and VOGEL (1961)

t°	d	t°	γ	
20	0.9861	20	36.06	
40	0.9681	40	33.74	
60	0.9488	60	31.17	
85	0.9255			

Refractive index: ibid.

t°	H_α	Na_D	H_β	H_γ	
20	1.50354	1.50698	1.51484	1.52272	

Dielectric constant, see KONDO and MATSUMOTO (1958)

Specific heat: McCULLOUGH, FINKE *et al.* (1954)

t°	c_p	t°	c_p	t°	c_p	t°	c_p
Crystals I				Crystals II		Crystals III	
−260.08	0.751	−188.02	13.130	−70.73	34.40	−30.02	33.29
258.26	1.123	187.69	13.156	69.70	34.69	25.85	33.48
257.96	1.191	182.96	13.623	69.15	34.71	20.12	33.77
256.59	1.517	182.09	13.705	68.68	35.07	16.19	33.98
256.03	1.659	177.02	14.164	67.68	35.50	14.38	34.08
254.87	1.951	170.35	14.781	67.56	35.64	12.85	34.19
254.28	2.114	163.49	15.418	66.68	36.46	8.64	34.41
252.99	2.465	156.45	16.071	65.80	34.62	4.65	34.67
252.52	2.607	149.67	16.715	65.69	34.99	− 2.44	34.82
251.05	3.014	143.12	17.398	65.55	33.94	+ 4.21	35.24
250.67	3.123	140.54	17.678	64.46	30.07	+11.29	35.75
248.80	3.658	136.40	18.125	63.78	30.14		
248.50	3.741	133.54	18.405	63.31	30.00	Liquid	
246.27	4.372	129.31	18.846	62.17	30.04		
245.88	4.466	125.71	19.222	61.64	30.09		
242.97	5.256	121.78	19.660	61.03	30.07	+22.47	38.84
239.79	6.031	124.02	20.563	59.90	30.19	27.07	39.18
236.43	6.749	106.09	21.603	59.51	30.26	27.42	39.21
232.90	7.434	102.21	22.133	56.19	30.70	32.97	39.63
229.06	8.103	97.59	22.860	55.52	30.78	36.66	39.73
224.81	8.796	94.22	23.454	54.97	30.95	41.17	40.32
220.22	9.440	89.07	24.489	51.76	31.38	49.56	40.94
217.60	9.797	87.65	24.790	50.25	31.64	58.79	41.71
215.35	10.081	84.15	25.739	49.89	31.73	+68.36	42.44
211.58	10.559	82.96	26.092	46.98	32.22		
205.77	11.207	79.00	27.608	46.62	32.31		
199.91	11.883	− 75.25	29.916	41.89	33.30		
−194.00	12.489	—	—	41.30	33.47		
				−40.26	33.68		

Heat of melting: 585.2 cal/mol McCULLOUGH, FINKE *et al.* (1954)

Heat of transition I: 1858.3 cal/mol   ,,
           II: 262.4 cal/mol   ,,

THIOPHENE C_4H_4S

Critical temperature: 579.4 CHENG, McCOUBREY and PHILLIPS (1962)

Boiling point: 84.20 B. E. (1959)
         84   JEFFERY, PARKER and VOGEL (1961)

Density

t°	d	
0	1.08806	B. E. (1959)
15	1.07044	,,
30	1.05277	,,
20	1.0644	JEFFERY, PARKER and VOGEL (1961)
40	1.0405	,,
60	1.0162	,,

Viscosity

t°	$\eta \cdot 10^5$	
15	697	B. E. (1959)
30.1	578	,,

Surface tension

t°	γ	
15	33.34	B. E. (1959)
20	32.62	,,
30	31.13	,,

Refractive index

t°	He_r	H_α	Na_D	He_y	He_bl	H_β	He_viol	
15	1.52578	1.52646	1.53135	1.53145	1.54113	1.54375	1.55125	B. E. (1959)
dn/dt	0.00057	0.00057	—	0.00056	0.00057	0.00057	—	,,
20	—	1.52385	1.52866	—	—	1.54109	—	JEFFERY, PARKER and VOGEL (1961)

Dielectric constant: PHILIPPE and PIETTE (1955) (two series)

t°	ε	t°	ε	
20.00	2.739	−160.0	2.758	
15.60	2.745	155.5	2.758	
− 3.0	2.774	145.0	2.759	
20.5	2.817	139.0	2.760	
36.5	2.890	119.0	2.762	
57.0	2.770	108.5	2.783	
74.0	2.778	105.0	2.793	
93.0	2.795	86.0	2.788	
135.0	2.760	52.0	2.768	
152.0	2.758	− 34.0	2.863	
163.0	2.757			
−168.5	2.757			

Specific heat: NAVEAU (1961)

t°	c_p	t°	c_p	t°	c_p	t°	c_p
−180.94	13.80	−158.27	16.43	−141.69	18.82	−127.22	17.04
178.71	13.88	156.29	16.74	139.49	19.49	126.42	16.89
175.95	14.08	152.77	16.94	138.33	19.58	124.24	17.17
167.76	15.05	151.37	16.98	136.29	20.77	118.23	17.28
163.12	15.87	149.25	17.13	135.92	19.51	108.98	18.14
162.35	16.16	147.98	17.24	134.18	18.42	107.52	18.20
161.95	22.87	145.40	17.99	132.54	17.11	105.97	18.41
160.38	17.61	145.23	18.31	−130.88	17.10	−103.44	18.52
−159.93	16.38	−144.18	18.37				

Heat of combustion: 675.55 kcal/mol HUBBARD, SCOTT *et al.* (1955)

3-METHYLTHIOPHENE C_5H_6S

McCULLOUGH, SUNNER *et al.* (1953)

Freezing point: −68.971   *Density* at 25°: 1.01647
Refractive index: n_D at 25° = 1.51758
Specific heat

t°	c_p	t°	c_p	t°	c_p	t°	c_p
			Crystals				Liquid
−260.76	0.797	−240.81	5.445	144.18	16.725	−66.15	32.734
260.47	0.850	237.52	6.153	140.96	16.976	60.72	32.825
259.54	1.029	233.68	6.930	138.49	17.173	54.34	32.979
258.91	1.156	229.24	7.750	138.29	17.187	47.03	33.168
258.19	1.302	224.25	8.609	135.85	17.372	38.80	33.401
257.38	1.468	219.19	9.379	132.01	17.682	29.68	33.705
257.02	1.540	219.11	9.399	130.84	17.794	20.18	34.044
255.81	1.825	213.31	10.207	127.13	18.267	10.32	34.423
255.73	1.838	206.66	11.051	124.78	18.442	6.24	34.591
254.11	2.217	200.51	11.732	124.67	18.499	− 0.11	34.854
254.04	2.236	194.38	12.394	121.94	18.710	+ 4.21	35.044
252.32	2.651	187.90	13.074	118.93	18.943	9.98	35.301
251.86	2.764	181.43	13.676	117.30	19.078	14.64	35.514
250.30	3.143	174.77	14.235	114.79	19.298	24.60	35.975
249.42	3.368	167.91	14.808	110.04	19.725	34.92	36.471
248.13	3.685	160.91	15.388	102.12	20.447	45.59	37.011
246.83	4.001	153.37	15.998	93.57	21.244	55.63	37.503
246.06	4.191	148.80	16.360	85.29	22.055	+64.13	37.951
−243.94	4.706	−145.70	16.607	− 76.49	22.990		

Heat of melting: 2518 cal/mol
Heat of combustion at 25°: 829.28 kcal/mol

For the ALKYLTHIOPHENES: see JEFFERY, PARKER and VOGEL (1961)

BENZOTHIOPHENE C_8H_6S

FINKE, GROSS *et al.* (1954)

Freezing point: $+31.32$

Transition point: -11.56

Density

$t°$	d	
35	1.1988	
40	1.1937	

Refractive index

$t°$	n_D	
35	1.6332	
40	1.6302	

Specific heat

$t°$	c_p	$t°$	c_p	$t°$	c_p	$t°$	c_p
Crystals II						**Liquid**	
-260.75	1.571	-208.90	10.903	-141.58	18.236	$+34.59$	45.549
259.55	1.906	207.30	11.063	134.57	18.901	39.27	45.920
257.92	2.341	203.30	11.460	11.16	33.399	40.64	45.974
255.69	2.952	200.79	11.701	10.03	33.566	48.62	46.575
253.10	3.639	197.14	12.062	5.06	34.450	$+56.52$	47.110
250.69	4.250	194.56	12.322	3.96	34.489		
248.39	4.803	193.99	12.368	1.79	34.877		
245.59	5.455	190.44	12.714	$-$ 1.41	34.783	**Crystals I**	
242.27	6.182	189.13	12.859	$+$ 0.90	35.294	see authors	
238.74	6.857	187.14	13.043	2.96	35.475		
234.90	7.502	183.94	13.360	4.99	35.711		
230.96	8.125	183.26	13.406	5.60	35.880		
226.69	8.734	179.83	13.693	10.69	36.594		
221.94	9.365	175.61	14.066	11.73	36.690		
218.88	9.750	172.05	14.390	13.31	36.943		
218.66	9.767	165.65	15.006	18.23	37.674		
217.16	9.956	160.04	15.755	18.78	37.802		
214.07	10.309	154.17	16.732	20.84	38.032		
-213.29	10.405	-148.39	17.490	$+$ 26.82	39.365		

Heat of melting: 2826.8 cal/mol

Heat of transition: 719.6 cal/mol

TRIFLUOROMETHANETHIOL   CHSF$_3$

DININNY and PACE (1960)

Saturated vapour pressure

t°	p mm	t°	p mm	
−105.41	9.20	−61.23	235.38	
97.84	18.17	54.64	337.64	
90.15	34.29	49.07	449.19	
82.68	59.94	42.57	611.12	
75.34	99.28	−37.13	792.51	
68.11	157.15	—	—	

Boiling point: −38.00

Melting point: −157.12

Specific heat

t°	c_p	t°	c_p	t°	c_p	t°	c_p
−260.63	1.869	−199.20	12.76	Liquid		−102.11	25.92
257.77	2.839	196.10	12.98			98.54	25.98
253.96	4.237	194.10	13.16			96.14	25.97
252.80	4.645	192.79	13.20	152.36	26.02	95.11	26.07
249.83	5.521	192.35	13.28	152.07	26.04	90.26	26.12
247.89	6.136	191.15	13.46	150.41	26.03	87.11	26.20
245.39	6.784	189.06	13.56	148.51	26.08	84.42	26.11
243.33	7.237	188.00	13.65	147.37	26.00	81.66	26.17
240.31	7.893	186.91	13.81	143.99	25.97	78.66	26.19
238.08	8.382	186.43	13.87	142.03	25.92	75.88	26.21
232.44	9.444	184.08	14.25	139.10	25.91	72.96	26.23
229.57	9.733	183.45	14.35	136.34	25.88	70.17	26.32
226.81	10.05	183.14	14.25	130.73	25.89	67.30	26.40
224.32	10.33	181.93	15.33	129.00	25.82	64.49	26.50
219.65	10.83	180.14	14.85	125.17	25.84	61.69	26.44
217.40	11.04	179.21	16.40	122.89	25.78	58.87	26.54
214.49	11.34	177.05	15.76	119.67	25.84	56.14	26.57
211.74	11.61	176.80	15.28	116.69	25.83	50.61	26.77
209.51	11.83	174.57	15.79	114.24	25.83	−45.81	26.84
206.55	12.11	172.18	16.48	110.57	25.87	—	—
204.37	12.30	169.58	17.99	108.86	25.90	—	—
−201.36	12.54	167.39	19.78	108.13	25.89	—	—
—	—	−165.77	21.47	−104.52	25.89	—	—

ALKYLBENZENESULPHONAMIDES VAUGHN and SEARS (1958)

DIMETHYLSULPHOXIDE C_2H_6OS

Density and *Surface tension:* CLEVER and SNEAD (1963)

t°	d	γ
20	1.098	43.54
25	—	42.86
30	1.0913	42.41
35	—	41.73
40	1.0816	41.17
50	1.0721	40.05
60	1.0616	38.94

Specific heat: MACKLE and O'HARE (1962)

t°	cal/mol
25	21.256
127	25.709
227	29.303
327	32.370
427	34.879
527	37.020
627	38.946
727	40.707

14. DERIVATIVES WITH OTHER ELEMENTS

METHYLSILANE CH_6Si

SHADE and COOPER (1958)

Saturated vapour pressure

t°	p mm
−29.0	2,340
0.0	6,310
+24.0	11,110
+35.7	14,800
+40.5	16,670
+47.2	18,920

Boiling point: —56.9

ALKYLSILANES see ALTSHULLER and ROSENBLUM (1955)

CHLOROSILANES see McKENZIE, MILLS and SCOTT (1950)

PHENOXYSILANES see SMITH (1955)

TRIMETHYLSILANOL $C_3H_{10}OSi$

Saturated vapour pressure: GRUBB and OSTHOFF (1953)

t°	p mm	t°	p mm	t°	p mm
18.0	13.9	37.7	47.0	64.5	193.9
22.9	19.3	41.6	59.3	68.9	234.4
24.5	21.2	46.6	77.0	76.4	329.2
29.7	29.5	54.1	115.4	79.1	374.9
32.7	34.9	61.1	161.8	84.7	468.0

TRIETHYLSILANOL $C_6H_{16}OSi$

Saturated vapour pressure: GRUBB and OSTHOFF (1953)

t°	p mm	t°	p mm	t°	p mm
24.5	1.8	67.9	19.1	104.9	122.2
41.0	4.6	74.4	28.3	116.0	189.0
48.2	6.5	84.6	48.0	120.5	218.5
55.2	9.2	93.6	73.7	135.2	390.4
60.8	12.4	100.5	99.0	140.2	471.2

HEXAMETHYLDISILOXANE $C_6H_{18}OSi_2$

SCOTT, MESSERLY *et al.* (1961)

Boiling point: 100.52°

Heat of fusion: 2849 cal/mol at —68.23°

Specific heat

$t°$	c_p	$t°$	c_p	$t°$	c_p
	Crystals			Liquid	
—261.58	1.641	—204.41	24.832	—64.21	66.776
260.38	2.087	197.64	27.241	56.20	67.398
258.80	2.757	190.89	29.610	50.81	67.766
257.37	3.402	185.18	31.840	46.29	68.133
256.51	3.795	180.93	32.812	41.87	68.465
255.51	4.256	177.44	33.847	36.49	68.910
254.53	4.709	172.61	35.237	26.32	69.769
253.47	5.195	164.76	37.433	15.80	70.651
252.68	5.566	157.29	39.436	— 5.39	71.601
251.67	6.029	150.16	41.277	+ 4.89	72.504
250.73	6.457	140.00	43.804	15.04	73.475
249.75	6.913	134.15	45.206	25.08	74.430
248.47	7.493	132.63	45.540	26.70	74.568
247.29	8.008	125.79	47.175	36.46	75.526
246.12	8.518	118.63	48.824	47.18	76.597
244.25	9.291	111.19	50.494	57.75	77.641
243.39	9.632	103.47	52.206	68.20	78.684
240.94	10.643	97.35	53.495	78.51	79.736
237.17	12.159	95.97	53.867	88.69	80.771
233.90	13.665	90.68	55.040	+97.74	81.667
229.48	15.117	89.93	55.230		
225.24	16.773	88.66	55.476		
222.93	17.694	83.32	56.704		
220.50	18.649	82.52	56.866		
216.98	20.028	— 75.29	58.551		
—210.70	22.501				

HEXAMETHYLCYCLOTRISILOXANE $C_6H_{18}O_3Si_3$

Saturated vapour pressure: OSTHOFF, GRUBB and BURKHARD (1953)

t°	p mm	t°	p mm	
Crystals		Liquid		
24.2	4.2	69.8	82.2	
27.8	6.1	76.9	110.0	
34.1	8.9	81.4	131.0	
39.8	12.6	85.0	150.6	
45.9	20.1	92.8	203.2	
51.0	27.1	99.0	251.1	
56.0	39.2	103.8	293.5	
62.4	54.1	108.4	338.6	
—	—	111.4	375.7	
—	—	114.8	412.7	

OCTAMETHYLCYCLOTETRASILOXANE $C_8H_{24}O_4Si_4$

Specific volume: ROSS and HILDEBRAND (1963)

t°	V (cc/mol)
22.26	311.09
24.45	311.93
25.00	—
29.56	313.90
35.65	316.27
44.84	319.91

N-DIMETHYLAMINODIBORANE $C_2H_{11}NB_2$

FURUKAWA, McCOSKEY, REILLY and HARMAN (1955)

Specific heat (cal/mol)

$t°$	c_p	$t°$	c_p	$t°$	c_p
− 65.42	29.95	− 59.46	31.98	− 51.67	34.10
63.74	30.15	57.18	41.94	50.55	34.12
61.88	30.47	56.13	67.70	47.70	34.28
59.87	30.93	55.75	104.22	42.88	34.56
57.94	35.04	55.48	170.11	37.89	34.85
56.38	64.90	55.30	268.91	32.90	35.08
55.36	260.60	55.11	446.40	27.91	35.47
53.38	62.25	53.96	80.01	23.03	35.79
50.36	34.07	− 52.13	34.02	− 18.17	36.10
− 47.47	34.24				
− 183.13	14.13	− 112.45	22.85	− 83.27	27.16
179.50	14.64	106.02	23.70	78.90	28.41
174.52	15.21	99.76	24.52	74.69	90.72
169.11	15.88	93.64	25.52	73.31	2803
164.35	16.47	87.67	26.45	73.24	9100
157.82	17.26	81.79	27.55	73.21	23010
149.97	18.23	− 76.21	33.94	71.94	270.6
142.43	19.15			− 69.84	29.79
135.20	20.03				
128.22	20.87	− 82.89	27.23	− 255.62	1.869
121.49	21.71	78.75	28.45	254.10	2.254
− 114.69	22.55	74.04	375.9	252.81	2.586
		70.10	29.83	251.44	2.934
− 70.83	29.63	67.43	29.98	249.99	3.305
68.35	29.80	62.88	30.36	248.70	3.666
62.49	30.31	− 55.50	73.25	246.68	4.161
55.13	83.13			243.83	4.857
− 50.68	34.10			240.76	5.573
				237.44	6.308
				233.70	7.036
− 25.95	35.65			228.64	7.922
20.44	36.01			223.04	8.834
15.59	36.34			217.65	9.627
9.59	36.73			211.84	10.45
− 2.45	37.27			206.13	11.23
+ 4.66	37.80			199.95	12.09
+ 11.75	38.42			193.32	12.87
				186.93	13.72
				− 180.09	14.56

FURUKAWA, McCOSKEY *et al.* (1955)

Saturated vapour pressure

$t°$	p mm	$t°$	p mm	$t°$	p mm
Series I		Series II		Series III	
−38.45	12.1	−53.37	4.8	−54.88	4.4
33.65	14.8	45.38	7.8	47.11	7.3
30.41	19.8	36.61	13.5	27.97	22.5
27.59	23.8	24.34	28.4	−13.01	52.3
23.87	29.0	17.18	41.6		
16.68	43.2	14.25	49.0		
11.21	57.7	12.63	53.8		
8.30	67.3	− 6.62	73.0		
4.27	82.4				
− 1.83	92.8				
+ 0.34	103.5				
+10.06	162.5				
+14.02	193.3				

Freezing point: −55.0

Heat of melting: 1407.6 j/mol

TRIALKYLBORANES, *Heat of combustion*: see JOHNSON, KILDAY and PROSEN (1961)

ALKYLPHOSPHONATES see KOSOLAPOFF (1955)

TRIBUTYL PHOSPHATE $C_{12}H_{27}O_4P$

Density and Viscosity: MOLE, HOLMES and McCOUBREY (1964)

$t°$	d	η	$t°$	d	η	$t°$	d	η
− 65	1.051	333	− 25	1.015	17.7	+ 25	0.972	3.39
55	1.042	121	15	1.007	11.1	35	0.963	2.77
45	1.033	56.6	− 5	0.998	8.50	45	0.954	2.23
− 35	1.024	32.9	—	—	—	+ 65	0.937	1.61

TRIS(2-ETHYLHEXYL) PHOSPHATE $C_{24}H_{51}O_4P$

Density and Viscosity: MOLE, HOLMES and McCOUBREY (1964)

$t°$	d	η	$t°$	d	η	$t°$	d	η
− 60	0.985	8080	− 20.5	0.955	133	+ 35	0.916	8.21
50	0.977	2560	10	0.947	—	45.5	0.908	6.07
38.5	0.969	—	0	0.941	—	65	0.893	3.76
− 30	0.963	260	+ 25.5	0.924	11.4	+ 75.5	0.886	3.12

TRIPHENYL PHOSPHATE $C_{18}H_{15}O_4P$

Density and Viscosity: MOLE, HOLMES and MCCOUBREY (1964)

t°	d	η	t°	d	η	t°	d	η
+ 50	1.205	10.04	+ 65	1.191	6.56	+ 80	1.180	4.61
+ 55	1.200	8.62	+ 70	1.188	5.77	+ 85	1.176	4.19
+ 60	1.196	7.34	+ 75	1.183	5.17	+ 90	1.172	3.86

TRIETHYLPHOSPHINE OXIDE $C_6H_{15}OP$

Density and Viscosity: MOLE, HOLMES and MCCOUBREY (1964)

t°	d	η	t°	d	η
+ 65	0.844	10.05	+ 85	0.831	5.48
+ 75	0.838	7.11	+ 98.5	0.821	4.02

TRIS(DIMETHYLAMINO)PHOSPHINE OXIDE $C_6H_{18}ON_3P$

Density and Viscosity: MOLE, HOLMES and MCCOUBREY (1964)

t°	d	η	t°	d	η
+ 10	1.037	4.85	+ 40	1.011	2.52
+ 18	1.030	3.94	+ 60	0.994	1.82
+ 25	1.024	3.34	+ 75	0.980	1.48

BIS(DIMETHYLAMINO)PHOSPHORYL CHLORIDE $C_4H_{12}ON_2PCl$

Density and Viscosity: MOLE, HOLMES and MCCOUBREY (1964)

t°	d	η	t°	d	η	t°	d	η
− 25	1.228	15.66	0	1.203	6.57	+ 40	1.161	2.64
− 20	1.222	12.75	+ 18	1.184	4.18	+ 60	1.142	1.92
− 10	1.213	9.04	+ 25	1.176	3.55	+ 75	1.127	1.54

ADDENDA

METHANE CH_4

Density and Viscosity: BARUA, AFZAL, FLYNN and ROSS (1964)

t°	P atm.	d	η	t°	P atm.	d	η
− 50.00	20.00	0.01936	88.20	+ 25.00	28.62	0.01974	114.79
	60.00	0.07762	108.75		54.73	0.03947	121.23
	80.00	0.12481	135.28		78.76	0.05900	129.23
	120.00	0.21065	216.41		113.50	0.08886	143.84
	140.00	0.23388	250.13		157.32	0.12633	167.31
	160.00	0.24998	273.10		175.23	0.14066	177.09
− 25.00	10.00	0.00822	95.55	+ 75.00	28.61	0.01649	130.37
	30.00	0.02636	99.80		54.92	0.03234	135.04
	60.00	0.05949	111.17		80.32	0.04811	141.19
	80.00	0.08640	123.90		119.60	0.07296	152.22
	100.00	0.11654	141.44		144.88	0.08886	160.66
	140.00	0.17352	186.92		174.23	0.10681	171.00
	160.00	0.19524	208.65				
0.00	14.01	0.01039	104.10	+ 150.00	11.55	0.00536	150.63
	25.88	0.01974	106.44		28.14	0.01311	152.33
	48.78	0.03947	112.64		56.05	0.02626	156.20
	69.22	0.05900	120.10		83.94	0.03947	160.55
	97.61	0.08886	134.54		125.50	0.05900	168.31
	131.77	0.12633	157.99		155.78	0.07296	174.96
	166.69	0.16147	184.87		170.00	0.07940	178.27

3,3-DIETHYLPENTANE C_9H_{20}

Dielectric constant: PHILIPPE and PIETTE (1955)

t°	ε	t°	ε	t°	ε
+ 44.95	1.997	25.4	1.891	+ 15.5	1.997
40.15	1.999	32.0	1.866	− 15.0	1.926
30.05	2.001	35.1	1.929	32.3	1.938
15.55	1.997	55.2	1.907	42.0	1.917
+ 5.10	1.982	− 74.9	1.894	− 64.8	1.900
− 5.3	1.957				

p-CYMENE (METHYL-*iso*PROPYLBENZENE) $C_{10}H_{14}$

STRUBELL (1964)

Saturated vapour pressure

p mm	t°	p mm	t°	p mm	t°
800	178.85	200	127.8	15	64.3
760	176.7	100	109.5	10	56.9
700	173.48	60	95.8	8	52.8
600	166.5	50	91.4	6	47.65
500	158.6	40	85.8	5	44.6
400	150.3	30	78.95	4	40.8
300	140.0	20	70.3		

Density

t°	d	t°	d	t°	d
0	0.8732	35	0.8435	130	0.7635
4	0.8701	50	0.8310	140	0.7550
8	0.8670	80	0.8000	150	0.7466
10	0.8654	100	0.7888	160	0.7361
15	0.8619	110	0.7805	170	0.7299
20	0.8571	120	0.7718	176	0.7251

Viscosity

t°	η	t°	η	t°	η
0	8.634	40	0.933	120	0.550
10	5.968	60	0.836	140	0.481
20	3.402	80	0.684	160	0.421
30	1.600	100	0.627	175	0.379

Specific heat (kg)

t°	cal/g	t°	cal/g	t°	cal/g
0	0.408	60	0.444	140	0.499
10	0.417	80	0.456	160	0.515
20	0.421	100	0.468	170	0.527
40	0.434	120	0.473		

Heat of vaporization

t°	cal/g	t°	cal/g
0	90.61	100	80.91
20	89.54	150	76.3
50	86.72	176.7	67.7

CARBON TETRACHLORIDE   CCl$_4$

WAXLER and WEIR (1963)

Density and Refractive index

t°	P atm.	d	n$_D$	t°	P atm.	d	n$_D$
24.80	0.99	1.58496	1.45731	54.34	0.99	1.52681	1.44067
	273.3	1.62639	1.47089		245.4	1.57176	1.45493
	516.6	1.65708	1.48037		446.7	1.60197	1.46428
	786.7	1.68637	1.48934		741.9	1.63918	1.47616
	1101.8	1.71597	1.49847		1045.1	1.67140	1.48617
34.50	0.99	1.56605	1.45197				
	252.1	1.60684	1.46481				
	474.5	1.63682	1.47426				
	746.1	1.66811	1.48381				
	1105.0	1.70329	1.49441				

TRIFLUOROMETHANE or FLUOROFORM CHF₃

VALENTINE, BRODALE and GIAUQUE (1962)

Saturated vapour pressure

t°	p mm	t°	p mm	t°	p mm
Vapour		**Solid**		**Liquid**	
− 127.802	20.4	− 233.15	$36.2 \cdot 10^{-24}$	− 153.15	$64.9 \cdot 10^{-2}$
115.070	71.0	223.15	$20.9 \cdot 10^{-17}$	143.15	$30.4 \cdot 10^{-1}$
108.949	123.4	213.15	$65.1 \cdot 10^{-13}$	133.15	11.1
103.968	178.8	203.15	$10.2 \cdot 10^{-9}$	123.15	33.1
100.326	234.5	193.15	$24.7 \cdot 10^{-7}$	113.15	84.5
96.724	302.5	183.15	$17.0 \cdot 10^{-5}$	103.15	190.1
93.801	368.8	173.15	$49.0 \cdot 10^{-4}$	93.15	385.4
91.150	439.3	− 163.15	$74.2 \cdot 10^{-3}$	− 83.15	718.5
89.268	495.1				
87.233	561.2				
85.261	633.4				
83.599	699.2				
− 81.973	768.9				

Boiling point: —82.18° (760 mm Hg)   *Triple point:* —155.18 (0.456 mm Hg)

Heat capacity

t°	cal/mol	t°	cal/mol	t°	cal/mol
Series I					
− 257.78	1.91	− 233.83	8.07	− 186.35	13.12
256.39	2.40	230.53	8.65	180.58	13.64
253.06	3.10	226.58	9.24	175.30	14.11
251.15	3.92	222.16	9.81	170.42	14.60
248.87	4.65	217.15	10.42	165.89	15.19
245.02	5.70	211.43	11.18	161.86	15.78
242.76	6.24	205.36	11.54	− 158.14	16.21
239.86	6.90	199.18	12.07	—	—
− 236.91	7.54	− 192.71	12.61	—	—
Series II		Series III			
− 192.18	12.58	− 150.42	20.25		
184.14	13.27	143.33	20.10		
179.82	13.69	135.22	20.02	− 92.33	30.37
175.28	14.13	126.83	20.00	− 83.82	20.59
171.05	14.56	118.55	20.02		
167.52	14.99	109.86	20.08		
− 164.91	15.33	− 101.20	20.20		

Heat of fusion: 970 cal/mol   *Heat of vaporization:* 3994 cal/mol

TETRAFLUOROMETHANE   CF$_4$

Douslin, Harrison, Moore and McCullough (1961)

Vapour pressure

t°	P atm.					
	d mol/l					
	0.75	1.0	1.5	2.0	2.5	3.0
0.00	15.480	20.086	28.559	36.149	42.974	49.150
25	17.194	22.453	32.339	41.486	50.000	58.012
30	17.538	22.923	33.087	42.538	51.387	59.764
50	18.898	24.792	36.057	46.720	56.893	66.701
75	20.591	27.116	39.749	51.903	63.709	75.279
100	22.275	29.426	43.412	57.049	70.468	83.789
125	23.952	31.725	47.047	62.155	77.175	92.224
150	25.625	34.021	50.671	67.233	83.830	100.617
175	27.296	36.304	54.274	72.282	90.460	108.963
200	28.964	38.585	57.868	77.316	97.066	117.270
225	30.627	40.860	61.455	82.331	103.639	125.550
250	32.289	43.132	65.034	87.334	110.200	133.807
275	33.949	45.398	68.596	92.326	116.738	142.032
300	35.609	47.661	72.165	97.306	123.266	150.212
325	37.266	49.924	75.723	102.278	129.773	158.415
350	38.921	52.187	79.273	107.240	136.267	166.576
t°	3.5	4.0	4.5	5.0	5.5	6.0
0.00	54.804	60.039	64.967	69.704	74.369	79.050
25	65.628	72.967	80.130	87.251	94.473	101.908
30	67.756	75.520	83.129	90.736	98.470	106.456
50	76.251	85.656	95.045	104.587	114.393	124.621
75	86.735	98.206	109.825	121.755	134.178	147.212
100	97.142	110.662	124.512	138.840	153.853	169.728
125	107.462	123.034	139.086	155.832	173.413	192.127
150	117.715	135.322	153.553	172.699	192.863	214.330
175	127.937	147.553	168.020	189.528	212.277	236.618
200	138.103	159.733	182.364	206.259	231.582	258.762
225	148.221	171.872	196.686	222.912	250.816	280.728
250	158.325	183.973	210.974	239.569	270.100	302.842
275	168.391	196.014	225.145	256.087	289.161	324.652
300	178.382	207.995	239.280	272.536	308.116	346.323
325	188.385	219.957	253.412	288.853	327.091	368.163
350	198.378	231.925	267.505	305.438	346.066	389.660

t°	P atm.					
	d mol/l					
	6.5	7.0	7.5	8.0	8.5	9.0
0	83.903	89.061	94.676	100.960	108.149	116.575
25	109.726	118.131	127.244	137.455	148.916	162.056
30	114.879	123.929	133.791	144.774	157.077	171.140
50	135.468	147.186	159.922	174.093	189.908	207.791
75	161.150	176.143	192.482	210.584	230.884	253.472
100	186.712	205.075	225.134	247.200	271.743	299.330
125	212.147	233.889	257.529	283.630	312.493	344.771
150	237.418	262.452	289.777	319.795	353.276	390.238
175	262.764	291.064	322.043	356.107	393.701	—
200	287.988	319.607	354.291	392.333	—	—
225	312.999	348.121	386.496	—	—	—
250	338.173	376.424	—	—	—	—
275	362.875	—	—	—	—	—
300	387.599	—	—	—	—	—

t°	9.5	10.0	10.5	11.0	11.5	12.0
0	126.561	138.458	152.884	170.481	192.000	218.629
25	177.339	195.101	216.126	241.054	270.777	306.072
30	187.469	206.428	228.708	254.939	286.356	323.269
50	228.320	251.970	279.425	311.330	348.658	392.619
75	279.421	308.736	342.440	381.498	—	—
100	330.350	365.751	—	—	—	—
125	381.244	—	—	—	—	—

t°	12.5
0	251.029
25	342.263
30	367.430

1,1,1-TRIFLUORO-2,2,2-TRICHLOROETHANE $C_2Cl_3F_3$

HIRAOKA and HILDEBRAND (1963)

Vapour pressure

t°	p mm	t°	p mm
14.05	230.1	27.55	405.2
15.05	240.1	30.05	444.8
17.55	265.1	32.05	478.2
20.05	295.0	34.05	511.0
22.55	325.0	36.05	544.0
25.05	361.1	—	—

1,1,2-TRIFLUORO-1,2,2-TRICHLOROETHANE $C_2Cl_3F_3$

HIRAOKA and HILDEBRAND (1963)

Vapour pressure

t°	p mm	t°	p mm
0.20	129.4	30.10	439.0
5.00	159.6	35.10	524.2
10.30	200.5	40.10	617.2
10.45	201.7	44.95	726.8
15.10	244.5	—	—
20.00	299.8	—	—
25.05	363.6	—	—

n-PROPYL ALCOHOL C_3H_8O

AMBROSE and TOWNSEND (1963)

Crit. temperature: 263.56°; *Crit. density:* 0.2754 g/ml; *Crit. pressure:* 51.02 atm

Saturated vapour pressure

t°	p	t°	p	t°	p
132.31	3.286	167.86	8.446	199.67	16.872
138.62	3.952	168.76	8.648	209.48	20.438
138.97	3.968	178.51	10.802	210.45	20.805
147.52	5.062	178.56	10.811	221.39	25.445
148.17	5.123	179.18	10.974	221.60	25.585
157.87	6.605	188.38	13.398	239.95	34.991
158.35	6.689	189.16	13.619	251.93	42.478
164.41	7.764	198.87	16.616	263.56	51.023

Orthobaric densities

t°	d		t°	d	
	L	V		L	V
141.65	0.6875	0.0091	225.12	0.5376	0.0618
154.18	0.6700	0.0135	232.54	0.5166	0.0742
165.85	0.6533	0.0173	240.11	0.4992	0.0885
176.93	0.6350	0.0220	245.33	0.4724	0.1034
186.29	0.6204	0.0270	250.22	0.4499	0.1187
197.77	0.6077	0.0314	254.61	0.4267	0.1357
201.01	0.5923	0.0384	256.69	0.4127	0.1474
206.40	0.5816	0.0413	—	—	—

Iso-PROPYL ALCOHOL C_3H_8O

AMBROSE and TOWNSEND (1963)

Critical temperature: 235.25°

Critical density: 0.2727 g/ml

Critical pressure: 47.02 atm

Saturated vapour pressure

t°	P	t°	P	t°	P
121.90	3.983	153.17	9.294	190.06	20.941
122.08	3.997	158.34	10.557	190.08	20.904
122.25	4.044	158.37	10.510	205.16	27.919
131.94	5.326	165.10	12.302	216.42	34.143
132.08	5.349	165.21	12.337	220.15	36.435
140.09	6.633	168.57	13.328	227.04	40.978
142.42	7.096	168.75	13.426	235.09	47.019
142.49	7.094	180.03	17.024	—	—
153.14	9.282	180.11	17.113	—	—

Orthobaric densities

t°	d		t°	d	
	L	V		L	V
134.12	0.6605	0.0146	201.74	0.5222	0.0669
149.18	0.6353	0.0193	207.25	0.5055	0.0762
163.23	0.6104	0.0278	213.19	0.4852	0.0888
170.57	0.5957	0.0332	218.05	0.4658	0.1029
177.55	0.5815	0.0389	222.64	0.4418	0.1196
185.30	0.5640	0.0456	227.28	0.4165	0.1389
191.98	0.5480	0.0535	231.07	0.3849	0.1660
196.69	0.5357	0.0597	233.53	0.3493	0.1975

n-BUTYL ALCOHOL $C_4H_{10}O$

AMBROSE and TOWNSEND (1963)

Critical temperature: 289.83°

Critical density: 0.2699 g/ml

Critical pressure: 43.55 atm

Saturated vapour pressure

t°	P	t°	P	t°	P
146.19	2.514	197.16	8.339	239.91	20.177
155.96	3.313	199.40	9.354	249.77	23.733
160.62	3.770	207.81	11.138	250.05	23.810
166.09	4.333	209.17	11.436	259.70	27.816
166.13	4.337	217.72	13.293	260.08	27.909
170.82	4.865	219.15	13.861	269.62	32.410
175.48	5.477	228.91	16.612	277.49	36.464
186.60	7.099	229.32	16.706	283.74	40.006
189.49	7.545	239.67	19.969	289.83	43.554

Orthobaric densities

t°	d		t°	d	
	L	V		L	V
166.93	0.6694	0.0142	226.57	0.5764	0.0409
178.57	0.6538	0.0176	235.08	0.5592	0.0482
188.90	0.6401	0.0203	242.44	0.5437	0.0563
196.32	0.6279	0.0238	248.05	0.5314	0.0623
202.62	0.6182	0.0266	256.95	0.5080	0.0740
208.75	0.6087	0.0283	260.90	0.4896	0.0880
216.63	0.5950	0.0341	275.70	0.4365	0.1224

Iso-BUTYL ALCOHOL $C_4H_{10}O$

AMBROSE and TOWNSEND (1963)

Critical temperature: 276.70°

Critical density: 0.2722 g/ml

Critical pressure: 42.39 atm

Saturated vapour pressure

t°	P	t°	P	t°	P
149.49	3.753	202.74	12.786	250.12	29.347
159.92	4.921	205.86	13.598	252.45	30.392
170.29	6.353	212.38	15.406	252.45	30.413
173.25	6.804	223.16	18.696	263.11	35.783
179.75	7.896	223.17	18.758	266.20	37.504
185.79	9.019	226.43	19.825	269.92	39.676
191.02	10.095	232.00	21.807	274.56	42.386
195.16	10.982	239.77	24.845	—	—
200.42	12.236	242.32	25.871	—	—

Orthobaric densities

t°	d		t°	d	
	L	V		L	V
148.01	0.6775	0.0098	223.89	0.5539	0.0490
161.25	0.6594	0.0140	229.31	0.5416	0.0553
181.16	0.6297	0.0211	236.17	0.5239	0.0657
186.40	0.6211	0.0238	242.15	0.5088	0.0732
193.89	0.6111	0.0254	248.70	0.4888	0.0852
203.73	0.5943	0.0317	252.91	0.4743	0.0965
213.94	0.5746	0.0397	262.29	0.4313	0.1275

Sec.-BUTYL ALCOHOL $C_4H_{10}O$

AMBROSE and TOWNSEND (1963)

Critical temperature: 262.80°

Critical density: 0.2755 g/ml

Critical pressure: 41.39 atm

Saturated vapour pressure

t°	P	t°	P	t°	P
148.96	4.681	180.53	9.812	211.89	18.530
150.44	4.845	190.11	12.005	221.44	21.408
159.68	6.146	190.79	12.155	221.81	22.466
160.05	6.161	200.79	14.768	232.39	25.762
170.06	7.838	201.10	14.844	242.19	30.199
170.37	7.840	211.01	17.772	252.76	35.557
179.94	9.800	211.30	18.115	262.80	41.392

Orthobaric densities

t°	d		t°	d	
	L	V		L	V
134.08	0.6944	0.0110	200.10	0.5871	0.0418
150.87	0.6701	0.0156	205.41	0.5758	0.0462
171.62	0.6377	0.0239	221.55	0.5390	0.0638
180.40	0.6233	0.0278	231.24	0.5132	0.0777
188.20	0.6092	0.0330	—	—	—

Tert.-BUTYL ALCOHOL $C_4H_{10}O$

Critical temperature: 233.0° Ambrose and Townsend (1963)

Critical density: 0.2700 g/ml *ibid.*   *Critical pressure:* 39.20 atm *ibid.*

Saturated vapour pressure: ibid.

t°	P	t°	P
103.27	2.131	153.68	8.729
115.41	3.150	159.67	10.033
125.40	4.217	170.70	12.733
135.63	5.559	172.78	13.330
146.22	7.306	233.00	39.200

Beynon and McKetta (1963)

t°	p
57.40	256.19
72.50	507.53
82.60	767.96
90.00	1020.32

Melting point: 25.82° Oetting (1963)

Orthobaric densities: Ambrose and Townsend (1963)

| t° | d | | t° | d | |
	L	V		L	V
146.67	0.6281	0.0217	192.66	0.5330	0.0597
160.46	0.6035	0.0289	200.37	0.5128	0.0701
174.08	0.5754	0.0395	207.41	0.4905	0.0835
183.05	0.5561	0.0474	—	—	—

Specific heat (cal/mol): Oetting (1963)

t°	c_p	t°	c_p	t°	c_p
		Series I			
C.II − 2.76	40.37	C.I + 19.45	35.94	42.00	56.24
+ 2.15	42.69	23.65	83.06	47.47	57.25
11.70	47.21	L. 30.80	53.78	52.86	58.09
+ 14.93	65.48	+ 36.45	55.10	58.19	58.99

t°	c_p	t°	c_p	t°	c_p
			Series II		
C.II − 257.63	1.352	− 172.05	14.52	− 56.67	28.50
256.04	1.649	167.02	15.13	51.29	29.27
254.18	2.133	162.16	15.76	46.02	30.08
252.21	2.566	157.45	16.27	35.85	31.89
250.23	2.964	152.86	16.80	30.89	32.84
248.09	3.523	148.39	17.35	26.03	33.72
245.72	4.065	143.03	17.88	21.27	34.77
243.13	4.545	139.76	18.33	16.61	36.00
240.28	5.121	134.72	18.93	9.97	38.24
237.30	5.700	128.94	19.55	7.17	39.24
234.01	6.358	123.30	20.21	− 1.72	40.85
230.21	6.993	117.79	20.89	+ 0.96	41.98
225.87	7.712	112.41	21.50	3.58	42.99
221.13	8.392	107.14	22.10	6.16	44.07
215.89	9.081	101.97	22.67	11.21	46.86
210.07	9.833	96.90	23.25	13.61	49.01
204.20	10.58	91.31	23.95	15.92	51.91
198.81	11.20	85.23	24.73	18.13	55.44
193.73	11.88	79.29	25.46	20.16	64.04
188.36	12.61	73.46	26.15	+ 21.77	69.76
182.68	13.29	67.75	26.91	−	−
− 177.26	13.90	− 62.15	27.67	−	−
			Series III		
C.II − 151.33	17.08	− 90.05	23.98	− 14.04	36.78
146.04	17.72	85.02	24.63	9.47	38.06
140.34	18.39	80.07	25.23	3.73	40.64
134.24	18.98	75.21	25.85	− 1.05	41.07
128.25	19.66	70.44	26.48	+ 1.61	41.87
122.43	20.28	65.74	27.24	4.22	43.26
116.74	20.89	61.12	27.90	6.77	44.53
111.18	21.58	56.58	28.31	9.27	45.59
105.75	22.30	51.10	29.20	16.44	52.60
100.41	22.82	32.69	32.35	18.62	56.80
− 95.18	23.45	− 20.19	35.12	+ 20.60	67.10
			Series IV		
C.II − 40.36	31.07	− 1.12	41.06	+ 19.21	34.92
35.33	31.92	+ 1.62	42.41	20.93	37.45
30.40	32.85	5.77	43.92	22.57	42.72
25.57	33.80	9.73	46.01	24.17	81.67
20.83	34.82	12.13	47.63	L. 30.42	53.77
16.21	36.09	14.56	49.83	36.06	54.91
9.77	38.25	15.87	701.43	41.60	56.03
6.86	39.12	C.I 16.51	33.45	47.05	57.02
− 3.96	40.58	+ 17.69	33.96	52.43	58.00

t°	c_p	t°	c_p	t°	c_p
Series V		Series VI		Series VIII	
C. II − 10.21	37.79	C. III 9.44	31.99	C. III 7.24	219.87
− 4.08	39.99	11.96	32.63	8.39	56.91
+ 2.92	42.76	14.45	32.74	10.41	32.41
7.60	44.38	16.99	33.51	11.27	32.00
9.84	45.95	19.51	35.15	13.87	32.58
12.00	47.37	22.64	79.38	17.04	33.88
13.91	48.92			19.99	35.87
15.56	51.01	Serie VII		−	−
16.94	51.63				
+ 17.86	53.03	C. I 9.99	32.77	−	−
−	−	12.29	33.15	−	−
−	−	14.67	33.46	−	−
−	−	17.07	34.20	−	−
−	−	19.48	35.28	−	−
−	−	21.92	40.30	−	−

Latent heat of vaporization: BEYNON and MCKETTA (1963)

t°	cal/mol
57.00	10147.3
66.50	9869.5
72.50	9660.5
75.50	9566.8
82.50	9327.6

Heat of melting: 1602.0 cal/mol OETTING (1963)

VALERIC ALDEHYDE $C_5H_{10}O$

SIMON (1929)

Boiling point: 103.7°

Melting point: − 91.5°

Refractive index and dn/dt

t°	He_r	H_α	Na_D	He_y	He_{gr}	H_β	He_v	H_γ
15	1.40552	1.40586	1.40800	1.40810	1.41209	1.41316	1.41615	1.41745
25	1.39981	1.40017	1.40233	1.40243	1.40638	1.40742	1.41035	1.41163
dn/dt	0.000571	0.000569	0.000567	0.000567	0.000571	0.000577	0.000580	0.000582

CARBON MONOXIDE CO

BARUA, AFZAL, FLYNN and ROSS (1964)

Density and Viscosity

t°	P atm.	d	η	t°	P atm.	d	η
− 50.00	13.48	0.02101	142.45	+ 25.00	25.43	0.02932	180.97
	25.00	0.03962	144.61		54.32	0.06283	186.81
	50.00	0.08217	152.77		87.30	0.10082	194.63
	75.00	0.12716	164.20		115.72	0.13276	202.53
	89.21	0.15310	172.60		150.33	0.17007	214.25
	100.00	0.17231	178.28		174.00	0.19433	223.26
− 25.00	12.86	0.01791	155.67	+ 75.00	29.97	0.02931	203.89
	25.00	0.03519	157.99		60.54	0.05887	208.55
	50.00	0.07143	163.12		90.06	0.08685	216.08
	75.00	0.10877	172.35		122.77	0.11691	224.20
	88.49	0.12883	177.69		152.95	0.14356	230.82
	100.00	0.14584	182.04		174.00	0.16148	236.39
0.00	17.38	0.02193	167.85				
	32.84	0.04176	170.73				
	53.14	0.06805	175.14				
	83.20	0.10713	184.19				
	103.23	0.13276	191.59				

CITRIC ACID MONOHYDRATE $C_6H_8O_7 \cdot H_2O$

EVANS, HOARE and MELIA (1962)

Heat capacity

t°	cal/g	t°	cal/g	t°	cal/g	t°	cal/g
Series 1		Series 2		Series 4		Series 6	
− 206.08	0.08863	− 74.67	0.2163	+ 7.57	1.210	− 251.27	0.0176
199.28	0.09811	68.35	0.2218	14.18	1.234	248.81	0.0221
191.74	0.1073	58.55	0.2294	+ 20.78	1.260	246.63	0.0259
183.04	0.1175	46.65	0.2391			244.67	0.0295
172.86	0.1262	35.17	0.2401	Series 5		242.39	0.0329
161.40	0.1389	24.62	0.2610			239.81	0.0374
149.59	0.1500	14.47	0.2694	− 207.17	0.0881	237.13	0.0396
137.86	0.1604	− 4.03	0.2789	197.58	0.1008	232.93	0.0413
126.95	0.1697			188.99	0.1117	227.39	0.0482
115.96	0.1784	Series 3		181.22	0.1204	222.00	0.0571
104.30	0.1884			170.65	0.1294	216.04	0.0657
91.82	0.1976	− 77.03	0.2124	157.64	0.1420	209.90	0.0840
− 79.25	0.2101	72.91	0.2163	145.62	0.1521	203.59	0.0931
		67.31	0.2217	134.35	0.1626	− 196.99	0.1016
		59.56	0.2304	123.67	0.1714		
		49.70	0.2401	− 112.35	0.1814		
		40.04	0.2462				
		30.63	0.2545				
		21.47	0.2631				
		12.57	0.2710				
		− 4.71	0.2782				

m-ETHYLPHENOL   C$_8$H$_{10}$O

BIDDISCOMBE, HANDLEY, HARROP, HEAD, LEWIS, MARTIN and SPRAKE (1963)

Vapour pressure

t°	p mm	t°	p mm	t°	p mm
4.96	0.0071	15.06	0.0197	25.05	0.0503
10.06	0.0116	20.05	0.0326	30.00	0.0811
172.071	199.14	194.711	400.23	209.302	599.72
178.846	247.81	198.819	449.98	212.412	651.09
184.980	299.82	202.582	499.82	215.101	698.21
190.094	349.68	206.047	549.53	217.955	751.15
35.06	0.123	44.98	0.282		
40.02	0.194	49.98	0.424		
220.520	801.37	229.592	1000.69		
222.970	851.82	—	—		
225.213	900.11	—	—		
227.399	949.31	—	—		

Density

t°	g/ml
20	1.01143
25	1.00758
30	1.00374

Heat of combustion at 25°: 35671.9 j/g (= 8525.6 cal/g)

o-ETHYLPHENOL   C$_8$H$_{10}$O

BIDDISCOMBE, HANDLEY, HARROP, HEAD, LEWIS, MARTIN and SPRAKE (1963)

Vapour pressure

t°	p mm	t°	p mm	t°	p mm
4.98	0.0251	15.01	0.0657	24.93	0.153
10.00	0.0388	20.01	0.103	29.53	0.231
150.425	153.45	176.74	349.73	192.115	549.31
158.137	199.08	180.808	400.46	195.266	597.82
164.876	247.49	184.869	449.63	198.382	649.01
171.143	300.67	188.565	498.49	200.845	691.87
34.84	0.344	45.00	0.772		
39.99	0.555	212.651	929.64		
204.350	756.71	215.149	987.39		
206.632	801.55	218.047	1057.81		
208.429	838.22	—	—		
209.854	868.29	—	—		

Density

t°	g/ml
20	1.01885 ± 0.00001
25	1.01459
30	1.01033 ± 0.00001

Heat of combustion at 25°: 35716.4 j/g (= 8536.1 cal/g)

p-ETHYLPHENOL $C_8H_{10}O$

BIDDISCOMBE, HANDLEY, HARROP, HEAD, LEWIS, MARTIN and SPRAKE (1963)

Vapour pressure

		Solid			
t°	p mm	t°	p mm	t°	p mm
5.00	0.0036	15.00	0.0121	25.03	0.0372
10.00	0.0068	19.99	0.0211	30.02	0.0632
35.00	0.107	43.97	0.256	—	—
39.99	0.175	—	—	—	—

		Liquid			
171.757	199.30	194.356	400.65	208.892	599.89
178.525	248.04	198.419	450.03	211.911	649.75
184.585	299.59	202.227	500.56	214.673	698.23
189.724	349.80	205.607	549.13	217.535	751.37
220.026	800.19	229.147	1000.72		
222.543	852.06	—	—		
224.769	900.04	—	—		
226.933	948.71	—	—		

Density at 25°: 1.054

Heat of combustion at 25°: 35589.0 j/g ($= 8505.8$ cal/g)

CAPROPHENONE $C_{12}H_{16}O$

SIMON (1929)

Boiling point: 265.2°   *Melting point:* 24.7°

Density and *Viscosity*

t°	d	$\eta \cdot 10^5$
25	0.95761	3207
30	0.95306	2906

Refractive index

t°	He$_r$	H$_\alpha$	Na$_D$	He$_y$	He$_{gr}$	H$_\beta$	He$_v$	H$_\gamma$
25°	1.49755	1.49812	1.50272	1.50277	1.51130	1.51340	1.51960	1.52230
30°	1.49556	1.49614	1.50066	1.50076	1.50926	1.51134	1.51752	1.52024
dn/dt	0.000398	0.000396	0.000412	0.000402	0.000408	0.000412	0.000416	0.000412

BENZOIC ACID $\qquad$ $C_7H_6O_2$

KOLESOV, SEREGIN and SKURATOV (1962)

Specific heat (cal/mol)

$t°$	c_p	$t°$	c_p	$t°$	c_p
− 251	3.150	− 188	13.83	− 68	24.96
249	3.674	183	14.31	63	25.47
247	4.200	178	14.78	58	25.99
245	4.720	173	15.24	53	26.52
243	5.230	168	15.70	48	27.04
241	5.727	163	16.15	43	27.57
239	6.207	158	16.61	38	28.10
237	6.667	153	17.06	33	28.63
235	7.108	148	17.50	28	29.17
233	7.530	143	17.95	23	29.70
231	7.934	138	18.39	18	30.24
229	8.321	133	18.84	13	30.78
227	8.692	128	19.28	08	31.33
225	9.047	123	19.73	− 03	31.87
223	9.387	118	20.18	+ 02	32.42
221	9.713	113	20.63	07	32.97
219	10.03	108	21.08	12	33.52
217	10.33	103	21.54	17	34.07
215	10.62	98	22.01	22	34.62
213	10.89	93	22.48	25	34.97
208	11.58	88	22.96	27	35.17
203	12.21	83	23.45	32	35.72
198	12.79	78	23.95	+ 37	36.27
− 193	13.33	− 73	24.45	−	−

SUCCINONITRILE $C_4H_4N_2$

WULFF and WESTRUM JR. (1963)

Heat capacity (cal/mol)

$t°$	c_p	$t°$	c_p	$t°$	c_p
Series I		Series II		Series III	
− 85.22	22.80	− 151.39	17.25	− 117.93	20.05
76.74	23.48	144.80	17.82	109.25	20.76
− 67.69	24.37	136.65	18.51	100.73	21.48
—	—	128.32	19.20	− 92.40	22.18
—	—	− 120.13	19.82	—	—
Series IV					
− 67.41	24.40	− 23.64	32.62	+ 13.21	34.16
58.08	25.32	14.71	32.97	22.67	34.64
48.80	26.22	− 5.37	33.35	+ 31.26	35.15
− 31.77	32.40	+ 3.97	33.74	—	—
Series V					
30.82	35.12	55.64	94.9	65.65	38.48
40.05	35.71	57.72	1320	70.03	38.56
49.34	36.38	62.17	126	74.48	38.73
Series VII					
− 268.15	0.026	− 256.93	1.398	− 226.06	8.439
267.73	0.053	255.14	1.780	222.30	9.123
267.15	0.067	253.06	2.253	218.04	9.837
266.35	0.097	250.64	2.837	212.97	10.64
265.56	0.16	247.92	3.515	204.32	11.47
264.48	0.26	245.00	4.241	200.59	12.33
263.49	0.36	242.42	4.883	193.51	13.19
262.44	0.48	239.64	5.558	186.63	13.99
261.34	0.621	236.00	6.396	− 179.54	14.70
259.99	0.821	231.81	7.294	—	—
− 258.55	1.081	− 227.02	8.251	—	—
Series VIII		Series IX		Series XI	
− 17.631	15.01	+ 67.99	38.56	− 111.79	20.56
169.22	15.66	Series X		103.51	21.26
162.39	16.28			94.71	21.97
− 155.31	16.91	− 45.33	26.53	− 85.41	22.81
—	—	43.45	26.74	—	—
—	—	− 37.20	32.28	—	—

t°	c_p	t°	c_p	t°	c_p	t°	c_p
Series XII		Transition runs A		Transition runs H		Melting runs J	
+ 53.27	36.94	− 42.094	62.0	− 41.790	27.06	57.12	237
55.17	40.05	39.937	2710	40.704	37.19	57.52	680
56.45	71.50	39.876	3580	40.142	639	57.68	1400
60.90	38.32	39.847	4820	39.927	3520	57.77	2300
64.29	38.40	39.805	2850	39.870	16100	57.82	4150
67.67	38.55	− 36.763	61.0	39.841	12700	58.52	133
71.04	38.67	—	—	− 39.105	212	—	—
+ 74.40	38.75	—	—	—	—	—	—

2-METHYLPYRIDINE C₆H₇N
or a-PICOLINE

Scott, Hubbard, Messerly, Todd, Hossenlopp, Good, Douslin and McCullough (1963)

Freezing point: − 66.739°

Vapour pressure

t°	p	t°	p	t°	p	p
79.794	149.41	110.472	433.56	142.207	1074.6	
85.853	187.57	116.736	525.86	148.683	1268.0	
91.942	233.72	123.038	633.99	155.201	1489.1	
98.074	289.13	129.387	760.00	161.761	1740.8	
104.252	355.22	135.773	906.06	168.356	2026.0	

Heat capacity

t°	cal/mol	t°	cal/mol	t°	cal/mol
Vapour					
115.10	31.02	195.05	36.76	—	—
140.05	32.91	227.05	38.84	—	—
165.05	34.72	—	—	—	—
Liquid					
− 63.25	33.881	− 12.51	35.776	+ 54.69	38.725
61.18	33.911	− 2.17	36.321	65.22	40.413
57.63	34.017	+ 8.04	36.883	75.60	41.089
52.06	34.159	18.09	37.456	85.80	41.828
42.12	34.487	27.01	38.051	+ 95.86	42.442
32.28	34.881	33.09	38.363	—	—
− 22.56	35.294	+ 43.98	39.043	—	—
Crystals					
− 260.78	0.810	− 239.51	5.623	− 165.38	15.769
260.50	0.873	235.95	6.403	162.61	16.005
260.37	1.070	231.99	7.208	159.25	16.289
259.11	1.132	227.86	7.988	153.26	16.785
257.95	1.347	223.26	8.809	146.97	17.301
257.75	1.394	218.18	9.652	145.61	17.399
256.63	1.619	217.64	9.740	140.37	17.814
256.18	1.722	212.72	10.503	138.25	17.973
255.04	1.972	212.23	10.579	131.08	18.512
254.28	2.144	206.77	11.350	124.10	19.074
253.05	2.424	201.13	12.053	117.30	19.601
252.29	2.592	195.31	12.751	110.66	20.110
250.91	2.928	189.43	13.459	107.93	20.323
250.30	3.071	186.20	13.829	104.16	20.622
248.59	3.493	183.47	14.099	101.38	20.844
248.21	3.584	180.39	14.393	101.38	20.855
245.81	4.132	177.77	14.647	94.94	21.371
245.79	4.133	174.80	14.913	92.90	21.580
243.26	4.759	171.74	15.191	88.63	21.920
− 242.77	4.875	− 168.87	15.459	− 84.59	22.335

Heat of combustion at 25°: —8764.45 cal/mol

3-AZABICYCLO[3,2,2]NONANE $C_8H_{15}N$

BARBER and WESTRUM JR. (1963)

Heat capacity (cal/mol)

t°	c_p	t°	c_p	t°	c_p
Series I		Series II		Series V	
− 19.87	36.04	+ 34.15	56.83	− 6.87	38.43
− 11.06	37.78	53.32	56.55	+ 1.79	40.32
− 2.23	39.38	62.67	56.48	−	−
+ 6.62	41.41	+ 72.22	56.57	−	−
Series III					
− 267.95	0.036	− 258.47	1.505	− 231.16	8.909
267.42	0.052	256.08	1.950	226.80	9.648
266.97	0.070	255.47	2.396	222.33	10.329
266.48	0.091	254.05	2.845	217.76	10.950
265.82	0.140	252.40	3.378	212.95	11.594
265.01	0.215	250.31	4.059	207.79	12.232
264.13	0.330	247.90	4.818	202.56	12.803
263.20	0.478	245.46	5.559	197.09	13.415
262.16	0.645	242.86	6.281	− 191.09	14.122
261.95	0.868	239.56	7.143	−	−
− 259.84	1.143	− 235.51	8.066		−
Series IV					
− 196.75	13.442	− 130.27	20.73	− 59.23	29.68
189.23	14.343	121.36	21.75	50.06	31.05
181.94	15.14	112.27	22.81	40.86	32.51
173.88	15.96	103.51	23.85	31.87	34.03
165.15	16.90	94.82	24.91	24.49	35.25
156.43	17.87	86.12	25.98	47.21	36.51
147.58	18.79	77.30	27.15	− 3.99	38.99
− 138.92	19.78	− 68.27	28.39	−	−

1,4-DIAZABICYCLO[2,2,2]OCTANE $C_6H_{12}N_2$
or TRIETHYLENEDIAMINE

TROWBRIDGE and WESTRUM JR. (1963)

Heat capacity (cal/mol)

$t°$	c_p	$t°$	c_p	$t°$	c_p
Series I		Series II			
29.28	37.06	46.88	40.09	133.88	54.83
34.51	38.74	53.48	41.62	143.19	55.81
48.19	40.65	61.21	43.62	150.46	56.33
57.95	42.86	68.49	45.64	155.51	56.56
67.64	45.50	74.45	47.83	156.45	56.96
				157.39	56.76
Transition runs A		Transition runs B		158.49	57.91
				159.29	64.55
85.36	50.58	82.14	50.16		
95.59	51.46	85.15	50.31	Fusion runs D		
105.82	52.23	86.40	50.40		
116.27	53.16	90.82	51.00	161.44	57.37
126.87	54.20	99.30	51.67	163.10	57.24
137.49	55.19	108.03	52.46	165.79	57.78
148.13	56.35	116.19	53.19	—	—
154.47	57.51	124.50	53.95	—	—
Series III		Series IV		Series VI	
71.61	46.38	26.74	36.44	160.51	57.23
74.94	47.74	30.18	37.14	161.04	57.26
76.79	47.88	34.94	37.94	161.39	57.26
		38.28	38.66	161.92	57.47
Series V		46.18	40.23	165.06	57.70
		55.41	42.09	168.76	57.96
80.87	49.86	65.03	44.82	170.65	58.19
84.34	50.54			172.68	58.36
92.65	51.26			174.86	58.64
103.68	52.20			—	—
—	—			—	—

L-ARGININE.HCl $C_6H_{15}O_2N_4Cl$

COLE, HUTCHENS and STOUT (1963)

Heat capacity (cal/mol)

$t°$	c_p	$t°$	c_p	$t°$	c_p
+ 25.61	62.70	− 226.81	12.60	− 74.25	45.44
+ 24.52	62.31	222.44	14.15	68.18	46.44
− 220.15	14.93	193.35	22.72	62.17	47.51
214.26	16.86	188.84	23.94	55.80	48.55
209.04	18.49	183.85	25.11	52.47	49.09
203.38	20.12	178.39	26.31	46.40	50.18
197.86	21.56	172.89	27.44	40.42	51.22
192.48	22.99	167.37	28.60	38.19	51.57
262.24	0.716	161.91	29.72	32.62	52.47
261.21	0.879	157.24	30.63	26.61	53.57
260.14	1.101	151.55	31.72	20.62	54.50
258.96	1.358	145.97	32.75	14.27	55.68
257.11	1.809	140.18	33.88	7.94	56.78
255.43	2.266	134.50	34.94	− 1.55	57.93
253.57	2.800	129.01	35.92	+ 5.17	59.06
251.74	3.368	123.33	36.92	11.30	60.07
249.67	4.066	115.12	38.39	17.51	61.12
247.21	4.932	109.57	39.36	24.17	62.26
244.24	5.988	103.68	40.39	+ 31.01	63.36
241.23	7.164	97.79	41.46	− 3.00	57.40
238.04	8.395	91.83	42.46	+ 3.02	58.33
234.63	9.691	85.57	43.48	+ 11.30	60.35
− 230.88	11.09	− 80.12	44.47	+ 18.54	61.61

L-HISTIDINE.HCl $C_6H_{10}O_2N_3Cl$

COLE, HUTCHENS and STOUT (1963)

Heat capacity (cal/mol)

t°	c_p	t°	c_p	t°	c_p
+ 28.51	60.95	− 103.36	38.62	− 261.76	0.615
− 215.30	16.37	97.59	39.59	260.76	0.758
209.98	17.94	91.76	40.51	259.54	1.031
204.49	19.44	86.28	41.30	258.14	1.361
198.81	20.86	80.38	42.32	256.61	1.783
193.65	22.13	74.39	43.26	254.93	2.286
188.89	23.29	68.55	44.24	252.98	2.907
183.61	24.48	62.91	45.13	250.77	3.667
178.48	25.49	52.22	46.90	248.37	4.498
173.12	26.54	46.25	47.83	245.93	5.451
167.58	27.59	40.03	48.75	243.28	6.477
161.98	28.66	33.78	49.82	240.30	7.637
156.27	29.70	27.37	51.07	236.90	8.938
152.30	30.39	21.73	51.76	233.07	10.38
146.63	31.36	15.05	52.93	228.84	11.91
141.01	32.39	8.43	54.14	224.25	13.53
135.41	33.34	− 2.02	55.21	219.06	15.20
129.81	34.23	+ 4.55	56.17	205.90	54.25
124.26	35.17	11.09	57.27	200.45	55.34
120.23	35.83	17.74	58.37	193.71	56.33
114.55	37.01	24.71	59.68	− 187.18	57.53
− 109.01	37.68	+ 32.14	60.69	—	—

L-LYSINE.HCl $C_6H_{15}O_2N_2Cl$

Cole, Hutchens and Stout (1963)

Heat capacity (cal/mol)

$t°$	c_p	$t°$	c_p	$t°$	c_p
+ 26.53	57.50	− 109.41	36.31	+ 25.17	57.08
− 221.59	13.36	106.31	36.76	+ 31.99	58.41
216.87	14.76	100.58	37.63	− 262.33	0.729
211.45	16.34	94.77	38.52	261.43	0.855
206.15	17.78	89.21	39.32	260.39	1.076
201.01	19.08	83.65	40.10	259.22	1.332
196.23	20.26	78.04	40.94	257.90	1.637
191.88	21.36	72.18	41.78	256.44	2.008
187.49	22.44	68.28	42.32	254.67	2.486
182.44	23.53	62.67	43.20	252.76	3.036
177.27	24.56	56.86	44.02	250.62	3.699
171.95	25.65	50.06	45.06	248.25	4.467
166.55	26.71	43.48	46.42	245.79	5.286
161.11	27.76	37.85	46.89	243.12	6.196
155.64	28.78	32.03	47.80	240.08	7.254
154.10	29.04	28.63	48.29	236.61	8.436
148.63	30.00	22.92	49.33	232.73	9.719
143.12	30.92	17.08	50.23	228.69	11.04
137.74	31.85	11.12	51.07	224.50	12.38
132.10	32.76	− 5.09	52.09	7.73	51.63
126.49	33.65	+ 0.87	53.02	− 2.62	52.49
120.99	34.52	6.89	53.98	+ 3.34	53.84
− 115.23	35.41	12.90	55.00	+ 10.98	54.65
		+ 18.80	56.00		

L-PHENYLALANINE $C_9H_{11}O_2N$

COLE, HUTCHENS and STOUT (1963)

Heat capacity (cal/mol)

t°	c_p	t°	c_p	t°	c_p
+ 21.38	49.26	− 115.28	27.46	+ 0.42	45.02
− 219.02	11.47	110.24	28.17	6.05	45.54
214.13	12.47	104.91	28.88	11.91	46.45
209.06	13.44	99.63	29.69	17.95	47.42
203.85	14.40	94.54	30.40	23.78	48.30
198.48	15.30	89.11	31.02	+ 29.53	49.17
193.58	16.18	83.71	31.90	− 261.84	0.845
188.95	16.96	78.24	32.73	260.33	1.120
184.30	17.67	73.49	33.38	258.69	1.483
179.25	18.44	67.83	34.18	257.17	1.823
174.19	19.15	62.19	35.02	254.53	2.487
168.88	19.95	56.41	35.82	251.38	3.312
163.30	20.74	50.46	36.64	248.12	4.154
157.82	21.53	45.27	37.59	244.39	5.189
152.35	22.29	39.59	38.44	240.80	6.193
147.01	22.98	33.88	39.28	236.70	7.300
141.79	23.74	28.07	40.27	232.23	8.440
136.50	24.50	22.27	41.11	227.34	9.616
131.20	25.22	16.80	41.92	− 221.95	10.83
125.90	25.92	11.03	42.89	—	—
− 120.61	26.67	− 5.50	43.74	—	—

L-PROLINE $C_5H_9O_2N$

COLE, HUTCHENS and STOUT (1963)

Heat capacity (cal/mol)

$t°$	c_p	$t°$	c_p	$t°$	c_p
+ 29.33	36.58	− 125.69	20.04	+ 11.36	34.47
− 220.19	8.970	119.71	20.68	+ 19.27	35.46
215.27	9.801	113.68	21.34	+ 28.37	36.66
209.57	10.70	107.47	21.96	− 261.75	0.457
203.90	11.51	100.90	22.69	261.01	0.545
198.37	12.24	94.18	23.40	259.72	0.726
192.97	12.96	87.31	24.15	258.28	0.960
188.09	13.56	80.29	24.90	256.51	1.286
182.68	14.18	73.76	25.60	254.45	1.713
177.09	14.79	66.92	26.26	251.94	2.252
171.40	15.37	59.90	27.02	248.80	2.968
165.63	15.96	52.70	27.79	245.88	3.632
161.37	16.40	45.86	28.54	242.88	4.330
155.60	16.99	38.33	29.29	239.58	5.088
149.84	17.59	30.49	30.06	235.97	5.894
144.10	18.14	22.71	30.96	231.91	6.750
138.10	18.79	14.86	31.78	227.36	7.666
− 131.65	19.42	− 7.02	32.64	− 222.55	8.572
		+ 1.77	33.56		

L-TRYPTOPHAN $\qquad$ $C_{11}H_{12}O_2N_2$

Cole, Hutchens and Stout (1963)

Heat capacity (cal/mol)

$t°$	c_p	$t°$	c_p	$t°$	c_p
− 261.30	1.505	− 193.97	18.21	− 85.32	36.90
260.30	1.778	189.31	19.14	79.93	37.93
258.97	2.144	185.25	19.82	73.99	38.95
257.64	2.565	180.32	20.73	68.19	39.90
256.23	2.982	175.30	21.57	62.63	40.91
254.76	3.444	170.35	22.50	57.09	41.90
253.20	3.932	165.10	23.32	51.20	43.01
251.46	4.444	159.67	24.27	45.61	43.89
249.46	5.100	154.38	25.15	40.21	44.91
247.14	5.816	149.20	25.97	34.53	45.92
244.39	6.614	145.39	26.65	29.13	47.03
239.97	7.930	140.15	27.54	23.41	47.91
236.83	8.820	134.79	28.48	17.64	49.15
233.04	9.770	129.39	29.43	11.98	50.08
228.93	10.79	123.98	30.26	6.19	51.14
224.38	11.92	118.56	31.25	− 1.08	52.17
219.83	12.94	112.81	32.20	+ 4.60	53.14
214.66	14.07	107.59	33.13	10.20	54.13
209.23	15.24	102.14	34.05	15.98	55.17
203.99	16.27	96.48	34.98	21.45	56.28
− 199.03	17.22	− 91.05	35.97	+ 27.41	57.36

L-TYROSINE $C_9H_{11}O_3N$

COLE, HUTCHENS and STOUT (1963)

Heat capacity (cal/mol)

$t°$	c_p	$t°$	c_p	$t°$	c_p
+ 28.76	55.31	− 116.45	28.68	+ 14.84	50.05
− 218.11	10.88	113.75	29.10	+ 22.17	51.19
212.93	12.07	107.97	30.05	+ 29.89	52.59
207.61	13.22	102.41	30.95	− 261.99	0.454
202.58	14.23	96.64	31.90	260.93	0.559
197.83	15.18	90.78	32.79	259.47	0.740
193.02	16.11	84.80	33.75	257.87	0.978
187.99	17.10	78.31	34.80	255.92	1.306
182.80	18.02	72.33	35.76	253.87	1.696
179.63	18.54	65.97	36.79	251.50	2.206
174.34	19.38	59.53	37.84	248.92	2.813
169.15	20.23	53.17	38.93	246.16	3.515
163.70	21.15	42.69	40.57	243.05	4.351
158.37	22.02	36.02	41.68	239.89	5.225
153.14	22.85	29.67	42.62	236.66	6.128
147.73	23.68	23.37	43.70	233.15	7.070
144.10	24.23	19.48	44.40	229.10	8.155
138.49	25.17	12.67	45.48	224.52	9.366
132.81	26.07	− 5.87	46.62	− 219.69	10.53
127.43	26.93	+ 1.00	47.87	−	−
− 122.00	27.76	+ 7.95	48.97	−	−

PERFLUOROPIPERIDINE $C_5F_{11}N$

GOOD, TODD, MESSERLY, LACINA, DAWSON, SCOTT and McCULLOUGH (1963)

Vapour pressure

$t°$	p mm
29.138	355.22
34.191	433.56
39.290	525.86
44.421	633.99
54.847	906.06
60.117	1074.6
65.437	1268.0
70.798	1489.1
76.201	1740.8
81.646	2026.0

Melting point: − 0.1679°

Heat capacity (cal/mol)

t°	c_p	t°	c_p	t°	c_p
C.III − 261.33	2.758	− 238.94	11.397	− 159.18	31.550
− 261.23	2.807	236.15	12.155	153.27	32.997
260.27	3.274	235.03	12.448	147.18	34.472
260.24	3.272	231.13	13.419.	140.99	35.964
258.93	3.944	230.98	13.469	135.76	37.186
258.85	4.000	226.60	14.493	135.07	37.377
257.42	4.697	225.72	14.728	134.47	37.535
257.13	4.836	221.66	15.721	130.05	38.586
255.72	5.509	218.44	16.510	129.25	38.800
255.25	5.727	213.31	17.799	128.27	39.068
253.82	6.361	208.12	19.122	− 122.75	40.739
253.21	6.613	202.75	20.450		
251.58	7.269	197.26	21.844		
250.96	7.515	191.69	23.322	C.II −110.39	50.332
249.05	8.259	187.25	24.530	109.08	50.603
248.38	8.522	186.03	24.844	108.18	50.857
246.39	9.172	182.67	25.699	107.48	50.835
245.50	9.474	177.12	27.071	105.95	51.217
243.46	10.085	171.33	28.548	105.30	51.303
242.41	10.409	− 165.25	30.029	− 104.61	51.403
− 240.20	11.048				

C. I − 92.86	49.969	L. 6.18	58.679
91.70	50.116	11.65	69.337
87.18	50.617	13.23	69.550
81.11	51.320	18.51	70.170
80.03	51.405	20.65	70.441
73.95	52.158	28.85	71.385
67.49	52.927	34.04	72.018
61.18	53.682	36.61	72.303
54.63	54.479	39.00	72.622
47.62	55.337	40.80	72.812
40.71	56.189	45.82	73.429
39.49	56.341	—	—
33.90	57.044	—	—
31.63	57.329	—	—
23.43	58.394	—	—
16.79	59.343	—	—
− 10.31	62.253	—	—

1,2-BIS(DIFLUOROAMINO)-4-METHYLPENTANE $C_6H_{12}F_4N_2$

GOOD, DOUSLIN and McCULLOUGH (1963)

Vapour pressure

t°	p mm
− 20.00	0.236
15.000	0.364
10.000	0.560
− 5.000	0.843
0.000	1.235
+ 5.000	1.743
10.000	2.466
15.000	3.478
20.000	4.812

REFERENCES

ADCOCK, D. S. and M. L. McGLASHAN, *Proc. Roy. Soc. (London)*, A226 (1954) 266.

ALBRIGHT, L. F. and J. J. MARTIN, *Ind. Eng. Chem.*, 44 (1952) 188.

ALTSHULLER, A. P., *J. Phys. Chem.*, 58 (1954) 392.

ALTSHULLER, A. P. and L. ROSENBLUM, *J. Am. Chem. Soc.*, 77 (1955) 272.

AMBROSE, D., *Trans. Faraday Soc.*, 52 (1956) 772.

AMBROSE, D., J. D. COX and R. TOWNSEND, *Trans. Faraday Soc.*, 56 (1960) 1452.

AMBROSE, D. and D. G. GRANT, *Trans. Faraday Soc.*, 53 (1957) 771.

AMBROSE, D. and R. TOWNSEND, *J. Chem. Soc.*, (1963) 3614.

ANDERSON, D. G., J. C. SMITH and R. J. RALLINGS, *J. Chem. Soc.*, (1953) 443.

ANDON, R. J. L., D. P. BIDDISCOMBE, J. D. COX, R. HANDLEY, D. HARROP, E. F. G. HERINGTON and J. F. MARTIN, *J. Chem. Soc.*, (1960) 5246.

ANDON, R. J. L., J. D. COX, E. F. G. HERINGTON and J. F. MARTIN, *Trans. Faraday Soc.*, 53 (1957) 1074.

ARMSTRONG, G. T., F. G. BRICKWEDDE and R. B. SCOTT, *J. Chem. Phys.*, 21 (1953) 1297.

ARNDT, R., H. H. GÜNTHARD and T. GÄUMANN, *Helv. Chim. Acta*, 41 (1958) 2213.

ASHTON, H. M. and E. S. HALBERSTADT, *Proc. Roy. Soc. (London)*, A245 (1958) 373.

ASTON, J. G., S. V. R. MASTRANGELO and G. W. MOESSEN, *J. Am. Chem. Soc.*, 72 (1950) 5287.

ASTON, J. G., P. E. WILLS and T. P. ZOLKI, *J. Am. Chem. Soc.*, 77 (1955) 3939.

ASTON, J. G., J. L. WOOD and T. P. ZOLKI, *J. Am. Chem. Soc.*, 75 (1953) 6202.

ASTON, J. G., T. P. ZOLKI and J. L. WOOD, *J. Am. Chem. Soc.*, 77 (1955) 281.

B. E., see TIMMERMANS and HENNAUT-ROLAND.

BARBER, C. M. and E. F. WESTRUM JR., *J. Phys. Chem.*, 67 (1963) 2373.

BARKER, J. A., I. BROWN and F. SMITH, *Discussions Faraday Soc.*, No. 15 (1953) 142.

BARROW, G. M., *J. Am. Chem. Soc.*, 73 (1951) 1824.

BARROW, G. M. and A. L. McCLELLAN, *J. Am. Chem. Soc.*, 73 (1951) 573.

BARTHOLOMÉ, E., G. DRIKOS and A. EUCKEN, *Z. Physik. Chem.*, B39 (1938) 371.

BARUA, A. K., M. AFZAL, C. P. FLYNN and J. ROSS, *J. Chem. Phys.*, 41 (1964) 374.

BATUECAS, T. and C. G. LOSA, *Anales Real Soc. Espan. Fis. Quim.*, Ser. B 50 (1954) 845.

BATUECAS, T. and G. G. MALDE, *Anales Real Soc. Espan. Fis. Quim.*, Ser. B 49 (1953) 405.

BEATTIE, J. A., D. R. DOUSLIN and S. W. LEVINE, *J. Chem. Phys.*, 19 (1951) 948; 20 (1952) 1619.

BEATTIE, J. A., S. W. LEVINE and D. R. DOUSLIN, *J. Am. Chem. Soc.*, 73 (1951) 4431; 74 (1952) 4778.

BEATTIE, J. A. and S. MARPLE JR., *J. Am. Chem. Soc.*, 72 (1950) 1449, 4143.

BENDER, P., G. T. FURUKAWA and J. R. HYNDMAN, *Ind. Eng. Chem.*, 44 (1952) 387.

BENOLIEL, *Thesis*, Penn. State Coll. (1941).

BERG, W. T., D. W. SCOTT, W. N. HUBBARD, S. S. TODD, J. F. MESSERLY, I. A. HOSSENLOPP, A. OSBORN, D. R. DOUSLIN and J. P. McCULLOUGH, *J. Phys. Chem.*, 65 (1961) 1425.

BERMAN, N. S. and J. J. McKETTA, *J. Phys. Chem.*, 66 (1962) 1444.

BEYNON JR., E. T. and J. J. McKETTA, *J. Phys. Chem.*, 67 (1963) 2761.

BIDDISCOMBE, D. P., E. A. COULSON, R. HANDLEY and E. F. G. HERINGTON, *J. Chem. Soc.*, (1954) 1957.

BIDDISCOMBE, D. P., R. HANDLEY, D. HARROP, A. J. HEAD, G. B. LEWIS, J. F. MARTIN and C. H. S. SPRAKE, *J. Chem. Soc.*, (1963) 5764.

BIRCH, S. F., R. A. DEAN, F. A. FIDLER and R. A. LOWRY, *J. Am. Chem. Soc.*, 71 (1949) 1362.

BJELLERUP, L., *Acta Chem. Scand.*, 15 (1961) 231.

BONAUGURI, E. and G. C. BERNARDI, *Z. Anal. Chem.*, 162 (1958) 241.

BOOTH, H. S. and W. C. MORRIS, *J. Phys. Chem.*, 62 (1958) 875.

BRADLEY, R. S. and T. G. CLEASBY, *J. Chem. Soc.*, (1953) 1690.

BROWN, O. L. I., H. E. CARY, G. S. SKINNER and E. J. WRIGHT, *J. Phys. Chem.*, 61 (1957) 103.

BROWN, O. L. I. and G. G. MANOV, *J. Am. Chem. Soc.*, 59 (1937) 500.

BROWN, H. C., S. JOHNSON and H. PODALL, *J. Am. Chem. Soc.*, 76 (1954) 5556.

BROWN, I., *Australian J. Sci. Res.*, A 5 (1952) 530.

BROWN, I. and A. H. EWALD, *Australian J. Sci. Res.*, A 3 (1950) 306; A 4 (1951) 198.

BROWN, I. and W. FOCH, *Australian J. Chem.*, 8 (1955) 361.

BROWN, I. and F. SMITH, *Australian J. Chem.*, 8 (1955) 62.

BROWN, J. A. and W. H. MEARS, *J. Phys. Chem.*, 62 (1958) 960.

BROWNE, C. C. and F. D. ROSSINI, *J. Phys. Chem.*, 64 (1960) 927.

BRYCE-SMITH, D. and K. E. HOWLETT, *J. Chem. Soc.*, (1951) 1141.

BUCK, F. R., B. B. ELSNER, T. HENSHALL, T. S. MOORE, A. R. MURRAY, S.H. MORRELL, G. MÜLLER, M. M. T. PLANT, J. C. SMITH and E. R. WALLSGROVE, *J. Inst. Petrol.*, 35 (1949) 631.

BUDDENBERG, J. W. and C. R. WILKE, *J. Phys. Chem.*, 55 (1951) 1491.

BURGER, L. L. and G. H. CADY, *J. Am. Chem. Soc.*, 73 (1951) 4243.

CALINGAERT, G. and H. SOROOS, *J. Am. Chem. Soc.*, 58 (1936) 635.

CAMIN, D. L., A. F. FORZIATI and F. D. ROSSINI, *J. Phys. Chem.*, 58 (1954) 440.

CAMIN, D. L. and F. D. ROSSINI, *J. Phys. Chem.*, 59 (1955) 1173.

CAPKOVA, A. and V. FRIED, *Collection Czech. Chem. Commun.*, 28 (1963) 2235.

CARMICHAEL, L. T., B. H. SAGE and W. N. LACEY, *Ind. Eng. Chem.*, 45 (1953) 2697.

CATHCART, J. A. and D. D. REYNOLDS, *J. Am. Chem. Soc.*, 73 (1951) 3504.

CHANG, S. S. and E. F. WESTRUM JR., *J. Phys. Chem.*, 64 (1960) 1547, 1551; *J. Chem. Phys.*, 36 (1962) 2571.

CHAVANNE, G. and H. VAN RISSEGHEM, *Bull. Soc. Chim. Belges*, 31 (1922) 87.

CHENG, D. C. H., J. C. MCCOUBREY and D. G. PHILLIPS, *Trans. Faraday Soc.*, 58 (1962) 224.

CHIURDOGLU, G., *Bull. Soc. Chim. Belges*, 60 (1951) 39.

CLARK, A. M. and F. DIN, *Trans. Faraday Soc.*, 46 (1950) 901.

CLEMENTS, H. E., K. V. WISE and S. E. J. JOHNSEN, *J. Am. Chem. Soc.*, 75 (1953) 1593.

CLEVER, H. L. and C. C. SNEAD, *J. Phys. Chem.*, 67 (1963) 918.

CLUSIUS, K. and F. KONNERTZ, *Z. Naturforsch.*, 4a (1949) 117.

CLUSIUS, K., U. PIESBERGEN and E. VARDE, *Helv. Chim. Acta*, 43 (1960) 2059.

COATES, J. E. and R. H. DAVIES, *Trans. Faraday Soc.*, (1950) 1194.

COLE, A. G., J. O. HUTCHENS, R. A. ROBIE and J. W. STOUT, *J. Am. Chem. Soc.*, 82 (1960) 4807.

COLE, A. G., J. O. HUTCHENS and J. W. STOUT, *J. Phys. Chem.*, 67 (1963) 1852, 2245.

COLMANT, P., *Bull. Soc. Chim. Belges*, 63 (1954) 5.

CONNOLLY, J. F., *J. Phys. Chem.*, 66 (1962) 1082.

COOK, D., *Can. J. Chem.*, 35 (1957) 268.

COOPS, J., D. MULDER, J. W. DIENSKE and J. SMITTENBERG, *Rec. Trav. Chim.*, 72 (1953) 785.

COPP, J. L., *Trans. Faraday Soc.*, 51 (1955) 1056.

COPP, J. L. and D. H. EVERETT, *Discussions Faraday Soc.*, No. 15 (1953) 174.

COSTELLO, J. M. and S. T. BOWDEN, *Rec. Trav. Chim.*, 77 (1958) 803; 78 (1959) 391.

COULSON, E. A., J. D. COX, E. F. G. HERINGTON and J. F. MARTIN, *J. Chem. Soc.*, (1959) 1934.

COULSON, E. A. and J. IDRIS JONES, *J. Soc. Chem. Ind.*, 65 (1946) 169.

COX, J. D., *J. Chem. Soc.*, (1954) 3183.

COX, J. D., A. R. CHALLONER and A. R. MEETHAM, *J. Chem. Soc.*, (1954) 265.

CROWE, R. W. and C. P. SMYTH, *J. Am. Chem. Soc.*, 72 (1950) 1098, 4009, 4427, 5281.

CROWELL, T. I. and G. L. JONES JR., *J. Phys. Chem.*, 58 (1954) 666.

CRÜTZEN, J. L., W. JOST and L. SIEG, *Z. Elektrochem.*, 61 (1957) 229.

CUMMINGS, G. A. M. and E. MCLAUGHLIN, *J. Chem. Soc.*, (1955) 1391.

CUTLER, W. G., R. H. MCMICKLE, W. WEBB and R. W. SCHIESSLER, *J. Chem. Phys.*, 29 (1958) 727.

DANA, L. I., A. C. JENKINS, J. N. BURDICK and R. C. TIMM, *Refrig. Eng.*, 12 (1926) 387.

DAVIDSON, D. W., *Can. J. Chem.*, 35 (1957) 458.

DAVIES, M. and D. G. JENKIN, *J. Chem. Soc.*, (1954) 2374.

DAVIES, M. and J. G. JONES, *Trans. Faraday Soc.*, 50 (1954) 1042.

DAVIS, H. S. and O. F. WIEDEMAN, *Ind. Eng. Chem.*, 37 (1945) 482.

DAWSON, L. R., T. M. NEWELL and W. J. MCCREARY, *J. Am. Chem. Soc.*, 76 (1954) 6024.

DAWSON, L. R., P. G. SEARS and R. H. GRAVES, *J. Am. Chem. Soc.*, 77 (1955) 1986.

DAY, H. O. and W. A. FELSING, *J. Am. Chem. Soc.*, 72 (1950) 1698.

DEAN, M. R. and J. W. TOOKE, *Ind. Eng. Chem.*, 38 (1946) 389.

DE BROUCKÈRE, L. and A. GILLET, *Bull. Soc. Chim. Belges*, 44 (1935) 473.

DE VRIES, T. and H. SOFFER, *J. Phys. Colloid Chem.*, 55 (1951) 406.

DENISON, J. T. and J. B. RAMSEY, *J. Am. Chem. Soc.*, 77 (1955) 2615.

DENNEY, D. J., *J. Chem. Phys.*, 27 (1957) 259.

DEREPPE, J. M. and M. VAN MEERSSCHE, *Bull. Soc. Chim. Belges*, 69 (1960) 466.

DEVER, D. F., A. FINCH and E. GRUNWALD, *J. Phys. Chem.*, 59 (1955) 668.

DEVINEY, M. L. and W. A. FELSING, *J. Am. Chem. Soc.*, 79 (1957) 4915.

DININNY, R. E. and E. L. PACE, *J. Chem. Phys.*, 32 (1960) 805.

DONALDSON, R. E. and O. R. QUAYLE, *J. Am. Chem. Soc.*, 72 (1950) 35.

DOOLITTLE, A. K. and R. H. PETERSON, *J. Am. Chem. Soc.*, 73 (1951) 2145.

DOUGLAS, T. B., G. T. FURUKAWA, R. E. McCOSKEY and A. F. BALL, *J. Res. Natl. Bur. Std.*, 53 (1954) 139.

DOUSLIN, D. R., R. H. HARRISON, R. T. MOORE and J. P. McCULLOUGH, *J. Chem. Phys.*, 35 (1961) 1357.

DOUSLIN, D. R. and H. M. HUFFMAN, *J. Am. Chem. Soc.*, 68 (1946) 173, 1704.

DOUSLIN, D. R., R. T. MOORE, J. P. DAWSON and G. WADDINGTON, *J. Am. Chem. Soc.*, 80 (1958) 2031.

DOUSLIN, D. R., R. T. MOORE and G. WADDINGTON, *J. Phys. Chem.*, 63 (1959) 1959.

DOW CHEMICAL COMPANY, unpublished (1956).

DREISBACH, R. R. and R. A. MARTIN, *Ind. Eng. Chem.*, 41 (1949) 2875.

DREISBACH, R. R. and S. A. SHRADER, *Ind. Eng. Chem.*, 41 (1949) 2879.

DREYER, R., W. MARTIN and U. VON WEBER, *J. Prakt. Chem.*, 273 (1954/55) 324.

DUNLOP, A. K., *J. Am. Chem. Soc.*, 77 (1955) 2016.

ECCLESTON, B. H., H. J. COLEMAN and N. G. ADAMS, *J. Am. Chem. Soc.*, 72 (1950) 3866.

EDWARDS, G., *Trans. Faraday Soc.*, 46 (1950) 423; 48 (1952) 513.

EUCKEN, A. and W. BERGER, *Z. Ges. Kälte-Ind.*, 41 (1934) 145.

EVANS, E. B., *J. Inst. Petrol.*, 24 (1938) 321.

EVANS, D. M., F. E. HOARE and T. P. MELIA, *Trans. Faraday Soc.*, 58 (1962) 1511.

EVANS, R. F., O. ORMROD, B. B. GOALBY and L. A. K. STAVELEY, *J. Chem. Soc.*, (1950) 3346.

FAIRBROTHER, D. M., H. A. SKINNER and F. W.

EVANS, *Trans. Faraday Soc.*, 53 (1957) 779.

FELDMAN, J., P. PANTAGES and M. ORCHIN, *J. Am. Chem. Soc.*, 73 (1951) 4341.

FINKE, H. L., M. E. GROSS, J. F. MESSERLEY and G. WADDINGTON, *J. Am. Chem. Soc.*, 76 (1954) 854.

FINKE, H. L., M. E. GROSS, G. WADDINGTON and H. M. HUFFMAN, *J. Am. Chem. Soc.*, 76 (1954) 333.

FINKE, H. L., D. W. SCOTT, M. E. GROSS, G. WADDINGTON and H. M. HUFFMAN, *J. Am. Chem. Soc.*, 74 (1952) 2804.

FISCHER, G. and A. S. BUCHANAN, *Australian J. Chem.*, 17 (1964) 481.

FORZIATI, A. F., *J. Res. Natl. Bur. Std.*, 44 (1950) 373.

FORZIATI, A. F., D. I. CAMIN and F. D. ROSSINI, *J. Res. Natl. Bur. Std.*, 45 (1950) 406.

FORZIATI, A. F., A. R. GLASGOW JR., C. B. WILLINGHAM and F. D. ROSSINI, *J. Res. Natl. Bur. Std.*, 36 (1946) 129.

FORZIATI, A. F., W. R. NORRIS and F. D. ROSSINI, *J. Res. Natl. Bur. Std.*, 43 (1949) 555.

FORZIATI, A. F. and F. D. ROSSINI, *J. Res. Natl. Bur. Std.*, 43 (1949) 473.

FOZ, O. R., J. MORCILLO, A. PEREZ MASIÁ and A. MÉNDEZ, *Anales Real Soc. Espan. Fis. Quim. (Madrid)*, 50 B (1954) 23.

FRASER, F. M. and E. J. PROSEN, *J. Res. Natl. Bur. Std.*, 54 (1955) 143.

FRENCH, C. M., *Trans. Faraday Soc.*, 47 (1951) 1056.

FRIED, V., A. CAPKOVA and J. SUSKA, *Collection Czech. Chem. Commun.*, 28 (1963) 3171.

FRIED, V. and J. PICK, *Collection Czech. Chem. Commun.*, 26 (1961) 954.

FUGE, E. T. J., S. T. BOWDEN and W. J. JONES *J. Phys. Chem.*, 56 (1952) 1013.

FURUKAWA, G. T., D. C. GINNINGS, R. E. McCOSKEY and R. A. NELSON, *J. Res. Natl. Bur. Std.*, 46 (1951) 195.

FURUKAWA, G. T., R. E. McCOSKEY and M. L. REILLY, *J. Res. Natl. Bur. Std.*, 52 (1954) 11.

FURUKAWA G. T., R. E. McCOSKEY, M. L. REILLY and A. W. HARMAN, *J. Res. Natl. Bur. Std.*, 55 (1955) 201.

FURUKAWA, G. T. and R. P. PARK, *J. Res. Natl. Bur. Std.*, 55 (1955) 255.

FURUKAWA, G. T., M. L. REILLY, J. H. PICCIRELLI and M. TENENBAUM, *J. Res. Natl. Bur. Std.*, 68A (1964) 367.

GARNER, J. B., L. ADAMS and R. M. STUCHELL, *Petrol. Refiner*, 21 (1942) 321.

GARRETT, A. B. and S. A. WOODRUFF, *J. Phys. Colloid Chem.*, 55 (1951) 477.

GELDOF, H., *Thesis*, Amsterdam (1951).

GEORGE, R. S., *Thesis*, Penn. State Coll. (1940).

GIAUQUE, W. F. and C. J. EGAN, *J. Chem. Phys.*, 5 (1937) 45.

GIAUQUE, W. F. and J. B. OTT, *J. Am. Chem. Soc.*, 82 (1960) 2689.

GLASGOW JR., A. R., N. C. KROUSKOP and F. D. ROSSINI, *Anal. Chem.*, 22 (1950) 1521.

GLASGOW, A. R. and J. TIMMERMANS, *Bull. Soc. Chim. Belges*, 70 (1961) 599, 623.

GLEW, D. N., *Can. J. Chem.*, 38 (1960) 208.

GOIG, S., *Compt. Rend.*, 189 (1929) 246.

GOMEZ-IBANEZ, J. D. and CHIA-TSUN LIU, *J. Phys. Chem.*, 67 (1963) 1388.

GOOD, W. D., D. R. DOUSLIN and J. P. MC CULLOUGH, *J. Phys. Chem.*, 67 (1963) 1312.

GOOD, W. D., J. L. LACINA and J. P. MCCULLOUGH, *J. Phys. Chem.*, 65 (1961) 2229.

GOOD, W. D., S. S. TODD, J. F. MESSERLY, J. L. LACINA, J. P. DAWSON, D. W. SCOTT and J. P. MCCULLOUGH, *J. Phys. Chem.*, 67 (1963) 1306.

GOODMAN, I. A. and P. H. WISE, *Natl. Advisory Comm. Aeronaut. Tech. Note* 2260 (1951).

GRAY, P. and P. L. SMITH, *J. Chem. Soc.*, (1953) 2380.

GREEN, S. J. and R. E. VENER, *Ind. Eng. Chem.*, 47 (1955) 103.

GREENLEE, ?, *Thesis*, Ohio State Univ. (U.S.A.) (1942).

GRIFFITHS, V. S., *J. Chem. Soc.*, (1952) 1326.

GRISWOLD, J., D. ANDRES and V. A. KLEIN, *Trans. Am. Inst. Chem. Engrs.*, 39 (1943) 223.

GROSS, M. E., G. D. OLIVER and H. M. HUFFMAN, *J. Am. Chem. Soc.*, 75 (1953) 2801.

GRUBB, W. T. and R. C. OSTHOFF, *J. Am. Chem. Soc.*, 74 (1952) 2108.

GRUNBERG, L., *Trans. Faraday Soc.*, 50 (1954) 1293.

GUTHRIE, G. B., JR., D. W. SCOTT, W. N. HUBBARD, C. KATZ, J. P. MCCULLOUGH, M. E. GROSS, K. D. WILLIAMSON and G. WADDINGTON, *J. Am. Chem. Soc.*, 74 (1952) 4662.

GUTHRIE, G. B., JR., D. W. SCOTT and G. WADDINGTON, *J. Am. Chem. Soc.*, 74 (1952) 2795.

GUTMANN, V. and K. UTVARY, *Monatsh. Chem.*, 89 (1958) 186.

HAINES, W. E., R. V. HELM, C. W. BAILEY and J. S. BALL, *J. Phys. Chem.*, 58 (1954) 270.

HAMMOND, L. W., K. S. HOWARD and R. A. MCALLISTER, *J. Phys. Chem.*, 62 (1958) 637.

HAMMOND, B. R. and R. H. STOKES, *Trans. Faraday Soc.*, 51 (1955) 1641.

HARDY, R. C., *J. Res. Natl. Bur. Std.*, 61 (1958) 433.

HARRISON, D. and E. A. MOELWYN-HUGHES, *Proc. Roy. Soc.*, A 239 (1957) 230.

HASELDEN, G. G. and P. SNOWDEN, *Trans. Faraday Soc.*, 58 (1962) 1515.

HAWKINS, J. E. and G. T. ARMSTRONG, *J. Am. Chem. Soc.*, 76 (1954) 3756.

HEIL, L. M., *Phys. Rev.*, 39 (1932) 666.

HELM, R. V., W. J. LANUM, G. L. COOK and J. S. BALL, *J. Phys. Chem.*, 62 (1958) 858.

HERINGTON, E. F. G., A. B. DENSHAM and P. J. MALDEN, *J. Chem. Soc.*, (1954) 2643.

HERINGTON, E. F. G. and J. F. MARTIN, *Trans. Faraday Soc.*, 49 (1953) 154.

HESTERMANS, P. and D. WHITE, *J. Phys. Chem.*, 65 (1961) 362.

HESTON JR., W. M. and C. P. SMYTH, *J. Am. Chem. Soc.*, 72 (1950) 99.

HIBBARD, B. B. and F. C. SCHMIDT, *J. Am. Chem. Soc.*, 77 (1955) 225.

HIEBER, W. and A. WOERNER, *Z. Elektrochem.*, 40 (1934) 252.

HILDENBRAND, D. L., W. R. KRAMER and D. R. STULL, *J. Phys. Chem.*, 62 (1958) 958.

HILDENBRAND, D. L., R. A. MCDONALD, W. R. KRAMER and D. R. STULL, *J. Chem. Phys.*, 30 (1959) 930.

HILDENBRAND, D. L., G. C. SINKE, R. A. MCDONALD, W. R. KRAMER and D. R. STULL, *J. Chem. Phys.*, 31 (1959) 650.

HIRAOKA, H. and J. H. HILDEBRAND, *J. Phys. Chem.*, 67 (1963) 916.

HOERR, C. W. and H. J. HARWOOD, *J. Phys. Chem.*, 56 (1952) 1068.

HOFFMAN, J. D. and B. F. DECKER, *J. Phys. Chem.*, 57 (1953) 520.

HOFFMAN, J. D. and C. P. SMYTH, *J. Am. Chem. Soc.*, 72 (1950) 171.

HOPKE, E. R. and G. W. SEARS, *J. Chem. Phys.*, 19 (1951) 1345.

HORYNA, J., *Collection Czech. Chem. Commun.*, 24 (1959) 3253.

HOWARD, F. L., T. W. MEARS, A. FOOKSON, P. POMERANTZ and D. B. BROOKS, *J. Res. Natl. Bur. Std.*, 38 (1947) 365.

HRYNAKOWSKI, K. and M. SZMYT, *Z. Physik. Chem. Leipzig*, A182 (1938) 110.

HRYNAKOWSKI, K. and M. SZMYTOWNA, *Z. Physik. Chem. Leipzig*, A171 (1934) 234.

HUBBARD, W. N., H. L. FINKE, D. W. SCOTT, J. P. MCCULLOUGH, C. KATZ, M. E. GROSS, J. F. MESSERLY, R. E. PENNINGTON and G.

WADDINGTON, *J. Am. Chem. Soc.*, 74 (1952) 6025.

HUBBARD, W. N., F. R. FROW and G. WADDINGTON, *J. Phys. Chem.*, 65 (1961) 1326.

HUBBARD, W. N., J. W. KNOWLTON and H. M. HUFFMAN, *J. Phys. Chem.*, 58 (1954) 396.

HUBBARD, W. N., D. W. SCOTT, F. R. FROW and G. WADDINGTON, *J. Am. Chem. Soc.*, 77 (1955) 5855.

HUBBARD, W. N. and G. WADDINGTON, *Rec. Trav. Chim.*, 73 (1954) 910.

HUET, J., R. PHILIPPE and D. BONO, *Bull. Soc. Chim. Belges*, 62 (1953) 436.

HUFFMAN, H. M., M. EATON and G. D. OLIVER, *J. Am. Chem. Soc.*, 70 (1948) 2911.

HUFFMAN, H. M., M. E. GROSS, D. W. SCOTT and J. P. McCULLOUGH, *J. Phys. Chem.*, 65 (1961) 495.

HUTCHENS, J. O., A. G. COLE and J. W. STOUT, *J. Am. Chem. Soc.*, 82 (1960) 4813.

ISAAC, R., KUN LI and L. N. CANJAR, *Ind. Eng. Chem.*, 46 (1954) 199.

ISNARDI, H., *Z. Physik*, 9 (1922) 153.

JAGER, L., J. BIROŠ and E. ERDOS, *Collection Czech. Chem. Commun.*, 20 (1955) 376.

JANNELLI, L., U. LAMANNA and O. SCIACOVELLI, *Gazz. Chim. Ital.*, 93 (1963) 1231.

JARRY, R. L., *J. Phys. Chem.*, 61 (1957) 498.

JASPER, J. J. and P. G. GRODZKA, *J. Am. Chem. Soc.*, 76 (1954) 1453.

JASPER, J. J., E. R. KERR and F. GREGORICH, *J. Am. Chem. Soc.*, 75 (1953) 5252.

JASPER, J. J. and E. V. KRING, *J. Phys. Chem.*, 59 (1955) 1019.

JASPER, J. J. and G. B. MILLER, *J. Phys. Chem.*, 59 (1955) 441.

JEFFERY, G. H., R. PARKER and A. I. VOGEL, *J. Chem. Soc.*, (1961) 570.

JOHNSEN, S. E. J. and J. W. FITZPATRICK, *Rec. Trav. Chim.*, 70 (1951) 823.

JOHNSON, W. H., M. V. KILDAY and E. J. PROSEN, *J. Res. Natl. Bur. Std.*, 65 A (1961) 215.

JONES, C. A., E. M. SCHOENBORN and A. P. COLBURN, *Ind. Eng. Chem.*, 35 (1942) 666.

JOSHI, S. S. and G. D. TULI, *J. Indian Chem. Soc.*, 28 (1951) 450.

JOURAVLEV, D. I., *J. Phys. Chem. USSR*, 9 (1937) 875/882.

JUREČEK, M., M. HUBIK and M. VEČEŘA, *Collection Czech. Chem. Commun.*, 25 (1960) 1458.

KAARSEMAKER, S. and J. COOPS, *Rec. Trav. Chim.*, 71 (1952) 125.

KARASHARLI, K. A. and P. G. STRELKOV, *Proc. Acad. Sci. USSR*, 131 (1955) 267 (568).

KARDON, S. and J. H. SAYLOR, *J. Am. Chem. Soc.*, 75 (1953) 1997.

KARR, A. E., W. M. BOWES and E. G. SCHEIBEL, *Anal. Chem.*, 23 (1951) 459.

KAY, W. B. and F. M. WARZEL, *Ind. Eng. Chem.*, 43 (1951) 1150.

KAZANSKII, B. A., M. I. ROZENGART, O. D. STERLIGOV and G. A. TARASOVA, *Zh. Anal. Khim.*, 8 (1953) 245.

KEMP, M. D., S. GOLDHAGEN and F. A. ZIHLMAN, *J. Phys. Chem.*, 61 (1957) 240.

KETELAAR, J. A. A. and N. VAN MEURS, *Rec. Trav. Chim.*, 76 (1957) 437.

KEYES, F. G., L. B. SMITH and D. B. JOUBERT, *J. Math. Phys.*, 1 (1922) 191.

KEYES, F. G., R. S. TAYLOR and L. B. SMITH, *J. Math. Phys.*, 1 (1922) 211.

KHALIBOV, KH., *Zh. Eksperim. Teor. Fiz. (J. Exptl. Theor. Phys.)* 9 (1922) 223, 229 [335].

KLIMENT, V., V. FRIED and J. PICK, *Coll. Czech. Chem. Commun.*, 29 (1964) 2008.

KLYUEVA, M. L., K. P. MISHCHENKO and M. K. FEDOROV, *Zh. Priklad. Khim.*, 33 (1960) 473.

KOEFOED, J. and J. V. VILLADSEN, *Acta Chem. Scand.*, 12 (1958) 1124.

KOHLER, F. and E. ROTT, *Monatsh.*, 85 (1954) 703.

KOLESOV, V. P., E. A. SEREGIN and S. M. SKURATOV, *Zh. Fiz. Khim.*, 36 (1962) 647.

KOMANDIN, A. V. and A. K. BONETSKAYA, *Zh. Fiz. Khim.*, 34 (1960) 845.

KONDO, S. and M. MATSUMOTO, *Bull. Chem. Soc. Japan*, 31 (1958) 319.

KORTÜM, G. and H. J. FREIER, *Monatsh. Chem.*, 85 (1954) 693.

KOSOLAPOFF, G. M., *J. Chem. Soc.*, (1955) 2964.

KOVALENKO, K. N. and N. A. TRIFONOV, *Zh. Fiz. Khim.*, 28 (1954) 312.

KREGLEWSKI, AL., *Roczniki Chem.*, 27 (1953) 125; 29 (1955) 95.

KRETSCHMER, C. B. and R. WIEBE, *J. Am. Chem. Soc.*, 76 (1954) 2579.

KRICHEVSKII, I. R., N. E. KHAZANOVA, G. M. SVETLOVA and R. S. PANINA, *Zh. Fiz. Khim.*, 34 (1960) 2160.

KURMANADHARAO, K. V., V. V. G. KRISHNAMURTY and C. VENKATARAO, *Rec. Trav. Chim.*, 76 (1957) 769.

KUSHNER, L. M., R. W. CROWE and C. P. SMYTH, *J. Am. Chem. Soc.*, 72 (1950) 1091.

KYLE, B. G. and T. M. REED, *J. Am. Chem. Soc.*, 80 (1958) 6170.

LABBAUF, A. and F. D. ROSSINI, *J. Phys. Chem.*, 65 (1961) 476.

LACINA, J. L., W. D. GOOD and J. P. McCULLOUGH, *J. Phys. Chem.*, 65 (1961) 1026.

LAFONTAINE, I., *Bull. Soc. Chim. Belges*, 67 (1958) 153.

LANGE, J. and J. BERGA, *Monatsh.*, 81 (1950) 921.

LEADER, G. R., *J. Am. Chem. Soc.*, 73 (1951) 856.

LIPLAVK, I. L. and E. P. BOLITER, *J. Appl. Chem. USSR*, 24 (1951) 207.

LOUGUIRINE, W., *Arch. Sct. Nat.*, 9 (1900) 5.

LOWITZ, D. A., J. W. SPENCER, W. WEBB and R. W. SCHIESSLER, *J. Chem. Phys.*, 30 (1959) 73.

McALLAN, D. T., T. V. CULLUM, R. A. DEAN and F. A. FIDLER, *J. Am. Chem. Soc.*, 73 (1951) 3627.

McCORMACK, K. E. and W. G. SCHNEIDER, *J. Chem. Phys.*, 18 (1950) 1269; 19 (1951) 845.

McCOUBREY, J. C. and N. M. SINGH, *Trans. Faraday Soc.*, 53 (1957) 877.

McCULLOUGH, J. P., D. R. DOUSLIN, W. N. HUBBARD, S. S. TODD, J. F. MESSERLY, I. A. HOSSENLOPP, F. R. FROW, J. P. DAWSON and G. WADDINGTON, *J. Am. Chem. Soc.*, 81 (1959) 5884.

McCULLOUGH, J. P., D. R. DOUSLIN, J. F. MESSERLY, I. A. HOSSENLOPP, T. C. KINCHELOE and G. WADDINGTON, *J. Am. Chem. Soc.*, 79 (1957) 4289.

McCULLOUGH, J. P., H. L. FINKE, M. E. GROSS, J. F. MESSERLY and G. WADDINGTON, *J. Phys. Chem.*, 61 (1957) 289.

McCULLOUGH, J. P., H. L. FINKE, W. N. HUBBARD, W. D. GOOD, R. E. PENNINGTON, J. F. MESSERLY and G. WADDINGTON, *J. Am. Chem. Soc.*, 76 (1954) 2661.

McCULLOUGH, J. P., H. L. FINKE, W. N. HUBBARD, S. S. TODD, J. F. MESSERLY, D. R. DOUSLIN and G. WADDINGTON, *J. Phys. Chem.*, 65 (1961) 784.

McCULLOUGH, J. P., H. L. FINKE, J. F. MESSERLY, R. E. PENNINGTON, L. A. HOSSENLOPP and G. WADDINGTON, *J. Am. Chem. Soc.*, 77 (1955) 6119.

McCULLOUGH, J. P., H. L. FINKE, J. F. MESSERLY, S. S. TODD, T. C. KINCHELOE and G. WADDINGTON, *J. Phys. Chem.*, 61 (1957) 1105.

McCULLOUGH, J. P., H. L. FINKE, D. W. SCOTT, M. E. GROSS, J. F. MESSERLY, R. E. PENNINGTON and G. WADDINGTON, *J. Am. Chem. Soc.*, 76 (1954) 4796.

McCULLOUGH, J. P., H. L. FINKE, D. W. SCOTT, R. E. PENNINGTON, M. E. GROSS, J. F. MESSERLY and G. WADDINGTON, *J. Am. Chem. Soc.*, 80 (1958) 4786.

McCULLOUGH, J. P., W. N. HUBBARD, F. R. FROW, I. A. HOSSENLOPP and G. WADDINGTON, *J. Am. Chem. Soc.*, 79 (1957) 561.

McCULLOUGH, J. P., R. E. PENNINGTON, J. C. SMITH, I. A. HOSSENLOPP and G. WADDINGTON, *J. Am. Chem. Soc.*, 81 (1959) 5880.

McCULLOUGH, J. P. and D. W. SCOTT, *J. Am. Chem. Soc.*, 81 (1959) 1331.

McCULLOUGH, J. P., D. W. SCOTT, H. L. FINKE, M. E. GROSS, K. D. WILLIAMSON, R. E. PENNINGTON, G. WADDINGTON and H. M. HUFFMAN, *J. Am. Chem. Soc.*, 74 (1952) 2801.

McCULLOUGH, J. P., D. W. SCOTT, H. L. FINKE, W. N. HUBBARD, M. E. GROSS, C. KATZ, R. E. PENNINGTON, J. F. MESSERLY and G. WADDINGTON, *J. Am. Chem. Soc.*, 75 (1953) 1818.

McCULLOUGH, J. P., D. W. SCOTT, R. E. PENNINGTON, I. A. HOSSENLOPP and G. WADDINGTON, *J. Am. Chem. Soc.*, 76 (1954) 4791.

McCULLOUGH, J. P., S. SUNNER, H. L. FINKE, W. N. HUBBARD, M. E. GROSS, R. E. PENNINGTON, J. F. MESSERLY, W. D. GOOD and G. WADDINGTON, *J. Am. Chem. Soc.*, 75 (1953) 5075.

McEACHERN, D. M. JR. and J. E. KILPATRICK, *J. Chem. Phys.*, 41 (1964) 3127.

MACEY, W. A. T., *J. Phys. Chem.*, 64 (1960) 254.

McKENZIE, C. A., A. P. MILLS and J. M. SCOTT, *J. Am. Chem. Soc.*, 72 (1950) 2032.

McKINLEY, C. and J. P. COPES, *J. Am. Chem. Soc.*, 72 (1950) 5331.

McKINNEY, W. P., G. F. SKINNER and L. A. K. STAVELEY, *J. Chem. Soc.*, (1959) 2415.

MACKLE, H. and P. A. G. O'HARE, *Trans. Faraday Soc.*, 58 (1962) 1912.

McLAUGHLIN, E. and A. R. UBBELOHDE, *Trans. Faraday Soc.*, 53 (1957) 628.

MALANOWSKI, S., *Bull. Acad. Polon. Sci., Ser. Sci. Chim.*, 9 (1961) 71.

MARECHAL, J., *Bull. Soc. Chim. Belges*, 61 (1952) 149.

MASI, J. F., *J. Am. Chem. Soc.*, 74 (1952) 4738.

MASI, J. F., H. W. FLIEGER JR. and J. S. WICKLUND, *J. Res. Natl. Bur. Std.*, 52 (1954) 275.

MATHEWS, J. F. and J. J. McKETTA, *J. Phys. Chem.*, 65 (1961) 758.

MATHIAS, S., *J. Am. Chem. Soc.*, 72 (1950) 1897.

MATHIAS, S., *Univ. Sao Paulo, Fac. Filosof. Cienc. Letras, Bol.* 246, Quim. 4 (1957).

MATHIAS, S. and E. DE CARVALHO FILHO, *J. Phys. Chem.*, 62 (1958) 1427.

MATHIAS, S., E. DE CARVALHO FILHO and R. G. CECCHINI, *J. Phys. Chem.*, 65 (1961) 425.

MATHIEU, M. P., *Acad. Roy. Belg., Classe Sci., Mem. Collection in 8°*, 28, No. 2 (1953).

MATTHEWS, J. B., J. F. SUMNER and E. A. MOELWYN-HUGHES, *Trans. Faraday Soc.*, 46 (1950) 797.

MAZZA, L., *Atti R. Academia*, 21 (1935 I) 434.

MEARS, T. W., A. FOOKSON, P. POMERANTZ, E. H. RICH, C. S. DUSSINGER and F. L. HOWARD, *J. Res. Natl. Bur. Std.*, 44 (1950) 299.

MEARS, W. H., R. F. STAHL, S. R. ORFEO, R. C. SHAIR, L. F. KELLS, W. THOMPSON and H. MCCANN, *Ind. Eng. Chem.*, 47 (1955) 1449.

MEARS, T. W., C. I. STANLEY, E. L. COMPERE JR. and F. L. HOWARD, *J. Res. Natl. Bur. Std.*, 67A (1963) 475.

MECKE, R., R. JOECKLE and G. KLINGENBERG, *Z. Elektrochem.*, 66 (1962) 239.

MECKE, R. and R. JOECKLE, *Z. Elektrochem.*, 66 (1962) 255.

MÉDARD, L. and M. THOMAS, *Mém. poudres*, 34 (1952) 421.

MICHEL, J., *Bull. Soc. Chim. Belges*, 48 (1939) 105.

MICHELS, A., R. J. LUNBECK and G. J. WOLKERS, *Physica*, 18 (1952) 128 (= *Commun. Van der Waals Fund* 121).

MICHELS, A., J. M. LUPTON, T. WASSENAAR and W. DE GRAAFF, *Physica*, 18 (1952) 121 (= *Commun. Van der Waals Fund* 120).

MICHELS, A., J. V. SENGERS and P. S. VAN DER GULIK, *Physica*, 28 (1962) 1216 (= *Commun. Van der Waals Fund* 176).

MICHELS, A., W. VAN STRAATEN and J. DAWSON, *Physica*, 20 (1954) 17 (= *Commun. Van der Waals Fund* 142).

MICHELS, A. and J. C. STRIJLAND, *Physica*, 18 (1952) 613 (= *Commun. Van der Waals Fund* 125).

MICHELS, A., A. VISSER, R. J. LUNBECK and G. J. WOLKERS, *Physica*, 18 (1952) 114 (= *Commun. Van der Waals Fund* 119).

MICHELS, A. and T. WASSENAAR, *Physica*, 16 (1950) 221 (= *Commun. Van der Waals Fund* 102).

MICHELS, A., T. WASSENAAR, P. LOUWERSE, R. J. LUNBECK and G. J. WOLKERS, *Physica*, 19 (1953) 287 (= *Commun. Van der Waals Fund* 132).

MICHELS, A., T. WASSENAAR and T. N. ZWIETERING, *Physica*, 18 (1952) 160 (= *Commun. Van der Waals Fund* 122).

MICHELS, A., T. WASSENAAR, T. N. ZWIETERING and P. SMITS, *Physica*, 16 (1950) 501 (= *Commun. Van der Waals Fund* 106).

MILLER, R. C. and C. P. SMYTH, *J. Am. Chem. Soc.*, 79 (1957) 20.

MILTON, H. T. and G. D. OLIVER, *J. Am. Chem. Soc.*, 74 (1952) 3951.

MIZUHARA, S. and W. F. SEYER, *J. Am. Chem. Soc.*, 75 (1953) 3274.

MOERSCH, G. W., *Pa. State Univ. Microfilms (Ann Arbor), Publ. No. 551, Abstracts*, 5 (1942) 301, Publ. 1943.

MOLE, M. F., W. S. HOLMES and J. C. MCCOUBREY, *J. Chem. Soc.*, (1964) 5146.

MOORE, E. M. and M. E. HOBBS, *J. Am. Chem. Soc.*, 71 (1949) 411.

MUELLER, C. R. and J. IGNATOWSKI, *J. Chem. Phys.*, 19 (1951) 845.

MUMFORD, S. A. and J. W. C. PHILLIPS, *J. Chem. Soc.*, (1950) 75.

MURRAY, F. E. and S. G. MASON, *Can. J. Chem.*, 33 (1955) 1399, 1409.

NECKEL, A. and H. VOLK, *Monatsh.*, 89 (1958) 754.

NEFF, J. A. and J. B. HICKMAN, *J. Phys. Chem.*, 59 (1955) 42.

NEILSON, E. F. and D. WHITE, *J. Am. Chem. Soc.*, 79 (1957) 5618.

NICHOLSON, A. J. C., *J. Chem. Soc.*, (1949) 1553.

NICKERSON, J. D. and R. MCINTOSH, *Can. J. Chem.*, 35 (1957) 1325.

NICKERSON, J. K., K. A. KOBE and J. J. MCKETTA, *J. Phys. Chem.*, 65 (1961) 1037.

NICOLINI, E., *Ann. Chim. (Paris)*, [12] 6 (1951) 582.

NITTA, I., S. SEKI, H. CHIHARA and K. SUZUKI, *Sci. Papers Osaka Univ.*, No. 29 (1951).

NOVAK, J., J. MATOUS and J. PICK, *Collection Czech. Chem. Commun.*, 25 (1960) 583, 2405.

NOYES, R. M., W. A. NOYES and H. STEINMETZ, *J. Am. Chem. Soc.*, 72 (1950) 33.

NÝVLT, J. and E. ERDOS, *Collection Czech. Chem. Commun.*, 24 (1959) 508; 26 (1961) 500.

OETTING, F. L., *J. Phys. Chem.*, 67 (1963) 2757.

OLIVER, G. D., S. BLUMKIN and C. W. CUNNINGHAM, *J. Am. Chem. Soc.*, 73 (1951) 5722.

OLIVER, G. D., M. EATON and H. M. HUFFMAN, *J. Am. Chem. Soc.*, 70 (1948) 1502.

OLIVER, G. D. and J. W. GRISARD, *J. Am. Chem. Soc.*, 73 (1951) 1688.

OLIVER, G. D., J. W. GRISARD and C. W. CUNNINGHAM, *J. Am. Chem. Soc.*, 73 (1951) 5719.

OSBORNE, N. S. and D. C. GINNINGS, *J. Res. Natl. Bur. Std.*, 39 (1947) 453.

OSBORNE, N. S., E. C. MCKELVY and H. N. BEARCE, *J. Am. Acad. Wash.*, 2 (1912) 95.

OSTHOFF, R. C., W. T. GRUBB and C. A. BURKHARD, *J. Am. Chem. Soc.*, 75 (1953) 2227.

OTHMER, D. F., S. A. SAVITT, A. KRASNER, A. M. GOLDBERG and D. MARKOWITZ, *Ind. Eng. Chem.*, 41 (1949) 572.

PACE, E. L. and R. J. BOBKA, *J. Chem. Phys.*, 35 (1961) 454.

PAQUOT, C. and L. DURRENBERGER, *Bull. Soc. Chim. France*, (1950) 402.

PARIAUD, J. C., *Ann. Chim. (Paris)*, [12] 6 (1951) 880.

PARKS, G. S., K. E. MANCHESTER and L. M. VAUGHAN, *J. Chem. Phys.*, 22 (1954) 2089.

PARTINGTON, J. R. and H. H. NEVILLE, *J. Phys. Colloid Chem.*, 55 (1951) 1550.

PEREZ MASIA, A. and M. D. ALVAREZ SONET, *Anales Real Soc. Espan. Fis. Quim. (Madrid)*, 58B (1962) 3.

PEREZ MASIA, A. and M. DIAZ PENA, *Anales Real Soc. Espan. Fis. Quim. (Madrid)*, 54B (1958) 661.

PEREZ MASIA, A. and A. ROIG, *Anales Real Soc. Espan. Fis. Quim. (Madrid)*, 54B (1958) 651.

PERRIN, R., *Bull. Soc. Chim. France*, (1963) 333.

PHIBBS, M. K., *J. Chem. Phys.*, 19 (1951) 1420.

PHILIPPE, R. and A. M. PIETTE, *Bull. Soc. Chim. Belges*, 64 (1955) 600.

PICK, J., E. HÁLA and V. FRIED, *Collection Czech. Chem. Commun.*, 24 (1959) 1589.

PLEBANSKI, T., *Bull. Acad. Polon. Sci., Ser. Sci. Chem.*, 8 (1960) 239.

POMERANTZ, P., *J. Res. Natl. Bur. Std.*, 48 (1952) 76.

POMERANTZ, P., A. FOOKSON, T. W. MEARS, S. ROTHBERG and F. L. HOWARD, *J. Res. Natl. Bur. Std.*, 52 (1954) 59.

POTTER, A. E., JR. and H. L. RITTER, *J. Phys. Chem.*, 58 (1954) 1040.

POTTER, J. C. and J. H. SAYLOR, *J. Am. Chem. Soc.*, 73 (1951) 90.

PROSEN, E. J., F. W. MARON and F. D. ROSSINI, *J. Res. Natl. Bur. Std.*, 42 (1949) 269; 46 (1951) 106.

PUTNAM, W. E. and J. E. KILPATRICK, *J. Chem. Phys.*, 27 (1957) 1075.

PYLE, W. R., *Phys. Rev.*, 38 (1931) 1057.

QUAYLE, O. R., R. A. DAY and G. M. BROWN, *J. Am. Chem. Soc.*, 66 (1944) 938.

QUITZSCH, K., C. NOWAK, P. WINKLER and G. GEISELER, *J. Prakt. Chem.*, [4] 20 (1963) 92.

RAMPOLLA, R. W. and C. P. SMYTH, *J. Am. Chem. Soc.*, 80 (1958) 1057.

RANDALL, M. and F. E. MCKENNA, *J. Am. Chem. Soc.*, 73 (1951) 4859.

RATHJENS JR., G. W. and W. D. GWINN, *J. Am. Chem. Soc.*, 75 (1953) 5629.

RAW, C. J. G. and H. TANG, *J. Chem. Phys.*, 39 (1963) 2616.

REHBERG, C. E. and M. B. DIXON, *J. Am. Chem. Soc.*, 72 (1950) 1918.

RIVENQ, F., *Bull. Soc. Chim. France*, (1963) 1606.

RÖCK, H. and L. SIEG, *Z. Physik. Chem. (Frankfurt)*, N.F. 3 (1955) 355.

RONDENKO, N. S., *J. Phys. USSR*, 9 (1944) 1078.

ROSS, M. and J. H. HILDEBRAND, *J. Phys. Chem.*, 67 (1963) 1301.

ROWLINSON, J. S. and R. THACKER, *Trans. Faraday Soc.*, 53 (1957) 1.

RUITER, L. H., *Thesis*, Amsterdam (1955).

RYBICKA, S. M. and W. F. K. WYNNE-JONES, *J. Chem. Soc.*, (1950) 3671.

SACKMANN, H. and A. BOCZEK, *Z. Physik. Chem. (Frankfurt)*, 29 (1961) 329.

SAGE, B. H. and W. N. LACEY, *Ind. Eng. Chem.*, 27 (1935) 1484.

SCHAERER, A. A., C. J. BUSSO, A. E. SMITH and L. B. SKINNER, *J. Am. Chem. Soc.*, 77 (1955) 2017.

SCHIESSLER, R. W. and F. C. WHITMORE, *Ind. Eng. Chem.*, 47 (1955) 1660.

SCOTT, D. W., W. T. BERG and J. P. MCCULLOUGH, *J. Phys. Chem.*, 64 (1960) 906.

SCOTT, D. W., D. R. DOUSLIN, M. E. GROSS, G. D. OLIVER and H. M. HUFFMAN, *J. Am. Chem. Soc.*, 74 (1952) 883.

SCOTT, D. W., H. L. FINKE, M. E. GROSS, G. B. GUTHRIE and H. M. HUFFMAN, *J. Am. Chem. Soc.*, 72 (1950) 2424.

SCOTT, D. W., H. L. FINKE, W. N. HUBBARD, J. P. MCCULLOUGH, G. D. OLIVER, M. E. GROSS, C. KATZ, K. D. WILLIAMSON, G. WADDINGTON and H. M. HUFFMAN, *J. Am. Chem. Soc.*, 74 (1952) 4656.

SCOTT, D. W., H. L. FINKE, W. N. HUBBARD, J. P. MCCULLOUGH, C. KATZ, M. E. GROSS,

J. F. MESSERLY, R. E. PENNINGTON and G. WADDINGTON, *J. Am. Chem. Soc.*, 75 (1953) 2795.

SCOTT, D. W., H. L. FINKE, J. P. McCULLOUGH, M. E. GROSS, J. F. MESSERLY, R. E. PENNINGTON and G. WADDINGTON, *J. Am. Chem. Soc.*, 77 (1955) 4993.

SCOTT, D. W., H. L. FINKE, J. P. McCULLOUGH, M. E. GROSS, R. E. PENNINGTON and G. WADDINGTON, *J. Am. Chem. Soc.*, 74 (1952) 2478.

SCOTT, D. W., H. L. FINKE, J. P. McCULLOUGH, M. E. GROSS, K. D. WILLIAMSON, G. WADDINGTON and H. M. HUFFMAN, *J. Am. Chem. Soc.*, 73 (1951) 261.

SCOTT, D. W., H. L. FINKE, J. P. McCULLOUGH J. F. MESSERLY, R. E. PENNINGTON, I. A. HOSSENLOPP and G. WADDINGTON, *J. Am. Chem. Soc.*, 79 (1957) 1062.

SCOTT, D. W., W. D. GOOD, S. S. TODD, J. F. MESSERLY, W. T. BERG, I. A. HOSSENLOPP, J. L. LACINA, A. OSBORN and J. P. McCULLOUGH, *J. Chem. Phys.*, 36 (1962) 406.

SCOTT, D. W., W. N. HUBBARD, J. F. MESSERLY, S. S. TODD, I. A. HOSSENLOPP, W. D. GOOD, D. R. DOUSLIN and J. P. McCULLOUGH, *J. Phys. Chem.*, 67 (1963) 680.

SCOTT, D. W., J. P. McCULLOUGH, W. D. GOOD, J. F. MESSERLY, R. E. PENNINGTON, T. C. KINCHELOE, I. A. HOSSENLOPP, D. R. DOUSLIN and G. WADDINGTON, *J. Am. Chem. Soc.*, 78 (1956) 5457.

SCOTT, D. W., J. P. McCULLOUGH, J. F. MESSERLY, R. E. PENNINGTON, I. A. HOSSENLOPP, H. L. FINKE and G. WADDINGTON, *J. Am. Chem. Soc.*, 80 (1958) 55.

SCOTT, D. W., J. P. McCULLOUGH, K. D. WILLIAMSON and G. WADDINGTON, *J. Am. Chem. Soc.*, 73 (1951) 1707.

SCOTT, D. W., J. F. MESSERLY, S. S. TODD, G. B. GUTHRIE, I. A. HOSSENLOPP, R. T. MOORE, A. OSBORN, W. T. BERG and J. P. McCULLOUGH, *J. Phys. Chem.*, 65 (1961) 1320.

SCOTT, D. W. and G. WADDINGTON, *J. Am. Chem. Soc.*, 72 (1950) 4310.

SCOTT, D. W., G. WADDINGTON, J. C. SMITH and H. M. HUFFMAN, *J. Am. Chem. Soc.*, 71 (1949) 2767.

Selected Values of Properties of Chemical Compounds, Agricultural and Mechanical College of Texas; American Petroleum Institute Research Project 44; see authors.

SEREGIN, E. A., V. P. KOLESOV, N. A. BELIKOVA, S. M. SKURATOV and A. F. PLATE, *Dokl. Acad. Nauk SSSR*, 145 (1962) 580.

SERYAKOV, G. V., S. A. VAKS and L. S. SIDORINA, *Zh. Obshchei Khim.*, 30 (1960) 2130.

SEYER, W. F., R. B. BENNETT and F. C. WILLIAMS, *J. Am. Chem. Soc.*, 71 (1949) 3447.

SHADE, R. W. and G. D. COOPER, *J. Phys. Chem.*, 62 (1958) 1467.

SHAW, W. G. and G. H. BROWN, *J. Am. Chem. Soc.*, 81 (1959) 2532.

SIMON, I., *Bull. Soc. Chim. Belges*, 38 (1929) 47.

SIMONS, J. H. and J. W. MAUSTELLER, *J. Chem. Phys.*, 20 (1952) 1516.

SIMONS, J. H. and R. D. DUNLAP, *J. Chem. Phys.*, 18 (1950) 335.

SINGH, R. and L. W. SHEMILT, *J. Chem. Phys.*, 23 (1955) 1370.

SINKE, G. C., D. L. HILDENBRAND, R. A. McDONALD, W. R. KRAMER and D. R. STULL, *J. Phys. Chem.*, 62 (1958) 1461.

SINOZAKI, H., R. HARA and S. MITSUKURI, *Bull. Chem. Soc. Japan*, 1 (1926) 59.

SKINNER, H. A. and A. SNELSON, *Trans. Faraday Soc.*, 56 (1960) 1776.

SMITH, B., *Acta Chem. Scand.*, 9 (1955) 1337.

SMITH, T. E. and R. F. BONNER, *Ind. Eng. Chem.*, 41 (1949) 2867; 43 (1951) 1169.

SMUTNY, E. J. and A. BONDI, *J. Phys. Chem.*, 65 (1961) 546.

SPAGHT, M. E., S. B. THOMAS and G. S. PARKS, *J. Phys. Chem.*, 36 (1932) 882.

SPEROS, D. M. and F. D. ROSSINI, *J. Phys. Chem.*, 64 (1960) 1723.

STAROBINETZ, G. L. and K. C. STAROBINETZ, *Zh. Fiz. Khim.*, 25 (1951) 759.

STAUDHAMMER, P. and W. F. SEYER, *J. Am. Chem. Soc.*, 80 (1958) 6491.

STEVENSON, R., *J. Chem. Phys.*, 27 (1957) 656, 673.

STEWART, J. W. and R. I. LaROCK, *J. Chem. Phys.*, 28 (1958) 425.

STREIFF, A. J., A. R. HULME, P. A. COWIE, N. C. KROUSKOP and F. D. ROSSINI, *Anal. Chem.*, 27 (1955) 411.

STREIFF, A. J., E. T. MURPHY, J. C. CAHILL, H. F. FLANAGAN, V. A. SEDLAK, C. B. WILLINGHAM and F. D. ROSSINI, *J. Res. Natl. Bur. Std.*, 38 (1947) 53.

STREIFF, A. J., E. T. MURPHY, V. A. SEDLAK, C. B. WILLINGHAM and F. D. ROSSINI, *J. Res. Natl. Bur. Std.*, 37 (1946) 331.

STREIFF, A. J., E. T. MURPHY, J. C. ZIMMERMAN, L. F. SOULE, V. A. SEDLAK, C. B. WILLINGHAM and F. D. ROSSINI, *J. Res. Natl. Bur. Std.*, 39 (1947) 321.

STREIFF, A. J., L. F. SOULE, C. M. KENNEDY, M. E. JANES, V. A. SEDLAK, C. B. WILLINGHAM and F. D. ROSSINI, *J. Res. Natl. Bur. Std.*, 45 (1950) 173.

STREIFF, A. J., J. C. ZIMMERMAN, L. F. SOULE,

M. T. Butt, V. A. Sedlak, C. B. Willingham and F. D. Rossini, *J. Res. Natl. Bur. Std.*, 41 (1948) 323.

Strubell, W., *J. Prakt. Chem.*, 26 (1964) 319.

Suryanarayana, C. V. and K. M. Somasundaram, *Acta Chim. Acad. Sci. Hung.*, 19 (1959) 337.

Swietoslawski, W. and J. Usakiewicz, *Roczniki Chem.*, 13 (1933) 495.

Takagi, S., H. Chihara and S. Seki, *Bull. Chem. Soc. Japan*, 32 (1959) 84.

Taylor, R. D., B. H. Johnson and J. E. Kilpatrick, *J. Chem. Phys.*, 23 (1955) 1225.

Teitelbaum, B. Y., T. A. Gortalova and E. E. Sidorova, *Zh. Fiz. Khim.*, 25 (1951) 911.

Thomas, G. A. and J. E. Hawkins, *J. Am. Chem. Soc.*, 76 (1954) 4856.

Thompson, F. W. and A. R. Ubbelohde, *Trans. Faraday Soc.*, 46 (1950) 349.

Timmermans, J. and M. Hennaut-Roland, *J. Chim. Phys.*, 52 (1955) 223; 56 (1959) 984.

Trowbridge, J. C. and E. F. Westrum Jr., *J. Phys. Chem.*, 67 (1963) 2381; 68 (1964) 255.

Tschamler, H. and F. Kohler, *Monatsh. Chem.*, 81 (1950) 463.

Valentine, R. H., G. E. Brodale and W. F. Giauque, *J. Phys. Chem.*, 66 (1962) 392.

Van der Waals, J. H., *Rec. Trav. Chim.*, 70 (1951) 101.

Van Gunst, C. A., *Thesis*, Techn. Hogeschool, Delft (1950).

Van Risseghem, H., *Bull. Soc. Chim. Belges*, 47 (1938) 194, 221.

Vaughn, J. W. and P. G. Sears, *J. Phys. Chem.*, 62 (1958) 183.

Vogel, A. I., W. T. Cresswell, G. H. Jeffery and J. Leicester, *J. Chem. Soc.*, (1952) 514.

Von Rautenfeld, F. and E. Steurer, *Z. Physik. Chem.*, 51B (1942) 39.

Wada, T., E. Kishida, Y. Tomiie, H. Suga, S. Seki and I. Nitta, *Bull. Chem. Soc. Japan*, 33 (1960) 1317.

Waddington, G., J. C. Smith, D. W. Scott and H. M. Huffman, *J. Am. Chem. Soc.*, 71 (1949) 3902.

Waddington, G., J. C. Smith, K. D. Williamson and D. W. Scott, *J. Phys. Chem.*, 66 (1962) 1074.

Ward, T. L. and W. S. Singleton, *J. Phys. Chem.*, 56 (1952) 696.

Waterman, H. I., J. J. Leendertse and D. W. van Krevelen, *J. Inst. Petrol.*, 25 (1939) 801.

Watson, R. W., J. A. R. Coope and J. L. Barnwell, *Can. J. Chem.*, 29 (1951) 885.

Waxler, R. M. and C. E. Weir, *J. Res. Natl. Bur. Std.*, 67A (1963) 163.

Weber, L. A. and J. E. Kilpatrick, *J. Chem. Phys.*, 36 (1962) 829.

Weissman, S. and S. E. Wood, *J. Chem. Phys.*, 32 (1960) 1153.

Westwater, J. W., *Ind. Eng. Chem.*, 47 (1955) 451.

Wheeler Jr., C. M. and F. S. Jones, *Anal. Chem.*, 24 (1952) 1991.

Whipple, G. H., *Ind. Eng. Chem.*, 44 (1952) 1664.

Whiteway, S. G. and S. G. Mason, *Can. J. Chem.*, 31 (1953) 569.

Whitmore, F. C., H. E. Whitmore and N. C. Cook, *J. Am. Chem. Soc.*, 72 (1950) 51.

Wibaut, J. P. and H. Brand, *Rec. Trav. Chim.*, 80 (1961) 97.

Wibaut, J. P., H. Hoog, S. L. Langedijk, J. Overhoff and J. Smittenberg, *Rec. Trav. Chim.*, 58 (1939) 329.

Wibaut, J. P. and B. Paulis, *Rec. Trav. Chim.*, 77 (1958) 782.

Williams, J. W. and I. J. Krchma, *J. Am. Chem. Soc.*, 49 (1927) 1676.

Willingham, C. B., W. J. Taylor, J. M. Pignocco and F. D. Rossini, *J. Res. Natl. Bur. Std.*, 35 (1945) 219.

Witschonke, C. R., *Anal. Chem.*, 26 (1954) 562.

Wood, S. E., S. Langer and R. Battino, *J. Chem. Phys.*, 32 (1960) 1389.

Wood, S. E. and C. M. Masland, *J. Chem. Phys.*, 32 (1960) 1385.

Wulff, C. A. and E. F. Westrum Jr., *J. Phys. Chem.*, 67 (1963) 2376.

Yang, C. P. and M. van Winkle, *Ind. Eng. Chem.*, 47 (1955) 293.

Yasumi, M., H. Okabayashi and H. Komooka, *Bull. Chem. Soc. Japan*, 31 (1958) 402.

Zhuravlev, D. I., *Russ. J. Phys. Chem.*, 9 (1937) 875.

Zieborak, K. and M. Zieborak, *Roczniki Chem.*, 29 (1955) 161.

Zinov'ev, A. A. and V. Y. Rosolovskii, *J. Inorg. Nucl. Chem. USSR*, 5 (1960) 1239 [2564].

CORRIGENDA TO THE REFERENCES OF VOLUME I

W. G. APPLEBY, instead of APPLEBEY (p. 634).

G. CALINGAERT, H. SOROOS et al., J. Am. Chem. Soc., 66, 1389 instead of 1398 (p. 637).

G. DARZENS, R. DELABY and J. HIRON, Bull. Soc. Chim. France, instead of Belg. (p. 639).

P. W. LUNT and M. A. G. RAU instead of RAN (p. 649).

L. MASSART, 1936 instead of 1916 (p. 649).

L. MOURADOFF-FOUQUET, add: Compt. Rend., 226 (1948) 1970 (p. 651).

F. D. ROSSINI, 6, 37 instead of 6, 1 (p. 654).

INDEX OF COMPOUNDS